WATER TOWERS OF BRITAIN

and their part in bringing water to the people

Barry Barton

THE NEWCOMEN SOCIETY

First published in 2003 by
The Newcomen Society
The Science Museum
London SW7 2DD
England

ISBN 0 904685 12 8

Typesetting, design and production by
Keld Fenwick
Cover design by
Prestige Typographics, Bury St Edmunds, Suffolk
Printed by
Antony Rowe Ltd, Chippenham, Wiltshire

ACKNOWLEDGEMENTS

This book could not have been written without the help of a large number and wide range of people who, in response to requests for information, gave generously of their time and resources to seek out the information required, sometimes on successive occasions. These individuals and the organisations they then represented, are listed below. It is inevitable that one or two names have inadvertently been omitted, and to anyone who has looked in vain for their rightful recognition I can only offer my sincere apologies.

First and foremost, my thanks are due to all my fellow members of the Institution of Civil Engineers' Panel for Historical Engineering Works who assisted the Water Towers Sub-Group in researching, locating, visiting and photographing water towers throughout Britain, and especially to Dr Bob Rennison, who undertook a peer review of the draft of the entire book, and Mike Chrimes, who reviewed the chapters concerned with reinforced concrete water towers, for their valuable and constructive comments and suggestions. Special thanks are also due to my fellow Sub-Group member, Dr Michael Gould, with whom I have worked in close harness throughout the project since the Sub-Group's inception in 1994, to Claire Delgal of the Institution of Civil Engineers Library for her consistently prompt and efficient responses to what must have seemed an endless stream of requests for copies of learned papers and technical articles, and to Dr Bob Otter for his help in finding a suitable publisher.

It was therefore through Dr Otter that I was fortunate to find myself in the capable hands of the publisher of the Newcomen Society's *New Studies in Engineering History* series, Keld Fenwick. For a whole year he patiently did everything necessary to bring this book to fruition. And finally I must express my gratitude to my wife, Margaret, and to my long-suffering family for their unfailing encouragment and for whom every family outing for years past has somehow been coupled with a visit to or search for yet another water tower.

Much of the basic information necessary for the project has of course come from the water undertakers themselves and thanks are due to Paul Allen and J W Lancaster (South East Water), K B Ball and Kevin Ensell (Hartlepool Water), J Bowyer-Lowe (North Surrey Water), Dave Brotherton (Welsh Water), Colin Cameron (West of Scotland Water), David Chatwin (Corby (Northants) & District Water), Mike Clark and Malcolm Bailey (Mid Kent Water), Stan Clarke (Severn Trent Water), Derek Clucas (North West Water), Paul Cousins (Northumbrian Water), Henry Edwards (Cholderton & District Water), Peter Edwards (Bournemouth & West Hampshire Water), B J Elliott (Cambridge Water), Vicky Evans (States of Guernsey WB), Richard Everitt and John Reade (East of Scotland Water), M J Green (South West Water), Dr Dave Harker and Ron Grant (Anglian Water), Tim Harris (Southern Water), Patrick Heaton-Armstrong (Isle of Man Water), M R Hedges and Brian Bunyard (Portsmouth Water), M Henderson (Tendring Hundred Water), Brian Lowen (Council of the Isles of Scilly), Ian McIntosh (Essex & Suffolk Water), Robin Nichols ('Landmark', Bracknell, for South East Water), Mike Pocock (Three Valleys Water), R J Rap (Sutton & East Surrey Water), Barbara Roberts (South Staffordshire Water), P Roberts (Dee Valley Water), John Saville (Mid Southern Water), Roger Smith (York Waterworks), Howard Snowden (Jersey New Waterworks), Barry Straughton (Bristol Water), Darren Towers (Thames Water) and Terry Williams (North of Scotland Water). Our gratitude must also be expressed to those from West of Scotland Water, Wessex Water, Yorkshire Water and Folkestone & Dover Water not named above who dealt directly with enquiries from Dr Gould or their local Panel members.

Thanks must also go to A R Ball of the Department of the Environment, Transport and the Regions in Whitehall whose reassurances were occasionally required to persuade some water undertakers that supplying the Panel with information on their physical infrastructure would not necessarily result in its destruction by terrorist action. It is heartening to be able to report that every statutory water undertaker in Britain, large and small, provided information on their water towers for the benefit of this research project, even though in one exceptional case — one of England's largest water companies — it took five years of persistent efforts to obtain a response.

Much useful information was also obtained from local authorities, particularly in respect of listed buildings and historical sites, either from their Archaeology Sections or their Sites & Monuments Record Officers. Thanks are therefore due to Duncan Brown (Hereford & Worcester), Martin Brown (East Sussex), Roy Canham (Wiltshire), S J Catney (Lincolnshire), Paul Charlton (Greater London), Dr Jill Collens (Cheshire), Stephen Coleman (Bedfordshire), Kim Cooper and Steve Hartgroves (Cornwall), Tony Crosby and S Gould (Essex), Mark Daniells (Plymouth), Ann-Marie Dick (Devon), Joanne Driffill (Nottinghamshire), David Evans (South Gloucestershire), G Falkingham (Humberside), Sarah-Jane Farr (Liverpool), Chris Godfrey (Cambridgeshire), Niall Hammond (Durham), Caroline Hardie and Liz Williams (Northumberland), Bette Hopkins (Cumbria), Bruce Howard (Hampshire), P D Iles (Lancashire), Bob Jones (Bristol), Jenny Kitchen (Northamptonshire), Catherine Marlow (Gloucestershire), Jim McNeil (South Yorkshire), Ian Morrison and Hanna Steyne (English Heritage pp Greater London), D L Motkin (Isle of Wight), Margaret O'Sullivan (Derbyshire), John Oxley (York), Alwen Pearson and Hilary White (West Midlands), Colin Pendleton (Suffolk), Claire Pinder (Dorset), Norman Redhead (Greater Manchester), Edwin Rose (Norfolk), Paul Stead (Kent), S J Warburton (Leicestershire), Penelope Ward (Shropshire), Chris Wardle (Staffordshire) and Chris Webster (Somerset) and Dr R E Yarwood and Helen Gomersall (West Yorkshire). If any area is not mentioned above it is probably because their Sites & Monuments Record included no water towers at the time an approach was made.

Local and regional historical and industrial archaeology societies have been exceptionally and unfailingly helpful and in this area thanks must therefore go to Ken Andrews (Bristol Ind Arch Soc.), David Bowler (SUAT, Perth), John Brace (Warwickshire Ind Arch Soc), Dr Rachel Brown (The

Marlow Soc), A W Brooks (Trevithick Soc, Camborne), David Cant (Yorkshire Arch.Soc.), Bill Firth (Greater London Ind Arch Soc), Bruce Hedge (Vale of the White Horse Ind Arch Gp), Chris Lester and John Turner (Soc Lincolnshire Hist & Arch), Christopher Mann (Surrey Ind Hist Gp), D J Manning (Norfolk Ind Arch Soc), Ron Martin (Sussex Ind Arch Soc), A P Moretti (Leicestershire Wolds Hist Org), Ron Moss (Black Country Soc), Paul Sowan (Croydon Nat Hist & Sci Soc), Geoffrey Starmer (Northants Ind Arch Group), Steve Stockley (Manchester Region Ind Arch Soc), Winifred Waterfall (Heanor & Dist Local Hist Soc) and Steven Worsley (Suffolk Ind Arch Soc).

Local libraries and museums have proved not merely to be a valuable source of local information but also of librarians, archivists and curators who have gone out of their way to look up and supply that information. These must include Paul Archibald (Lanark), Alan Bell (Perth), Rachel Benvie and Mrs C Donald (Montrose), Dawn Bradley (Skegness), Stuart Burroughs (Bath), Tony Carr (Shrewsbury), Christine Conboy (Dunstable), Andrew Crabtree (Boston), Mrs E Curtis (Holsworthy, Devon), Rosemary Fletcher (Burton-on-Trent), Deborah Gahan (Barnstaple), Scott Hastie (Hemel Hempstead), Jackie Heaton (Knutsford), Mark Higginson (Derby), Roger Hull (Liverpool), Mike Jobling (Ilkeston), Alan King and Diana Gregg (Portsmouth), Anne-Marie Knowles (Chesterfield), Anne Leigh (Ormskirk), Nigel Lutt (Bedford), Peter McNabola (Morpeth), Eileen Moran (Dundee), Ruth Neller (Mablethorpe), Lesley O'Connell-Edwards (Bromsgrove), Julie Noble (Bournemouth), Jenny Parker (Middlesbrough), Corinne Phillips (Nottingham), Lois Pratt (Sheerness), Bruce Purvis (Salisbury), Martin Rickard (High Wycombe), Jan Ruhrmund and Liz Le Grice (Penzance), Mrs D Scriven and Hugh Mayfield (Wakefield), Kath Shawcross (Sutton), J Strong (Bishop Auckland), Mark Stubbs (Luton), Jane Sutton (Nuneaton), D J Taylor (Scunthorpe), Philippa Taylor (Kings Lynn), M Waite (Cromer), Mr P & Mrs M White (Darlington), D Whitham (Chorley), Mrs E Williams (Chester) and an anonymous librarian at Ellesmere Port.

Officers or representatives of other organisations, both public and private, who have responded generously to requests for information or have allowed access to sites normally inaccessible to the public include Barry Abraham (Airfield Research Gp), Cressida Annesley (Canterbury Cathedral Archives), Helen Blackman and Dr Amanda Draper (Manchester Museum of Science & Industry), Dr Julian Bommer and Dr David Smith (Soc for Earthquake & Civ Eng Dynamics), W R Burns (York University Estate Services), Maj R E Chatten, Flt Lt D J Curwen, Chris Jeff, Flying Officer J A J Milnes and Flt Lt A Pemberton (RAF), Vivienne Chesterfield and Kelly (Kier Group plc), T P Clarke (Grimsthorpe & Drummond Castle Trust), Reg Davies (Midland Rly Soc), Alastair Dick-Cleland (The Landmark Trust), M L Dunley (Cromarty Firth Industrial Park), Paula Fahey (*Country Life* Magazine), P N Greenwood (Resident Agent, Newby Hall, Ripon), Mike Harding (National Museum of Science & Industry, London), Dr R J Holder (The Victorian Society), Mark Hurn (British Standards Institute), Jeremy Lake (English Heritage) who kindly reviewed the section on Military Water Towers, R J S Miller (Agent,

Cholmondeley Estates), Dr Mike Osborne (Defence of Britain Project), M J O'Lone (Agent, Sandringham Royal Estate), Charlotte Samuels (British Museum), Alison Sands and Edwin Trout (British Cement Assn), Mrs P Shah (Science Museum, London), Dennis Sherer (Vauxhall Motors), Janet Skidmore (Victoria & Albert Museum, London), D R Sladdin (Director of Estates, Leeds University), Peter Stonor (Stonbury Ltd, Cranfield), Richard Taylor (National Railway Museum, York), Trevor Todd (RIBA), Matt Wheeler (Dacorum Heritage Trust), Emma Whinton (National Monuments Records Centre, Swindon), Andrew Whitmarsh (RAF Museum, Hendon), Isabel Wilson (AIA, Ironbridge) and Alec Worraker (Advanced Concrete Protection Ltd, Peterborough).

And last but far from least, the following private individuals have also been most helpful; Elspeth Beard (Munstead, Surrey), Gordon Biddle (Kendal), S J Blackwell and David Burnett (Sudbury, Suffolk), Dr J W Bland (Berkswell, Coventry), Bruno Del Tufo (Rolvenden, Kent), E Cossor (Upper Norwood), Allan Gill (Selby), Vivienne Graham (Old Windsor), Gwenda Grange (Flackwell Heath, Bucks), Jack Green & S D Robertson (Dorking), Henry Gunston (Wallingford), Terry Hardy (Bath), Brian Hayes (an old friend and colleague, Littleport, Cambs), Roger Holden (Stockport), Keith Horne (Ross on Wye), Dr J M Illston (Salisbury), Joan Leach (Knutsford), Elizabeth Leggatt (Woodstock, Oxon), Bruce Osborne (Tadworth, Surrey), Jon Sass (Keelby, Lincs), Margaret Smith (Tisbury, Wilts), Anne Upson (Woodbridge, Suffolk), Frank Williams (alias the Vicar in *Dad's Army*, Edgware, Middx) and Martin Williams (Swinstead, Lincs).

Illustrations

Adam, R (ICE/PHEW): 2.3;
Angus Council: 3.1;
Bowler, D P (SUAT Ltd): 3.2;
British Concrete Ass: 5.1; 5.2; 6.17;
British Museum: 2.1,
Cragg, R (ICE/PHEW): 6.10;
Crosby, A: 8.7
Cross-Rudkin, P (ICE/PHEW): 3.6;
Fenwick, K: 3.12;
Greenfield, D (ICE/PHEW): 6.7;

Hartlepool Water plc: 3.11;
Hedge, B: 6.11; 7.2;
Holden, R N: 8.1
Kier Construction: 9.5;
Liverpool Central Library: 3.3;
Portsmouth Central Library
(D G Dine):8.10;
Shropshire CC: 9.1;
Vauxhall Motors: 7.7;
Author: All others

Abbreviations

Readers may encounter the following abbreviations

Co	Company	Ln	Lane	RN	Royal Navy
Crt	Court	NHS	National Health Service	Sch	School
Cty	County	MPD	Motive Power Depot	St	Street
Gn	Green	Pk	Park	Stn	Station
Gt	Greater	Ptnrs	Partners	Twr	Tower
Hl	Hill	RAF	Royal Air Force	UDC	Urban District Council
Hosp	Hospital	RDC	Rural District Council	Univ	University
Jctn	Junction	Rly	Railway	Wks	Works

CONTENTS

LIST OF ILLUSTRATIONS

PREFACE

The Institution of Civil Engineers' Panel for Historical Engineering Works, under whose auspices this book was written, was established in 1970 to identify, assess and record all works considered to form an important or significant part of the civil engineering heritage of Britain and Ireland. Each of the 20 or so members appointed to the Panel represents a particular region or area.

For the first two decades of its existence the Panel concentrated on this primary task, and its archives in the Institution's library in Great George Street, Westminster, contains detailed entries for well over two thousand historical engineering works. New entries are still being added to the archive as hitherto undiscovered or overlooked works come to light but, inevitably, the pace at which the archive is growing has slowed.

Because of this, the Panel took the decision in 1994 to review its strategy and start to focus on specific aspects of our civil engineering heritage. As a pilot scheme, a number of small sub-groups were set up to study certain well defined topics — cast iron bridges, masonry arch bridges, dams, dry docks, windmills and water towers. Each sub-group consists of two, three or four members of the Panel whose task, starting with the archive material to hand, is to research the origins, evolution and technical development of their subject throughout Britain and Ireland and to derive a methodology for assessing the relative merit of any particular structure in its class.

The author of this book was one of the two Panel members appointed to form the Water Towers Sub-Group. Early in the Sub-Group's researches it became clear that this was a subject on which very little work had previously been done, and even less written. The need for a book on water towers, of use and interest to Civil Engineers whilst still being comprehensible to the interested layman, soon became apparent. This book is an attempt to meet that need.

The Panel was awarded a grant by the Institution's Research and Development Enabling Fund so that a detailed survey of water towers in Britain and Ireland could be made. Without this grant the Water Towers Sub-Group's study could not have been undertaken as comprehensively as it has, and this book would not have been written. The water towers of Ireland have been the subject of a separate paper published in the Journal of the Institution of Engineers of Ireland in 1999.

INTRODUCTION

The water tower is a familiar feature, particularly of the lowland landscape, throughout much of Britain. In urban areas it has been an accepted part of the townscape for almost 150 years and although water towers in rural areas are a largely 20th century phenomenon, here too their presence is accepted and largely unremarked. Given modern aesthetic and environmental sensibilities this is perhaps surprising.

Water towers are, of necessity, large solid structures and are almost invariably built on ridges or hilltops. They often therefore assume a prominent position on the skyline and make a major visual impact on nearby communities. Despite this, water towers seem never to have been subject to the same hostility and dislike that is so often directed against electricity pylons and radio masts or, more recently, wind power generators. Why is this, when in a modern society, mains electricity and electronic communications are regarded as of equal importance to piped water?

One possible reason is the sheer variety of water towers. Variations in size, shape and form seem endless. Everyone can feel that their local water tower is distinctive, if not unique. This, too, is odd. Since the prosaic function of any water tower is to support a given volume of water at a predetermined height above the ground in a safe, technically efficient and cost-effective manner it might be supposed that, for any particular construction material, there would be a single, optimum solution and that all designs would result in structures of almost identical appearance. If that were so then this book would have been a much slimmer volume.

This book will not attempt to delve too deeply into the origins or the archaeology of the water tower, which has been around in one form or another since early medieval, possibly even since Roman times. Any water supply system, especially one that involved pumping, also required a means of storing the water but those early, primitive systems were usually small scale private water supplies of limited extent and capacity. The water towers with which this book will primarily concern itself are those of the great (and small) public water supply undertakers who saw it as their principal function to supply an entire city, town or village — and latterly, as undertakings have coalesced and expanded, entire regions — with a safe, pure, reliable and constant supply of potable water.

Our detailed study of water towers commences therefore with the advent of the municipal water supply system in the early Victorian era. The initial, uncontrolled urban expansion of the early industrial revolution with its attendant population explosion had resulted in unredeemed urban squalor. Rather belatedly came the recognition that living conditions for everyone in towns, rich and poor alike, could only be made tolerable when public health was safeguarded by the combination of a sewerage system and a wholesome, piped water supply. Next came the arrival, here and there, of rural water supplies, often under the patronage of the great country estates and occasionally in association with their 'model' villages. The formation of rural district councils in 1894 eventually gave rise to the spread of piped water supplies throughout the countryside, particularly in the decades either side of the second world war.

It is important to define clearly what, for the purposes of this book, is meant by a water tower. The term 'water tower' is one to which, it would seem at first sight, only one meaning could be ascribed, namely an engineering structure built for the purpose of storing a large quantity of water above ground level. This definition however gives no indication as to the precise purpose for which the water is stored. This may be for public water supply but can also include a variety of single-function uses such as water for an industrial process, for firefighting or for a private supply of potable water to a hospital, military base, school or even a large house. Our study of water towers will however be principally concerned with those built, or adapted, by a water undertaking for public water supply purposes — the supplying of a wide and unrestricted range of customers with potable water.

But this definition is also imprecise at the margins. What is a 'public' water supply? From earliest times water supply undertakers have included both public and private organisations; individual municipalities, water boards (a consortium of municipal undertakings) and subsequently water authorities, water companies (both public and private) and even wealthy individuals. The word 'public' thus relates to the consumer rather than the supplier and the definition given above is intended to be sufficiently broad to embrace a fully representative range of structures.

Whilst this study has concentrated on water towers intended for a public supply, the exclusion of single-function water towers would obviously carry with it the risk of overlooking structures of historical significance or technical merit. This risk is thought to be relatively small, as the great majority of industrial or single-function water towers are simple and straightforward adaptations of established designs. There are, nevertheless, some inevitable exceptions and where other towers of particular importance or interest have come to our attention they have been included in this book and a chapter has been devoted to water towers built for purposes other than public water supply. Where such a tower has been mentioned or described elsewhere in the text its function has been indicated.

As originally drafted, the text of this book was liberally littered with references. Whilst entirely appropriate in a learned paper or an academic work, it was felt that they were out of place in a more general book that this sets out to be, so instead of references in the text there is a bibliography at the end of this book, arranged under chapter headings. To avoid needless repetition, each book, learned paper or article cited appears only once, at the end of the first chapter to which it has relevance. It is hoped that the derivation of most key statements or salient items of information in the text should be readily apparent from the context in which they appear and a perusal of the bibliography. Only those publications which the reader has a reasonable chance of tracking down are listed. If readers find the bibliography a rather scrappy miscellany this simply reflects the almost complete absence of books on water towers. There was at one time a thin trickle of papers and articles on individual water towers in technical journals but few of a generic nature.

The neglect of water towers as a subject for study is puzzling. Public libraries and bookshops offer books on bridges, on windmills, on RAF airfields, on dovecotes but nothing on water towers. Books on architecture ignore them. Even a book on 'Towers' mentions almost every conceivable sort of tower except water towers. On the continent they do things a little differently and at Brussels in 1991 the Belgian Association Nationale des Services d'Eau devoted an entire symposium to water towers, with contributions from France, Germany, Britain and the Netherlands as well as the host country. These demonstrated that, at least in Belgium, a serious and systematic study of that country's water towers had already been attempted, something the Panel for Historical Engineering Works' Water Towers Sub-Group has tried to emulate.

This book is entitled *Water Towers of Britain* and the more cosmopolitan reader may regard this as regrettably and unnecessarily insular. Just as there exists a wide variation in types and styles of water tower within Britain, the differences between, say, Britain and Europe or between Britain and the United States are equally marked. One has only to follow the Tour de France on television as it snakes its way through the French countryside or to watch an American 'road' film set in the wide open spaces of the Mid-West to appreciate this. Despite their variety British water towers are sufficiently distinctive to warrant a book of their own.

CHAPTER ONE

The Function of the Water Tower

The principal components of any public water supply system are a source of raw water, a means of treating that water to potable standards, somewhere to store the treated water, and a network of pipes for distributing the water to the consumers. Before going any further an apology should be made to those water engineers for whom the words 'supply' and 'distribution' have specific and distinct meanings, but as this book is also intended for the non-specialist reader to whom the distinction is of little concern, the words are used in their more general sense throughout this book. A word of apology too, to women readers who may be irritated by the exclusive use of the male pronoun. This is not to suggest that water engineering is in any way a male preserve but merely a device to avoid clumsy and repetitive circumlocutions.

The source of supply may be a reservoir or lake, a river, a shallow well, or a deep borehole. In upland areas the source will usually be a reservoir in the hills, from which water can flow under gravity to and through the treatment works and throughout the whole distribution system without recourse to pumping. In less favoured areas the source of supply may be a river or a borehole in which case it will be necessary to pump the water from the source up to the treatment works and from there into short term storage. If this storage is placed at the highest point in the system the treated water will flow under gravity to the consumers. Figure 1.1 shows a typical lowland water supply system in a simplified and diagrammatic form.

But why the need for short term storage? At this point we come up against one of the fundamental problems facing the water supply engineer. His treatment works, like any industrial process, operates most efficiently with water flowing through it at a constant rate. His pumps (until recently) are designed to perform at a near-constant discharge and pressure. If only he could supply his water at a constant rate all would be in complete harmony. Unfortunately his consumers are not so accommodating. They spend a lot of time asleep and almost all choose to do so at the same time. Then they get up at the same time, have their meals at the same time, go to work at the same time and, if the weather is fine, they all decide to wash their cars and water their

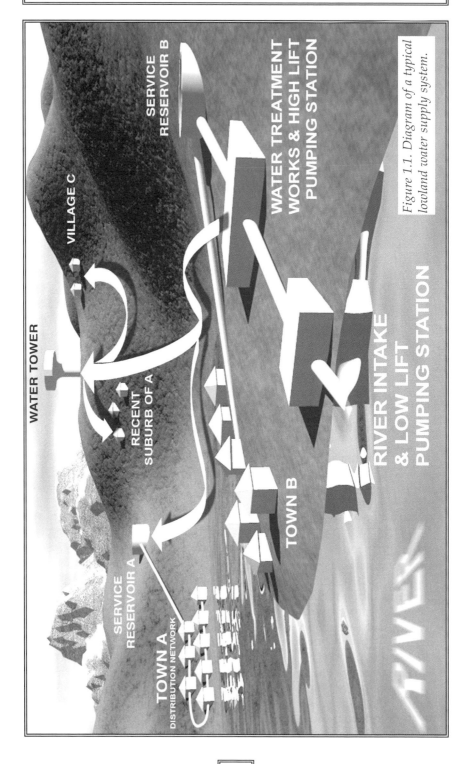

Figure 1.1. Diagram of a typical lowland water supply system.

Labels within the diagram:

SERVICE RESERVOIR B

WATER TREATMENT WORKS & HIGH LIFT PUMPING STATION

VILLAGE C

WATER TOWER

RECENT SUBURB OF A

RIVER INTAKE & LOW LIFT PUMPING STATION

SERVICE RESERVOIR A

TOWN B

TOWN A
DISTRIBUTION NETWORK

RIVER

gardens on the same summer evening.

The result is that demand for water in residential areas exhibits a complex but pronounced diurnal pattern, peaking in the early mornings and evenings, dropping off somewhat in the middle of the day and falling back almost to zero (or to whatever is leaking out of the pipes) late at night. This pattern of demand, though always essentially diurnal, varies widely and in each supply zone will exhibit its own unique characteristics. Marked variations to the basic domestic pattern may be created by the effects of industrial or agricultural users within that zone. The type of residential area — detached suburban houses with large gardens, streets of terraced houses, tower blocks — will also influence the pattern, as will the weather and the changing seasons. Traditionally, Monday mornings — washday — imposed a particularly heavy demand on the system, up to three times the average in some instances.

It is impractical to attempt to match treatment and pumping rates with every change in demand, and uneconomic to provide plant capable of meeting brief and infrequent surges in demand. The only way of balancing a highly variable flow pattern with a steady output from the pumps and treatment works is to incorporate short term storage into the system, designed to fill up during the night and to be available throughout the day to meet sudden surges in demand. This is illustrated in Figure 1.2 which shows how the volume of water held in storage in a service reservoir or water tower varies with the changing demand placed upon it by a typical suburb or small town with its mix of housing, trade and light industry. Based on a crude average per capita consumption of 40 gallons/day Figure 1.2 suggests that, for this particular area, a 100,000 gallon storage capacity should be adequate for a population of about 10,000. But this storage also performs another function. In the event of a pump breaking down or a water main bursting the water engineer has at least a few hours to carry out repairs before the consumers' taps start to run dry. The storage in the system should similarly be capable of responding to the sudden and unquantifiable demand placed upon it in an emergency by the local fire brigade.

The obvious question now arises as to why a water tower should be built at all when its task could as easily be performed by a service reservoir sited on a hilltop. After all, a service reservoir — a large storage tank or cistern built at or just below ground level — can usually be constructed considerably more economically, gallon for gallon, than a water tower with its elevated tank and the expensive structure required to support it.

Although a service reservoir may be the water supply engineer's initially preferred option, a service reservoir might not always be feasible, for a number of reasons. The first is that there may not be a sufficiently elevated site available in the locality upon which to build a service reservoir and still provide an acceptable pressure of water in all

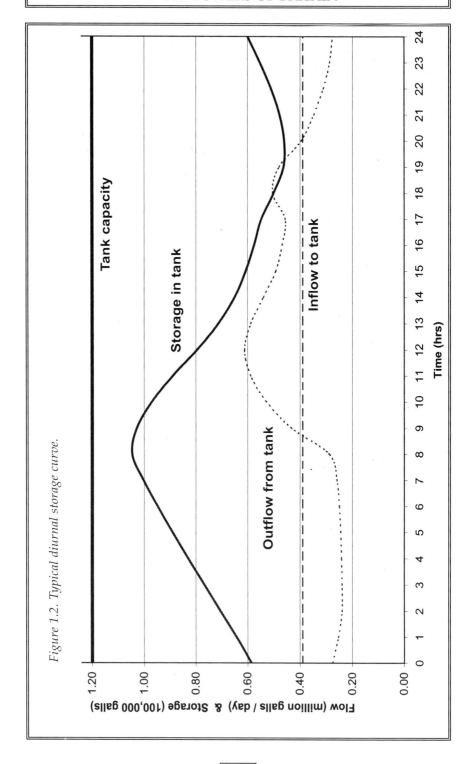

Figure 1.2. Typical diurnal storage curve.

parts of the supply network. A second and more usual reason is that urban development has spread up the hillside and onto the hilltop itself, or a hilltop settlement already exists. In either case a service reservoir would not be high enough to supply the neighbouring hilltop properties. In many such situations a small water tower is often located on the same site as a service reservoir, the one feeding a small, high level distribution system and the other a much larger, low level area. This arrangement has the disadvantage of two separate pipework systems in the same area operating under different pressures. Another reason is that a new water tower is needed to replace an earlier, life-expired structure, one that may originally have been built both quickly and cheaply to meet a particular need, without having to reconfigure an established pipe network. Alternatively it may be necessary to supplement an existing tower which, though still serviceable, is no longer large enough to meet increased demands.

The water tower's function requires that it has pipework connections to the local water mains. These normally consist of three vertical pipes below the tank; an inlet pipe through which water is pumped into the tank and which discharges into the tank above top water level, an outlet pipe to the distribution network from the base of the tank, and an overflow pipe of greater capacity than the inlet pipe to prevent the tank from overfilling (Figure 1.3). Connected into the latter is usually a valved drain-off pipe from the base of the tank to allow the tank to be emptied for maintenance or repair, during which time the bypass between the inlet and outlet pipes would be opened to permit a supply to consumers to be maintained. The need to protect all these pipes from frost or unauthorised interference means that they are, except in the most utilitarian towers, enclosed within the tower's walls or supporting shaft.

The configuration shown in Figure 1.3 has the inlet pipe discharging at the top of the tank. An alternative discharge position at the base of the tank would require the insertion of a reflux (non-return) valve in the pumping (or rising) main feeding the water tower, in order to prevent water running back to the pumping station when pumping ceases. The next logical progression is to combine the inlet and outlet pipes in a single vertical pipe. Some towers have been built with this configuration, but the reliance on a reflux valve and the loss of the float valve on the tank inlet both introduce small but additional elements of risk into the system with which some engineers are uncomfortable. A few water towers incorporate a pumphouse built into the base of the tower at ground level but these are a small minority as the pumps that feed the tower are normally at a sourceworks or treatment works remote from the tower.

Where, as is usually the case, the water tower is remote from the pumphouse, the problem of when to start and stop pumping water into the tank without wasteful overflow or, more seriously, allowing the tank to empty, is as old as water towers themselves. In a modern

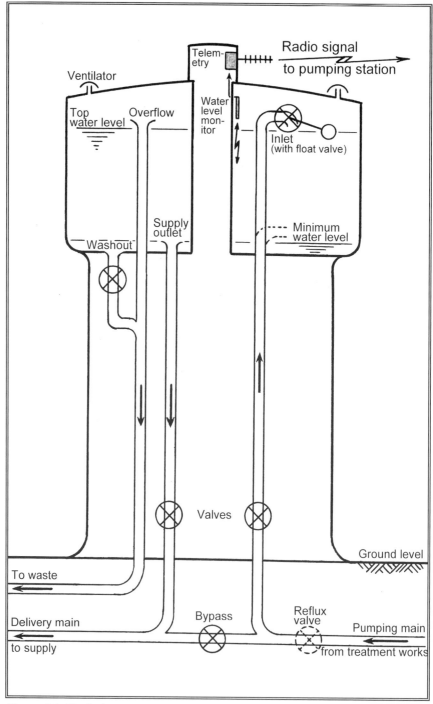

Figure 1.3. Typical water tower pipework layout.

water supply system, water levels are monitored electronically and the information relayed back to the pumping station by telemetry using a radio or landline link. The pumps are then programmed to stop and start automatically as the situation demands. In the 19th century the problem was addressed by fitting a float valve, a greatly enlarged version of the domestic ballcock, to the end of the inlet pipe at the top of the tank. If pumping was still taking place when the tank became full and the valve fully closed, damagingly high pressures could occur in the mains, but since the pumphouse was continuously manned the pump operator would observe the sudden rise in water pressure and stop the pumps. Even so, in an era of low technology, cheap labour and manned sites it was sensible to equip water towers with a visual indication of the water level in the tank, and this was achieved by the simple expedient of a float-and-pulley operated target sliding up and down a calibrated gaugeboard fixed to the outside of the tank. Although now disused and redundant, the remains of these devices can still be seen on considerable numbers of older water towers. An interesting variation on the gauge board appeared at Topsham (Devon) in 1917 where the float was connected to a large copper ball which rose and fell on a vertical pole on the roof of the tower.

Telemetry is thought of as a modern technology but methods for monitoring water towers by telemetry have existed in some form or other since the end of the 19th century and were described in some detail in a 1900 textbook. Lincoln's comprehensive new water supply system installed in 1910/11, with the water tower 22 miles from the sourceworks pumping station, was equipped with just such a system. Typically this would have consisted of a float actuated, battery powered electro-mechanical device installed in the tower which transmitted electric current pulses with each rise (eg, one inch) or fall of water level along a dedicated telegraph wire to a distant recorder. A float operated valve would nevertheless be installed at the top of the inlet pipe as a precaution against telemetry failure and the consequent wasteful overflow. Fully automatic (closed loop) control of a water supply system is only possible in practice with electric pumps. Lincoln's scheme, as with almost all large water supply schemes of that era, was powered by steam engines which, like the big, low speed internal combustion engines which succeeded them, were not amenable to automatic stopping and starting. But the use of small, electrically driven pumps had already begun and a fully automatic pumping system was reported to be in operation at Wykeham (Yorkshire) in 1903. This was a rare exception, and the widespread adoption of fully automatic electrically powered pumps would have to await the arrival of mains electricity.

Since public supply water towers almost always contain water that has already been treated to potable standards it is essential that there is no deterioration in the quality of the water whilst it is temporarily held in the tower. It is therefore necessary for the tank to be roofed to keep out airborne pollution, perhaps the most serious of which is bacterial contamination from passing birds. For the same reason the tank must also be sufficiently secure and well enclosed to keep out all birds and animals, including humans. Having said that, the interior of the tank must still be accessible for inspection, maintenance and repair purposes, normally down through a hatch in the roof of the tank. How to make this hatch safely accessible to maintenance staff is part of water tower design and the solutions adopted vary widely, depending on the type of tower.

Access to the roof of the tank may either be by an external ladder or by an internal ladder or staircase within the tower or a central shaft. In many concrete towers this shaft is carried up through the centre of the tank to a small turret or shelter above, with a door opening from it onto the tank roof. Some early brick towers had a smaller, adjoining access tower to one side, a feature reverted to by some designers of modern concrete water towers. Strangely there never seems to have been a consensus as to what this shelter should be called and various names are encountered, such as cabin, cupola, penthouse, belvedere, turret and lantern. None of them are entirely apposite but 'cupola' is as good as any and will be used throughout for consistency. Readers may have other preferences.

Even though the water stored is potable, a thin layer of sediment will gradually accumulate on the inside of the tank and this must periodically be cleaned out. The drain-off pipe or a cross-connection from the outlet to the overflow allows the tank to be emptied for cleaning, but the tower is then out of service. An early solution to this problem, something more satisfactory than a simple bypass, was to build a low internal wall around the outlet pipe. This permitted the larger part of the tank to be emptied and cleaned while some water remained for supply. Subsequently this wall was raised to above top water level giving, for a circular tank, two concentric compartments. With square or rectangular tanks this is achieved by a simple cross-wall. It is not clear when the first twin-compartment water towers came into use but the concrete tower built at Hatfield, near Doncaster, in 1916 had two separate chambers in its tank, then described as a 'novel feature.' Presumably this was a novelty only in respect of concrete towers as Hartlepool's 1891 water tower had a twin-compartment iron tank. Only exceptionally are tanks with more than two separate compartments encountered, though York's massive Siwards How tower (1956) has four, each of 250,000 gallons.

The pressure of water at a consumer's tap will depend on the rate at which he (and thousands of others) are using water at any instant, the length and diameter of the water mains between him and the water tower, and the level of water in the tower itself. It is this 'head' of water which creates the pressure which causes the water to flow through the pipe network. This head will of course vary with the amount of water in the tank so it is obviously desirable to keep fluctuations of water level to a minimum to maintain as constant a pressure in the system as possible. If a water tower is designed with a very wide, flat tank the fluctuations in level as the volume of water in the tank varies will be very small. On the other hand, the most economical shape for storing a given volume of water (considered in terms of surface area of the container per unit volume enclosed) is a sphere. Not only will the broad, flat tank itself be an inherently uneconomical shape to build but it will also require a relatively expensive structure for its support. In addition, it is more difficult to ensure a thorough circulation of water between inlet and outlet in a very broad tank and thus avoid areas of 'dead' water. The shape of the tank and indeed the whole water tower will therefore be an uneasy compromise between conflicting hydraulic and economic ideals and this goes some way to explain the bewildering variety of water towers that will be encountered.

The provision of storage, whether water tower or service reservoir, in any water supply system is, inevitably, expensive. No water engineer knowingly wishes to incur excessive capital costs in unnecessary storage, so how much storage is required? How little can the water engineer get away with without jeopardising the security and reliability of the public supply? An analysis of a mass diagram, such as Figure 1.2, would suggest that the storage capacity of a water tower should be between a quarter and a third of the average daily consumption in the area it serves. In practice a more conservative allowance of around 50% of the maximum daily consumption is usually made, though if consideration is given to the effects of contingencies such as burst water mains or a major firefighting incident, even this volume of storage can be drawn down with alarming rapidity.

If, however, the rate at which water is pumped into the system can be made to match the rate at which water is withdrawn from the system then, in theory, storage capacity becomes unnecessary. As has already been alluded to, modern variable speed pumps can go a long way to achieve this, provided that there are standby pumps on hand to cover mechanical breakdowns and standby generators ready to start up automatically in the event of mains electric power failures. Even if some storage is incorporated in the system to even out the load at the treatment works it need not be located at the highest point if an alternative means can be found to maintain a constant pressure in the system. Modern pump technology has made the pump-pressurised system a viable alternative to the traditional simple pump-and-storage system. As might be expected, professional opinion varies widely and there is still no general consensus. Most supply engineers are understandably wary of having to operate a system which could, however remote the risk, suffer a sudden, widespread and potentially catastrophic failure. The consequences of failure are compounded by the problems that can arise from a loss of pressure in the mains network and the dangers to public health of air or, far worse, untreated water being drawn into the pipes. If an underground pipe is leaking, water can, depending on relative pressures inside and outside the pipe, flow in either direction.

Pump pressurised water supply systems are not entirely recent. As long ago as 1907 they were described optimistically in an engineering textbook as 'now possible with electric high speed centrifugal pumps' although 20 years later another textbook dismissed them rather loftily as 'an American practice ... not favoured by British engineers.' By the 1960s it was becoming accepted that pump-pressurised systems were suited to flat, densely populated urban areas with Hull being cited as an example, although the divergence of opinion within the water industry was as acute as ever. As recently as the 1980s, even within the same regional water authority one divisional engineer could still be embarking on the construction of a batch of replacement water towers while his counterpart in an adjoining division would be resolutely demolishing them. What tends to happen in practice is inevitably more pragmatic. A service reservoir will provide the necessary storage and maintain pressure in most of the system, but can also be used to feed a small, local high level supply zone by means of a pump-pressurised system for which a separate water tower would otherwise be needed. This type of arrangement is certainly not new. Before World War I a hydraulic accumulator was installed at the base of Shrewsbury's now demolished St Mary's water tower from which this device was pump-fed and supplied the uppermost part of the town.

Another device no longer seen is the standpipe, a prominent feature of some early water supply systems which were, in effect, pump-pressurised. These were tall vertical iron pipes usually about 60 to 80 feet high, although there were two notably loftier examples in London, at Kew Bridge and Campden Hill. They were connected directly to the delivery main from the pumping station and could be either single and open ended or double ('up and over'). A 1914 textbook went as far as to state, a little contentiously, that the water tower was 'sometimes employed as an alternative to a standpipe though the purpose is the same' but went on to concede that 'the water tower has certain decided advantages,' one of which was that pumping need not be continuous. This is of course a consequence of the water tower's much greater storage capacity. For a standpipe to have an equivalent capacity its diameter would have to be substantially increased and, whereas it is not difficult to manufacture a relatively narrow iron pipe to withstand the hydrostatic pressure at ground level beneath a tower (considerably higher than that at the base of an elevated tank), the cost of fabricating a large diameter shaft to withstand that same pressure at ground level could be prohibitive. The brief popularity and rapid demise of the standpipe is clearly demonstrated at York's Severus Hill water tower which, when built in 1914, incorporated an existing up-and-over standpipe, erected only 18 years previously, as its inlet and overflow pipes. Despite actual practice, a water supply textbook published in 1931 was still describing standpipes in some detail in its 1950 edition.

The water tower and service reservoir on the same site is common-place and there are many examples of water towers designed to be structurally and architecturally integral with the service reservoir upon which were built. So if it is operationally convenient for water to be stored at two different levels on the same site why not at two different levels in the same tower? The author has only come across three public supply examples of a 'double decker' tank arrangement in Britain. The earliest was Ormskirk's Victoria tower (1897) though here the upper tank held a mere 17,000 gallons compared with the main tank's 80,000. There then seems to have been a long gap until 1950 when Glasgow's Priesthill water tower appeared, followed by the recent (1989) tower at Dunkeswell in Devon. (Croydon's Victorian Park Hill water tower came close with a low level tank in the basement but this was, in effect, an integral service reservoir.) Yet the type is not unusual in Europe. The most extreme example is perhaps at Oostburg in the Netherlands where the concrete tower, completed in 1950, has no fewer than six elevated tanks, one above the other.

Another occasional continental practice is the grouping of identical water towers (as opposed to successive generations of towers) together on the same site. Groups of three, four and seven (Gentofte, Denmark) are known but the spectacular cluster of nine Swedish designed 'wineglass' type water towers in Kuwait — if they survived the Gulf War — must surely be the record. Is the rationale behind this practice an economic one, that of phased development, or to do with aesthetic reasons discussed in a later chapter? The only corresponding occurrence in Britain is the pair at Beanfield on the outskirts of Corby (Northants) which, although of the same design, are of different sizes.

A water tower's function, and those features of its design dictated by that function, are common to all types and categories of tower, both ancient and modern. The following chapters will, after a short historical review of the origins of the water tower, explore and describe the principal types of water tower with which readers will be familiar, and the way in which the design of each type has evolved to provide most effectively those essential features and hence fulfil that function.

CHAPTER 2

The Origins of the Water Tower

A definition of what we mean by a water tower has been given in the Introduction but readers should be aware that this definition is not the only one they may encounter. In medieval times a 'water tower' was a bastion in a city wall or a castle's defences which gave direct access to open water. Such a tower still exists at Chester, on the River Dee. A very similar tower at York will be described in more detail later in this chapter.

By Tudor times the term 'water house' had emerged to describe a building erected over a well. Such a well-house at Hever Castle in Kent appears in the statutory list of protected structures as a 'water tower', as does the combined well-house and dovecote (hardly conducive to a hygienic water supply) at Abington Park, Northampton, though this 'water house' was subsequently adapted for use as a water tower. Conversely, the expression 'water house' has in some instances been used to describe what are clearly water towers.

A 'water tower' is listed at the Stonehouse Naval Hospital complex in Plymouth, but the structure was described in 1795 as 'the engine house for forcing water up to the top of the different buildings to supply the wards and the reservoirs for furnishing the water to cleanse the common sewers.' Was this a water tower? The description leaves room for doubt, though we now know that it was. Some of these very early elevated tanks erected on or within buildings at Royal Naval dockyards are of considerable interest and will be encountered again in a later chapter. Unfortunately some of the references in which 'water tower' is cited as a key word may simply represent a straightforward misuse of the term. The Middlesbrough Dock hydraulic tower is one example.

When the term 'water tower' came to mean an elevated reservoir is uncertain. Early service reservoirs built in stone were often called cisterns. A fine example still exists at Rye in Sussex. The Rye cistern (1735), which is listed as a 'water tower,' does have a shaft through the centre but apparently this shaft only provides access and no doubt helps to support the domed roof. Conversely, the term 'cistern' was also applied to some early water towers, such as that built at Montrose in 1841. The three storey octagonal tower on North Esk Road, the oldest purpose-built municipal water tower still extant in Britain, is still known as the Lochside Cistern.

Even at the start of the twentieth century, when water towers as we know them today had become commonplace, the use of the term was still not universal. In the decade before the first world war the firm of consulting engineers, L G Mouchel & Partners, was pre-eminent in the design of reinforced concrete water towers and its archives show the use, in almost equal numbers, of the terms 'water tower,' 'tower tank' and 'elevated reservoir' for job numbers allocated at that time. Even today some engineers still use the term 'elevated tank', although usually to denote a prefabricated sectional tank supported on a steel lattice framework. The term 'elevated reservoir' was still being used to describe water towers well into the 1930s. An engineering textbook of 1967 distinguished between a 'water tower' and an 'elevated tank' by the height of the tank base above the ground. If this distance was greater than 20 feet the structure was a water tower, otherwise merely an elevated tank, but this definition never seems to have been generally accepted.

As has been made clear in the previous chapter, the water tower is essentially a feature of a pump-fed water supply system. This in turn means that water towers would not be expected to appear in any number until the advent of steam, although waterwheel, horse or even manpowered pumps had been in use since at least Roman times, albeit on a very limited scale. Roman engineering at its finest is exemplified by its water supply systems and aqueducts. Bath houses and public sewers were common features of Roman towns and these required a copious supply of water. This could not be achieved by the primitive pumps then available (though the Romans are known to have used force pumps for raising water) so these systems were gravity fed. Hence the need for aqueducts, often of remarkable length, to bring water from a distant source at a higher elevation. The aqueduct itself provided all the storage capacity the system required and the Romans had little or no need for water towers. One intriguing exception to this pattern appears to be the water supply to the Roman colony at Lincoln. Here the source of supply, the Roaring Meg spring, is at a lower elevation than the Roman town to which it is linked by a $1^1/3$ mile rising main consisting of 6in internal diameter earthenware pipes encased in 'concrete.' Some form of pump must clearly have been an integral part of the system, but what type was it, what powered it, and did the system also incorporate a water tower?

In the pre-industrial rural community, water supply needs could adequately be met from wells, streams or springs, but this would not be the case in towns, especially as the size of towns increased. By modern standards most medieval towns were very small, little more than overgrown villages. By the end of the 15th century even London had a population of only 60,000, but high urban population densities meant that wells and cesspits were effectively interconnected. The resulting health risks were probably not understood, although the foul tasting water would certainly have been. There is, nevertheless, a wealth of documentary and archaeological evidence that many medieval towns had a piped water supply of sorts. These developed piecemeal as a result of civic, ecclesiastical or private initiatives. All of them served a very restricted range of customers, usually within a limited area. Apart from the difficulties associated with pumping, pre-industrial technology struggled to provide solutions to the intractable problems then associated with pipework and the storage of water.

Cisterns which once formed part of the local water supply system, or at least the buildings that enclosed them, are still remarkably common throughout Britain, in towns and villages alike, and date from medieval times to the start of the industrial era. These cisterns, almost invariably located at the downstream end of a gravity-fed system, consisted of a small, overflowing lead-lined or stone tank, sometimes with a tap or valved outlet at the base, to which people could bring flagons, jugs or barrels, to fill with water for domestic or trade use. The function of the cistern was essentially twofold; to allow customers to fill their containers beneath the overflow or valve with minimum inconvenience and to provide an element of buffer storage at busy times, though without a valved outlet customers might have to immerse their vessels in the tank. The ground around the cistern would need to be paved to avoid becoming a trampled quagmire. The tank itself would have to be raised slightly above ground level to facilitate the placing of containers beneath the overflow or outlet. Despite the 'elevated tank,' it would be wrong to suggest that such structures should be regarded as water towers though it could possibly be argued that cisterns were the precursors of the water tower.

In a gravity fed system a considerable amount of leakage can be tolerated, but if all the water has to be pumped, involving both effort and expenditure, leakage presents a serious handicap. The designer of any large water storage vessel is faced with two imperatives; the need to minimise leakage and to ensure that the vessel does not burst. The pressures imposed on the walls of a large tank by the water contained within it are considerable, as is the load on the supporting structure if the tank is elevated. With a cistern at or below ground level its structural integrity can be ensured by the passive support of the surrounding earth. If, however, in order to feed a pipe network the tank is elevated, it has to be entirely self-supporting and of a material that will resist the outward pressure of the water — a watertight material that combines the ability to resist tensile stress with a high strength-to-weight ratio so as to minimise the load on the supporting structure.

For the medieval engineer the only readily available material capable of meeting these criteria was lead, but because lead is a relatively weak metal, larger lead tanks would require secondary support from iron hoops or timber casing. The elevated lead tank is therefore a feature of many medieval water supply systems and with it we see the early forerunners of the water tower. Very few examples now remain, although such a tank, dated to 1160, still exists at Canterbury Cathedral. This gravity-fed tank which originally supplied the whole ecclesiastical community is housed in a small, octagonal tower with a conical roof, 25 ft high to the eaves. Monastic establishments in towns often had their own private water supplies and at the reformation many of these were taken over for public use by the civic authorities. Most, if not all, appear to have been spring-fed. Having remained at roughly the same size for centuries, the inexorable growth of towns from their medieval base seems to have begun at about this time, pre-dating the industrial revolution. London, for example, doubled in size during the reign of Elizabeth I.

It is towards the end of the 16th century that pumped water supply systems first begin to appear, and with them the need for elevated storage. Most towns were situated beside rivers and the breakthrough came when the flow of the river was utilised to drive a waterwheel which in turn provided the power required to pump water from the river. The rotating shaft of the waterwheel could be linked, either directly or by primitive gearing, to a crank and thus operate a reciprocating force-pump. Just such a system was in operation on the River Dee at Chester in 1573 and was leased in 1600 to John Tyrer who built a water tower near the river in Bridgegate, not to be confused with the defensive 'water tower' at the end of what is now Tower Street. By about 1670 Chester's water supply system was operated by a Thomas Evans who had replaced the waterwheel by a horse. This suggests that fluctuations in river levels, especially at times of flood, could pose serious problems for the operation of waterwheel powered systems.

In 1595 Bevis Bulmer was providing Londoners with a water supply of sorts from the Thames by means of a horse-powered chain pump at Queenhythe, though a rival waterwheel driven system already existed nearby. This was the famous London Bridge water supply system, inaugurated in 1580/2 by a Dutchman, Peter Morris (or Morice) who had installed a set of force pumps under one of the arches of London Bridge. Morris' waterwheels rotated in either direction, depending on the ebb and flow of the tide, but his original system must have been successful because he leased a second arch in 1583. Despite competition from the gravity-fed New River Scheme and from other Thames-side pumped systems, the London Bridge waterworks continued in use until 1822, by which time its waterwheels and pumps (and those of the Southwark Waterworks Company on the south bank) occupied five of its 19 arches and had become an unacceptable hazard to navigation. They were also, according to contemporary accounts, extremely noisy. London Bridge was rebuilt in 1824/31, without any of its predecessor's mechanical accretions.

We know that the London Bridge pumps fed some sort of water tower (a possible structure, directly under the words 'The Water Works', appears on John Norden's superbly detailed 18th century drawing of the bridge) but no details survive. A rival undertaking, the York Buildings Waterworks Company, took water from the Thames by means of horse-driven pumps at the bottom of Villiers Street, off the Strand, and a contemporary (1797) water colour painting by J P Malcolm of their waterworks — complete with tall wooden water tower — can be seen in the British Museum (Figure 2.1). It is clear that urban public supply water towers of this type must have existed fairly widely throughout the 17th and 18th centuries but they seem to have been utilitarian and essentially ephemeral structures and have gone virtually unrecorded. Stephen Switzer's *Hydrostaticks and Hydraulicks* (1729), the best known hydraulic engineering textbook of its day, describes what are clearly service reservoirs but makes no mention of water towers and no urban water tower from this era has survived.

Throughout the 17th and 18th centuries, urban water supplies struggled to keep up with the ever growing demand. Responses varied widely, ranging from the professionally engineered, gravity fed New River system which supplied part of London with Hertfordshire spring water, through the increasingly numerous waterwheel-powered systems to the ramshackle but probably fairly typical small town system which supplied Gainsborough. Here three horse-gin driven pumps lifted water from the tidal River Trent into a collection of lead tanks on timber trestles in Ship Inn yard, providing a woefully inadequate standpipe supply in a few nearby streets. In between the two extremes we have the situation at York where the Lendal Tower (Figure 2.2), originally part of the city's medieval defences (a 'water tower'!) was converted to a water tower in 1616 by the installation of an internal tank. This was, presumably, filled from the adjacent River Ouse but whether by a wind, horse or waterwheel-driven pump is uncertain. Whatever means were employed, the system was not a success and had fallen into disuse by the early 1630s.

A second attempt was made to utilise Lendal Tower as a 'waterhouse' when in 1682 Henry Whistler erected a waterwheel to pump water up into the tank, but wide natural fluctuations in river level caused persistent problems and Whistler's wheel was dismantled after only two years. But Lendal Tower and its elevated tank remained in service, using either horse or wind power at different periods to drive the pumps. In 1752 the waterworks were purchased by Colonel Thornton. Four years later he raised money by mortgaging the works and a pump powered by a Newcomen atmospheric steam engine was installed. This raised water 72ft to a lead-lined cistern at the top of the tower. John Smeaton, a shareholder in the water undertaking, rebuilt the engine in 1784 and Lendal Tower continued to function as a pumphouse and water tower until 1846. Although the topmost storey was removed with the tank, the tower is still in use as the offices of the York Waterworks Company (now part of Yorkshire Water) thus maintaining an association with the city's water supply for nearly four centuries.

In the context of waterwheel-powered supply systems mention has

Figure 2.1. York Buildings waterworks, Villiers Street, London, c 1726

to be made of George Sorocold of Derby, about whom tantalisingly little has been discovered. Inspired, it is said, by the system in use to supply the French royal palace and gardens at Versailles, Sorocold devised and installed a similar system for a water supply to his native Derby from the River Derwent in 1692. Sorocold utilised a variable-level waterwheel (possibly designed by his partner and collaborator, John Hadley) to cope with fluctuations in river levels. This system remained in use until 1829. He was then engaged to erect comparable systems at Leeds and Norwich in 1694 and at Bristol in 1696. His reputation

Figure 2.2. Lendal Tower, York, converted to water tower c 1684

spread nationally, and he is known to have installed his waterwheel-powered systems in towns and cities as far afield as Macclesfield, Wirksworth, Sheffield, Chester, Great Yarmouth, Portsmouth, London (Marchant's Waterworks), Kings Lynn, Deal and finally at Bridgnorth in 1706, where Sorocold's water supply system lasted until 1857. His Leeds system utilised a service reservoir but at other locations, certainly those with a more gentle topography, there can be little doubt but that he would have had to erect water towers.

Sorocold's renown was such that in 1702 he was also brought in by Morris' successors to refurbish the London Bridge system and to extend it under a fourth arch. His new 20ft diameter, 14ft wide wheel was reported to have powered four four-throw reciprocating pumps and delivered 880 gallons per minute to a height of 120ft, though this latter figure is questionable. By this time all four London Bridge waterwheels (there was also one on the south bank) were recorded as driving a staggering total of 52 pumps capable of supplying 1,820 gallons per minute. This equates to 2.6 million gallons per day but was probably considerably less in practice because of slack tide periods and pumps under repair. The figure of 52 pumps almost certainly relates to individual pump cylinders, counting (for example) a three-throw pump as three pumps. Sorocold was also employed by London's New River Company in 1708 to install a windpump-powered system to pump water up to a service reservoir to supply new urban development in the more elevated parts of Islington. The intermittent nature of wind power proved problematical and the windpump was replaced by horse-power in the 1720s.

During the same period, the water tower gradually developed, growing in size and sophistication though technically still not far from its medieval origins. As the extent and scale of the undertakings grew, and with them the capital investment necessary for development, civic authorities took over from private individuals as the local water undertaker. In 1694 land was leased by the Oxford City Council 'at Market Hill in Cornmarket' for the construction of an elevated cistern. Local historical research at Warwick has identified the locations of structures erected circa 1693 and in the late 18th century, and revealed an intriguing sequence of water towers in the city, culminating in Warwick's mid-Victorian water tower of 1857. This last tower was essentially a modern water tower and thus falls properly within the next chapter.

Until the industrial revolution, the evolution of water supply systems was constrained primarily by the development of pump and pipe technology. The force pump — essentially a combination of a piston moving in a cylinder and non-return valves — was in use again by the end of the 16th century. Camden had seen and noted a 'forcer' (ie, a water pump) at work in Norwich in 1583. By the early 18th century this device had evolved into a three or occasionally even four-cylindered affair driven through a crude crankshaft to enable a rotating power source to give a reciprocating motion; what became known as the three-throw (or four-throw) pump. Notwithstanding the commercial availability of centrifugal pumps from the 1850s onwards, reciprocating pumps continued to be synonymous with waterworks pumping plant until the early years of the 20th century.

As we have already seen, a range of motive power was used to operate the pumps. Steam arrived on the scene as early as 1726 when a Newcomen engine was in operation at London's York Buildings Waterworks (It may have replaced an even earlier but very short-lived Savery engine.) In that year a Swiss visitor to London, M de Saussure, noted that

'This piece of machinery and the two pumps are placed at the foot of a wooden tower which is, I think, about one hundred feet in height, in breadth diminishing, after the manner of the pyramids, gradually. [Is this the water tower seen in J P Malcolm's 1797 painting?] At the summit of the tower, which is octagonal, there is a small leaden cistern . . . which receives the water the pumps send up and from thence it flows into the great reservoir or pond of Marylebone. The inventor of this machinery is a very clever mathematician, Dr Desaiguillieres (*sic*).'

This was, of course, an atmospheric steam engine, but they were thermodynamically very inefficient and their excessive fuel consumption made them uneconomic to operate — except at coal mines. The York Buildings Waterworks steam engine was out of use by 1731. It had been a false dawn and another 100 years were to pass before steam engines started to become widely acceptable for waterworks pumping.

Water supply pipes were commonly of wood; reamed-out tree trunks with crude spigot-and-socket joints, but these could not withstand any great pressure and were only really suitable for gravity-fed systems. Nevertheless they were still being installed at the start of the 19th century, sometimes being used to replace lead pipes. The use of lead pipework goes back to Roman times and a three inch diameter lead pipe was in use as a water main in Edinburgh from 1676. Neither timber nor lead proved very satisfactory in use. The former had a limited life and suffered from leaking joints whilst the latter was expensive and larger diameter lead pipes tended to collapse under any substantial load. Cast iron pipes were in use at Versailles as early as 1664 and in 1729 Switzer wrote of iron pipes:

'. . . which are now growing into use . . . the best sizes being from seven or eight to five, four or three inches diameter. They are cast about two yards, and sometimes three yards long and that but seldom. They are joined together by flanchets (flanges) as may be seen in the water works on London Bridge . . .'

Cast iron pipes were certainly in use in Edinburgh in 1755 and their use must have become widespread as the century progressed, for between 1777 and 1786, J&W Wilkinson of Wrexham exported 40 miles of cast iron pipes to Paris. *Après nous le déluge.*

The development of comprehensive pipe networks was however handicapped by the lack of reliable and leakproof fittings. The in-line gate (or sluice) valve did not appear until 1839 followed by the hydrant in about 1850 and mechanical flow meters from 1852. It is difficult to avoid the impression that 18th century water undertakers were not keen to encourage increased consumption but, beset as they were by the limitations of the technology available to them, one can feel a certain sympathy with their plight. In 1770 Bath Corporation threatened to disconnect one of their customers, a Mr Melmoth, unless he agreed to stop using their piped water to flush his water closet. Even in places where resource availability was not a problem, supplies could still be extremely intermittent. In 1800 the Plymouth Dock Waterworks Company 'guaranteed' their customers a supply for two hours each day and in York, as late as 1846, one half of the city had a two hour supply on Mondays, Wednesdays and Fridays and the other half on Tuesdays, Thursdays and Saturdays. Obviously the Victorian link between cleanliness and godliness had yet to be established.

Unfortunately there are very few surviving water towers from this pre-industrial age. One example, although probably of early 19th century origin, is the water tower at Court Lodge, Wrotham, in Kent. (Figure 2.3) Here a simple octagonal brick tower housed both a 680 gallon elevated lead-lined tank (only the octagonal wooden frame remains, the lead was sold to pay for bathrooms when mains water arrived) and a pony or donkey-worked pump over a well in the base of the tower. The latter machinery, although originally intended for a private supply, subsequently fed a row of nearby cottages until World War I and has survived almost intact. Other, more grandiose examples of structures built to provide elevated water storage in connection with private pumped systems at stately homes started to appear in the 18th century. A tiny handful of these have survived.

With the industrial revolution now fully established, the accelerating expansion of towns in the first quarter of the 19th century, especially in the industrial areas, soon outstripped the available water sup-

Figure 2.3. Court Lodge water tower, Wrotham, Kent, mid 19th century

plies, even where they had previously been adequate. A few towns, where local conditions were favourable, already relied on water brought in from considerable distances outside by means of open leats. Sir Francis Drake's leat at Plymouth, completed in 1591, and London's New River are the best known but they existed elsewhere too, some appreciably earlier. In the last decade of the 14th century, water was being brought to Hull across the Humber estuary by boat, and in 1401 the corporation excavated a channel to convey water to the town from chalk springs at Anlaby. This was bitterly resented by the people of Anlaby and the neighbouring villages who dammed the channel and filled it with rubbish. The mayor and burgesses of Hull responded by petitioning the Pope to have the delinquent villagers excommunicated. The matter was eventually resolved by a stern letter from the College of Cardinals in Rome in 1415. This leat was still in use in 1616 when, in order to provide piped water supplies within the town, a company was formed and a primitive water tower, filled by a horse-pump, was erected at the northern end of Waterhouse Lane. These 'water works' are clearly marked as such on Antony Bower's 1786 map of Hull, by which time the horse had been replaced by a steam engine. In 1830 the 1616 site was abandoned and a new waterworks established on Spring Bank, on the western edge of the town. Here the corporation erected a 60,000 gallon iron tank above the brick engine house, 40 feet high. The water tower as we would recognise it today had begun to take shape. Hull's new waterworks was well in the technological vanguard in other respects, as water taken from the open channel was routinely filtered, one of the earliest recorded instances of water treatment in Britain.

The urban water undertaker's problems were exacerbated by the advancing living standards of an emergent middle class. An increasing number of consumers were no longer content to rely on communal standpipes and conduits in the street for their domestic water supplies and began to demand a supply piped into their own homes, and for somewhat more than a meagre two hours each day. The results of this were twofold; an increased *per-capita* consumption and the need for higher operating pressures within the supply network. These trends, combined with the by now explosive growth in urban populations, placed the already inadequate water supplies in towns and cities under an intolerable strain and by the start of Queen Victoria's reign it was increasingly obvious that the situation nationally was becoming unsustainable. The creation of the statutory framework necessary for the provision of municipal water supply systems capable of meeting the needs of industrial towns and cities, the provision of those systems and with them the appearance of the prototypes of the modern water tower will be the subject of the next chapter.

CHAPTER THREE

The Victorian Municipal Water Tower

The provision of water supplies in towns up to the early years of the 19th century has been described in the preceding chapter. The diverse and piecemeal character of this provision was in keeping with the nature of local government up to that time. In many respects still reflecting its medieval and ecclesiastical origins, local government, such as it was, found itself increasingly ill-equipped to deal with the physical and administrative problems of an industrialised urban society. Local authorities lacked statutory powers and such powers as they did possess were uncertain and poorly defined. Before the 19th century only a small minority of towns enjoyed public water supplies and until 1835, despite earlier initiatives, there were hardly any supplies in England that could be described as a municipal undertaking. One rare exception was Macclesfield, which claims to have had a municipal supply continuously from 1682 until 1961. The situation in Scotland, where many boroughs never relinquished municipal control, was somewhat different.

Even if these problems were recognised and acknowledged, parliament was not inclined towards strengthening local government to deal with them. This attitude was perhaps understandable since local government itself seemed, by and large, to have given up any attempt to tackle the problems that so beset them. In any case, the first half of the 19th century was an era of unbridled economic liberalism and parliament merely echoed the political establishment's deep suspicion of public ownership. Consequently the setting up of joint stock companies to provide public utilities was actively encouraged, and from 1820 onwards an average of two water supply companies were being incorporated each year. It is of some interest that in many towns, particularly the smaller ones, gas and water were supplied by the same company. By 1845, when only 10 out of 190 municipalities possessed their own waterworks, there were already 65 privately owned water supply companies in operation. This was perhaps the heyday of those early urban water companies, for even though this figure had increased to 145 by 1865 the tide had already begun to turn.

The burgeoning industrial towns and cities were by now, in the absence of any coherent town planning, experiencing potentially overwhelming problems with inadequate housing, urban transport, policing, the provision of public utilities and amenities and, above all, public health. In the 1840s, only 1450 houses out of 18,500 in Newcastle and Gateshead had individual supplies. In Bristol only 5000 out of a population of 13,000 had a domestic water supply. Elsewhere the position was very similar. Worse still, the situation was actually deteriorating. Consumption of water in Manchester fell from 14 gallons per customer per day in 1832 to ten gallons in 1841. In Leeds there was a fall in per-capita consumption from one and a half gallons per day in 1801 to little more than half a gallon in 1831, whilst the number of households supplied fell from 9% in 1811 to 6% in 1841. It had become starkly apparent, even to the most *laissez faire* liberal, that the situation was getting progressively out of hand and that the existing legal and administrative framework was wholly incapable of addressing, let alone solving, the daunting problems facing the industrial towns and those that lived and worked in them. There was certainly no adequate legal framework for the provision of piped water supplies, let alone the allocation of water resources.

The problems faced by the private water companies were twofold. Firstly, as the urban areas grew and coalesced, they were forced to look increasingly far afield for their sources of supply as local sources became both polluted and subject to the conflicting demands of navigation, water power, and industrial abstraction. The capital costs of new works increased alarmingly, together with the problems of financing them. At the same time their customer base was, at best, static as most of the urban population were unable to afford piped water at a price at which it was economic for the companies to supply, especially if they were to finance new works and pay a dividend to their shareholders. The fact that there would be immense external benefits to the nation at large from improved water supplies was immaterial to the water companies and, within their own remit, they acted rationally in disregarding them.

There does appear to have been a modest improvement in both water quality and security of supply from about 1850, but from a very low base. Despite the notable success of Chadwick and his collaborators, there were other equally important influences at work. As industrialisation spread, the industrialists themselves found their own private sources of water, hitherto literally on their own doorsteps, were being increasingly derogated in both quality and quantity by their upstream neighbours. To escape the ensuing 'free for all,' industrialists were forced to turn to the piped supply offered by the local private water undertaker but these supplies were all too often intermittent, polluted and at too low a pressure to be suitable for use in the new multi-storey factories and mills. Intermittent supplies could cripple firefighting and polluted water was unacceptable in many industrial processes, especially those involving textiles. There was therefore an increasingly vocal and hard-nosed pressure group of industrial water users pressing for radical improvements to their local public water supplies.

Predictably perhaps, the landscape was transformed, both politically and literally, by the initiatives taken in the 1840s by a growing number of large industrial conurbations where the problems outlined above had become most acute. Encouraged by the changing political climate they promoted large, professionally-engineered schemes to harness substantial water resources well outside their own municipal boundaries. To do so, the municipal authorities concerned utilised not the relatively weak permissive powers in the Chadwick-inspired Acts 1847 and 1848 but their own new-found power and influence in order to promote and obtain private Acts of Parliament, though it is clear that the pattern had been established before the late 1840s. (It should also be noted that in a few cases these schemes were promoted by the larger private companies.)

Suddenly there was a succession of large industrial towns and cities obtaining Acts of Parliament for their own water supply schemes — Leeds (1837), Bradford (1844), Manchester, Glasgow, Sheffield and Dundee (1845), Bristol and Newport (1846) Liverpool, Edinburgh and Leicester (1847), and so on. These schemes were all relatively modest compared to the massive schemes in North Wales (Liverpool), Mid-Wales (Birmingham) and the Trossachs (Glasgow) which were to come later in the 19th century but, significantly, they were all based on impounding reservoirs. These were not the first schemes to bring clean water from a source well outside the town that built them — Plymouth's Drake's Leat (1591), London's New River (1613) and Edinburgh's lead pipeline from Comiston Springs (1676, extended into the Pentland Hills 1760) pre-dated them by a couple of hundred years but all these schemes used technology the Romans would have been familiar with.

The storage capacity created by damming an upland river or stream enabled a constant and reliable supply of clean water to be had throughout the year. Furthermore, since these reservoirs were invariably located at a considerably greater elevation than the towns that built them, they were able to supply those towns by gravity. Pumping was not necessary, and hence there would, by and large, have been no initial need for water towers. This may explain why the classic 'Victorian' water tower did not appear in any numbers for at least another decade.

One of the most common characteristics of pre-industrial water supply systems was the intermittent supply, especially where the water had to be pumped or, even if gravity fed, was derived from a spring or stream whose natural discharge could exhibit marked seasonal variability. If the storage capacity in the system was limited, as was almost always the case, then the supply to consumers would have to be interrupted on a daily cycle to allow the cisterns to refill, or simply to restrict demand. The gravity fed water supplies to the big industrial towns inaugurated in the 1830s and 40s were supported by large impounding reservoirs. Resources were, at least in the new scheme's early years, virtually unlimited. Not only was there no need for an intermittent supply, it would have been a pointless and time consuming chore. Furthermore, cutting off the flow in the mains could also reduce the pressure in the pipes to the point where any leakage would be reversed and water drawn into the pipes from the surrounding ground, a potential public health hazard.

The continuous supply thus became the expected norm, even though adherents of the old intermittent supply concept proved remarkably tenacious. As early as 1847 the Waterworks Clauses Act, an attempt to standardise waterworks practice, included provisions for constant supplies but the good intent was effectively nullified by a clause stating that it need not be implemented unless four fifths of the local inhabitants requisitioned it. The Metropolis Water Act of 1871 confirmed that the provision of a continuous supply in London was still optional but edged towards it by stipulating that water must be supplied on Sundays as well as on weekdays. It was not until 1899, shortly before the formation of the Metropolitan Water Board in 1902, that the whole of London finally came to enjoy a continuous supply. Even as recently as 1938 continuous supply was still being discussed in an engineering textbook in terms of its advantages and disadvantages. Faced with the commitment to provide a continuous supply, the water engineer could no longer cope with the consequences of inadequate storage in his supply network simply by shutting off the water. Maintaining a continuous supply demanded sufficient storage capacity to balance the daily peaks and troughs in demand and this meant water towers of a substantial size, much larger than the elevated cisterns of the past.

The large municipal schemes of the late 1830s and 40s acted as a spur for the more modest industrial towns to follow them down the same route. Between 1846 and 1865 only two towns per year had adopted municipal supplies, but by the 1860s the tide was in full flood and municipalisation of water supplies grew rapidly. Between 1866 and 1878, 43 public water supply undertakings transferred from private to municipal control and from 1865 to 1905 this trend was running at an average of six undertakings per year. Initially at least, the process appears to have been one of mutual convenience for it was not until 1888 that statutory powers were first used by a local authority for the compulsory acquisition of its water supply, when Sheffield Corporation took over the city's water company 'on the grounds of public policy' at a cost of £2,092,014. Not that municipalisation had been much less contentious elsewhere. Birmingham had taken over its water supply, sanctioned by Act of Parliament in 1875, after a bruising campaign by Joseph Chamberlain who, echoing the report of the 1869 Royal Commission on Sanitary Reform, declared that "whereas there should be a profit made on the gas undertaking, the waterworks should never be a source of profit as all profit should go in the reduction of the price of water."

By 1907, 81% of public water supplies were in municipal hands, by which time the rump of private companies that remained were the most efficient of their kind. The level of service they provided was equal to that of any of the municipal undertakings and the impetus for municipalisation had abated. This *status quo* persisted until the 1980s by which time the steady amalgamation of municipal water undertakings during the preceding half century had diminished the once distinctive local character — and accountability — of many of those undertakings, and the tide started to turn once more in favour of private enterprise. Coincidentally or not, the era of municipalisation saw an inexorable rise in the *per-capita* consumption of water. In Leeds it rose from eight gallons per day in 1851, the year before municipalisation, to over 20 gallons in 1871, and in Manchester it soared to over 32 gallons per day by 1878. There is however some evidence that the earlier falls in consumption had been reversed before municipalisation.

The reader may have found the preamble to this chapter a little protracted but for a proper appreciation of the Victorian water tower it is essential to understand it within its historical context. A note of explanation, justification even, must also be given for the use of the word 'Victorian' in the title of this chapter. The term 'Victorian' has been used as a convenient shorthand description for what the reader will immediately recognise as the typical water tower of the 19th century — a substantial iron tank supported on or within a properly engineered masonry or brick tower — but it was not a uniquely Victorian design. Apart from the Round House at Perth, it is not inconceivable that other very early examples were being built before Queen Victoria ascended the throne, and water towers of this type continued to be built up to first world war, and even later. Essex, for some reason, seems to have been the last outpost of this design. Although the 'Victorian' design was entirely superseded by the reinforced concrete water tower in a relatively short period, effectively over two decades, the transition did not occur overnight. As is often immediately apparent, the Victorian water tower was more than just a utilitarian structure for the storage of water, it was an expression of civic pride, characteristic of a nation approaching the height of its imperial power even if, in engineering terms, the Victorian water tower was simple and uncomplicated, both structurally and hydraulically.

As mentioned in the previous chapter, the oldest surviving Victorian municipal water tower is the Lochside Cistern at Montrose in Scotland. This is a recognisably modern water tower (Figure 3.1). It was opened in September 1841, superseding an earlier (1804, enlarged 1828) ten thousand gallon town centre cistern. Initially gravity fed from a spring source at Glenskenno, its location and capacity (40,000 gallons) were suitable when a pumped supply from Kinnaber was

Figure 3.1. Lochside Cistern, Montrose, Tayside, 1841

introduced about 1860. The Lochside Cistern (the archaic name was retained) had a circular, 27ft diameter, cast iron tank fabricated by the Montrose Foundry Company enclosed within an empinnacled octagonal masonry tower, 36ft across opposite faces and 64ft high. The tank was carried on ten cast iron beams spanning the full width of the shaft but supported on two internal cross-walls within the tower.

Whether or not the Lochside Cistern can claim to be the oldest surviving municipal water tower in Britain depends upon the definition of a water tower and, in particular, to what extent it should have been built for that purpose. It is not uncommon to find water towers which incorporate pumphouses at ground level, at the base of the shaft or in the space between the columns. With compact modern electric pumps it is very easy to do this without compromising the essential function of the tower or significantly influence its basic design. The pumps in question can be either boosters or, if the tower is located over a borehole, primary abstraction pumps. Small oil-engine driven pumps are now virtually obsolete but it is still possible to come across older 'Victorian' type water towers containing the remains of such pumps, usually only concrete machine bases but occasionally with the engine or pump still *in situ*. These pumps, though less compact than their electric successors, could also be accommodated without undue difficulty on the ground floor of a water tower.

This brings us to the Round House at Perth (Figure 3.2). This building is worth considering in some detail because even if it does not meet the strict definition of a water tower, which is debatable, it is a notable landmark in the development not only of urban water supply

Figure 3.2. The Round House, Perth, Tayside, 1832

systems but also of water towers themselves. Throughout the latter half of the 18th century, Perth suffered the usual deficiencies in its water supply of any expanding and industrialising town of that period. In 1810 the Town Council appointed Dr Adam Anderson, Rector of Perth Academy — the local headmaster — to investigate the problem and propose a solution. This he did. A variety of options were considered and at first nothing happened but the steadily deteriorating situation finally compelled action. A scheme was agreed and, in 1829, an Act of Parliament was obtained to sanction it.

Anderson's water supply scheme was based upon large, shallow wells on Moncreiffe Island in the River Tay, in effect a river abstraction scheme with inbuilt filtration. The island was connected to the town by a 12 inch cast iron pipeline laid under the bed of the river and terminating in a 23 foot deep cast iron lined sump directly opposite the island at the corner of Marshall Place and Tay Street. The Round House was erected over the sump. This was not the originally intended site for the Round House but it was relocated to avoid routing the pipeline close to a cemetery and the perceived risk to public health. The relative prominence of the new site then gave rise to concerns about the visual impact of the building in the Perth townscape. Dr Anderson responded by designing the Round House as a circular, domed rotunda in a formal classical style modelled on the Roman Pantheon, together with a rectangular extension to the north in the same elegant style. A chimney, designed to appear as a classical stone column on a pedestal, surmounted by a vase, completed the work. The resulting effect was both imposing and dignified. The rectangular extension housed the boilers which fed the two beam-engine pumps, the second being installed only three years after the scheme was completed in 1832.

The rotunda itself, the Round House proper, housed what was for its time a massive 146,000 gallon sectional cast iron elevated tank, cylindrical in shape and decorated externally with Ionic pilasters and an ornate frieze incorporating Perth's coat of arms. The rotunda's domed roof was also of cast iron. It is not entirely clear whether either of the beam engines was actually housed within the rotunda, directly beneath the tank. Anderson ingeniously made provision for steam to be bled off from the boilers to pass through heating coils inside the tank as protection against frost. The town's steady growth away from the river eventually rendered the tank redundant and in 1862 it was superseded by a service reservoir on higher ground outside the town. The base of the tank was subsequently dismantled and its internal supporting walls demolished to give additional clear space inside the rotunda. The beam engines themselves were replaced with a pair of triple-expansion reciprocating steam engines installed in 1898 and 1904 respectively. These were in turn replaced by electrically driven pumps in 1954 until a new pumping station was built on a different site in 1965 whereupon, after 133 years of continuous service, the Round House became redundant.

Both the Round House and Adam Anderson deserve to be better known. Perth's water supply scheme aroused widespread interest when it was first commissioned, at least on the continent, for in 1837 the King of Prussia sought and obtained a set of drawings from Dr Anderson with the intention of providing a similar system for Berlin. Nearer home, the Town Council were more grudging in their appreciation of Anderson's success and voted to pay him 300 guineas, a sum which he apparently regarded as insufficient for the work he had undertaken on their behalf. He wrote to the Council in 1834 to protest at their treatment of him, and again in 1837 to complain that he had not received a reply to his previous letter. Perhaps it is not surprising that the 'schoolmaster engineer' as he had become known seems to have abandoned his engineering career at this juncture and taken up an appointment as the Professor of Natural Philosophy at St Andrews University.

In many respects Anderson's comprehensive scheme, and the philosophy it embodied, was almost a generation ahead of its time. The unity, scale, and solidity of the engineering involved bore little comparison with what, as far as we know, had gone before and yet it failed conspicuously to provoke emulation elsewhere in Britain. One can only speculate as to why. Whether the Round House may or may not be accepted as a water tower, as opposed to an engine house incorporating an elevated tank, is almost immaterial given its historical significance as a key component of Anderson's pioneering work at Perth and thus a notable milestone in water supply engineering. It may be worth pointing out that the Round House is, in fact, pre Victorian.

It cannot be claimed that either the Round House or the Lochside Cistern were Britain's first municipal water towers, or even the first with cast iron tanks. Other municipal water supply systems with water towers were undoubtedly being built elsewhere in the early 19th century but, as far as is known, none was remotely comparable with Adam Anderson's waterworks at Perth. Typical of this pre-Victorian generation of waterworks was that at Kings Lynn in Norfolk. As we have already seen, Kings Lynn was one of the towns where George Sorocold was active. In 1780 the old 'water engine' was renewed but within a few years the Corporation, in a fit of enthusiasm, suddenly decided to abandon the recently renewed waterwheel and replace it with a steam engine. Kings Lynn being remote from the newly industrialised areas of the country, the Corporation were perhaps unfamiliar with with the latest advances in technology and purchased, not an up to date Boulton & Watt machine but a Newcomen 'atmospheric' steam engine. This was a disaster, as the ratepayers rapidly discovered that they could neither afford to fuel it let alone maintain it in working order. Their steam engine, by now an embarrassing dead white elephant, was left to rust and the waterwheel recommissioned.

With the town steadily expanding, this reversion could only be a temporary expedient and in 1830 a new waterworks was established at Kettle Mills on the Gaywood River, a chalk stream on the northern edge of the town where a 10HP pumping engine by George Stephenson was installed in a 54ft high circular engine house. As at Perth, this building also housed a cast iron tank but at Kings Lynn this held a derisory 'upwards of 1400 gallons,' not much larger that a modern domestic heating oil tank. Contemporary sketches of the Kettle Mills waterworks show a range of ill-assorted, bucolic looking buildings, more akin to a large farmstead than an industrial site. Prominent among them was the circular masonry(?) tower with its conical tiled roof capped with a weathervane. A thin, square brick chimney protrudes from a lean-to building, presumably the boiler house. The overall effect is quaint and distinctly ramshackle, totally unlike Anderson's impressively well engineered works at Perth. To Kings Lynn's credit the water was abstracted 'after percolation through a bed of sand' and the town's elm-log water mains were renewed with cast iron as part of the overall scheme.

The apparent time lag between the initial wave of big municipal water supply schemes of the 1840s and the appearance of the 'Victorian' water tower in significant numbers from the 1850s onwards has already been touched on. It is no coincidence that the spate of professionally engineered schemes of the 1840s were gravity-fed systems. With the exception of London, the great industrial towns and cities had grown up in the coalfields that fuelled their growth, hilly areas in the main, where the topography and geology lent itself to upland reservoirs and, initially at least, gravity-fed supply systems. Elsewhere in Britain the older towns were not so fortunate but they could not fail to follow the example set by their industrial counterparts in providing their inhabitants with modern water supplies. If geography, financial constraints and, quite possibly, landed interests precluded them from developing impounding reservoirs they had to rely, as they had always done, on abstractions from rivers and wells. With up-to-date engineering, the water from such sources might now be cleaner and give a more reliable supply than hitherto, but it still needed pumping — and pumping involved water towers. And even in those areas where the original scheme may have been entirely gravity-fed, as the demand for water and the area of supply expanded inexorably, the distribution networks became increasingly complex and, here too, water towers started to appear. Notable early municipal water towers are to be seen at Aubrey Street, Liverpool (1854), Boughton, Chester (1856) and Broadstairs (1859).

Elaborate design and extravagant ornamentation were characteristic of almost all Victorian municipal buildings and were certainly not confined to water towers. Nevertheless, water towers, because of their prominent, sometimes dominating physical presence in the local townscape lent themselves particularly to public expressions of municipal self-confidence. No doubt, especially with the close proximity of considerable numbers of small, independent urban boroughs in the larger industrial areas, there was also an element of municipal rivalry at work. It was an essentially urban phenomenon, for as yet the rural hinterland still relied on private wells, springs and cisterns for its water supplies. Towards the end of the century when, here and there, 'model' villages on the large landed estates were supplied with piped water the water tower would be a smaller and more modest affair. Even so, the same prevailing tendencies are apparent.

The transition from the primitive, pre-industrial raised cistern to the Victorian municipal water tower coincided with the transition from relatively small lead-lined timber framed tanks to the use of much larger iron tanks, and for much of the 19th century iron became the dominant, indeed almost the only material used for large tanks and similar water retaining structures. Throughout this period iron tanks came in two quite distinct and very different forms — those assembled on site using prefabricated cast iron panels, or those constructed of rivetted wrought iron (or latterly steel) plates. Each was the product of a well established industrial technology and each had its own specific advantages. Neither type seems to have gained a dominant position in the market or to have come anywhere near to displacing the other, right up to the time when both types were superseded by reinforced concrete and the pressed steel sectional tank, though cast iron tanks do seem to have been the more numerous of the two. The choice of material by the engineer concerned was probably determined by the nature of the local engineering industry and the availability of particular engineering skills in that locality. In an area with a shipbuilding or boilermaking tradition a rivetted tank would presumably be the favoured choice.

The use of uniform cast iron panels bolted together to form a water-retaining structure dates back at least to the late 18th century and the building of Thomas Telford's aqueduct at Longdon-on-Tern for the Shrewsbury Canal in 1796. The first canal aqueduct to be constructed in cast iron, its nine foot wide 186 foot long trough is made up of large cast iron panels but perhaps the most intriguing feature of the structure is the irregularity and distortion of the individual castings. It is obvious that the ironfounder had experienced considerable difficulties in casting the plates, either in the moulding or the cooling. The problems which must have been encountered in assembling the trough, let alone making it watertight, are all too apparent yet Telford's aqueduct gave satisfactory service for almost 150 years.

Nevertheless these early problems with producing cast iron panels of consistent quality and to the close dimensional tolerances essential for ease of assembly must have been quickly overcome to give Telford sufficient confidence to attempt what was to become his masterpiece, the Pontcysyllte aqueduct above the River Dee near Llangollen, completed in 1805. Here the sectional cast iron trough is nearly 12 feet wide but 846 feet long, without any of the obvious imperfections clearly to be seen at Longdon. After Pontcysyllte there could have been no doubt as to the suitability of cast iron for large water retaining structures, and that those early problems, whatever their cause, were entirely overcome is equally obvious from a close inspection of any Victorian water tower with a cast iron tank, where the ability of ironfounders to cast plates and other components with a high degree of uniformity and precision is evident.

The first sectional cast iron tanks, like the iron troughs made for Telford's aqueducts, would almost certainly have been produced specifically for a particular structure as 'one off' commissions by the ironfounders concerned. Nevertheless, as water towers began to proliferate the advantages of standardisation and mass production of cast iron tank components must have become obvious to water undertakers, engineers and ironfounders alike. In fact it is clear that the technology had been developed and was available for some time before municipal water towers started to appear in any numbers from the 1850s, since railway water towers of appreciable size were in all probability being built in significant numbers a decade or more earlier. It is apparent from an inspection of the railway water towers at York and Curthwaite (Cumbria) described in Chapter 8 that prefabricated cast iron plates intended specifically for water towers were being produced as early as the end of the 1830s.

Expressed in terms of the relationship between the capacity of the tank and the area of its walls and floor — the most economic use of materials — a hemispherical or cylindrical tank is considerably more efficient than a square or rectangular one. Yet cast iron tanks were almost always square or rectangular in plan, with vertical walls and a horizontal floor. The reason is not hard to find. It is much easier to cast an iron panel on a flat, horizontal surface than it is to produce the curved plates required to form a cylindrical tank. A rectangular tank could also be erected on a rectangular tower which, with its rectilinear surfaces, would be no more expensive to build than an equivalent cylindrical tower, where any savings in materials would be outweighed by the additional labour costs. This would certainly be the case if building in stone rather than brick. Circular cast iron tanks are not however unknown. As has been seen, Perth's Round House incorporated a cylindrical tank as did Liverpool's Everton (Aubrey Street) water tower, although it is certainly the case that nearly all later Victorian towers had square or rectangular tanks. Everton (Figure 3.3) is unusual in that its tank is externally buttressed with raked iron stanchions.

It could be argued that the benefits of both approaches can be combined by making the tank polygonal in plan, but few water towers of this shape have been identified. There is a good practical explanation for this. Standard panels intended for rectangular tanks have their flanges set at right angles to the plane of the plate; they can

Figure 3.3. Everton water tower, Liverpool, Merseyside, 1854

therefore be bolted together to form a tank with a floor area of any number of shapes and sizes. On the other hand, a standard panel fabricated for a polygonal tank would have two of its flanges set at an angle less than 90 degrees and it could therefore only be used for one specific size and shape of tank. To achieve a range of polygonal tank sizes, a number different types of panel would be needed and the benefits of standardisation would thus be largely forfeited. (A square or rectangular cast iron panelled tank does, of course, require special corner pieces. A polygonal tank avoids the need for corner pieces up the sides but, if of any size, still requires corner pieces of at least two different types between walls and base not to mention the differently shaped panels needed for the base itself.) Despite all this, water towers with polygonal cast iron tanks were occasionally erected.

Mention has already been made of the precision with which cast iron tank panels could be produced, although it became normal practice for the mating faces of the panels to be lightly machined and for the bolt holes to be drilled to jig. This precision is particularly apparent with tanks fabricated from plates with internal flanges when the joints on the external fair faces are sometimes surprisingly difficult to identify without careful inspection. Apart from a neater appearance, the use of internal flanges also facilitates the use of internal cross-bracing to tension the sides in order to resist bending moments imposed on the otherwise unsupported walls of the tank by the pressure of water, particularly important in tanks with a large, undivided base area. As regards appearance, the use of internal flanges was only important where the tank was intended to be free-standing and exposed, rather than enclosed within the tower and hidden from view. On the face of it, since it would be as easy to produce panels with internal as external flanges, the more aesthetically pleasing internally-flanged type might have been expected to predominate, but it did not. Here again, a simple practical consideration could be the reason. With external flanges the edges and corners of the tank can be formed by the use of simple angle irons in the 90 degree gap between adjacent plates. With internal flanges special quite complex castings are needed to serve the same purpose, although by making a virtue of necessity the outer faces of these castings can be rounded to give a smooth curve to the edges and corners of the tank, reinforcing the impression of a 'seamless' structure. Examples of cast iron tanks with internal and external flanges respectively are shown in Figures 3.4 and 3.5.

Despite the clean lines of tanks fabricated from internally-flanged panels, their appearance would still have been regarded as utilitarian and Victorian sensibilities were such that the majority of municipal water towers, certainly those in the larger towns and cities, were of the enclosed tank type. This was despite the fact that for a given capacity and top water level, the exposed-tank design was obviously cheaper to

Figure 3.4. Externally flanged cast iron water tank, Charfield railway station, Avon, probably 1844

Figure 3.5. Internally flanged cast iron tank, Wivenhoe water tower, Essex, 1901

construct, even though the tank would still need to be roofed to keep out birds and airborne pollutants. The rather stark effect of exposed cast iron panels could to some extent have been ameliorated by the use of ornate castings and decorative iron trimmings, although the problem of what to do about the inherently unsightly tank access ladder and walkways would still remain, and a comparison with industrial water towers was unavoidable. Considerations of maintenance must also have played a part in the decision. An enclosed tank is not exposed to the elements — an advantage for the safety of workmen as well as for reduced corrosion — and is better insulated against frost. Examples of each type are shown in Figures 3.6 and 3.7.

The weight of water contained within a typical water tower with,

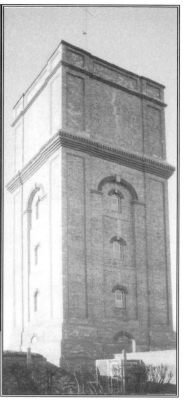

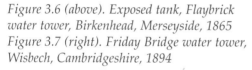

Figure 3.6 (above). Exposed tank, Flaybrick water tower, Birkenhead, Merseyside, 1865
Figure 3.7 (right). Friday Bridge water tower, Wisbech, Cambridgeshire, 1894

say, a 50,000 gallon capacity 40ft x 60ft x 10ft tank, would be 223 tons. Whilst this would be a relatively modest load for the masonry tower itself, the cast iron tank could not have carried this load unaided and, as well as the internal bracing already mentioned, structural support would have been required beneath the tank floor. This took the form of cast or wrought iron beams spanning horizontally between the opposing walls of the tower. The three pipes from ground level to the tank — the supply pipe from the water treatment works, the delivery pipe to the consumers and the overflow pipe — would also have been of cast iron. The joints between adjacent tank panels were usually caulked with 'rust cement' or, later on, with bituminous gaskets.

The disadvantages of cast iron tanks are their dead weight (compared to wrought iron), the proliferation of joints to be sealed, and their inflexibility in the event of differential settlement of the supporting structure. They are also nearly always square or rectangular. Rivetted iron tanks were, by contrast, almost invariably circular in plan, with a dished base (which, incidentally, avoided the areas of 'dead' water in the corners of rectangular tanks). This meant that the supporting structure could be either square or circular — or both, as at Lincoln's Westgate tower (1910), where the rivetted iron tank is supported on a circular brick shaft encased within a massive square masonry 'Norman keep', intended to blend in with the nearby castle and cathedral (Figure 3.8). The voids in the corners between the brick and stone structures are utilised for stairwells giving access to the tank and tower roof.

It might be supposed that demand for cast iron tanks would have been killed off by reinforced concrete and pressed steel panel tanks but in 1927 an engineering textbook could still advise its readers that 'the cast iron system has much to recommend it' and the firm of Mather & Platt was still advertising standardised sectional cast iron tanks in the late 1940s. It is not known for certain when cast iron tanks passed into history, but they can occasionally be found at military airfields, indicating that they were still being produced as recently as the second world war. A British Standard for cast iron tanks was issued in 1949 but this must have been obsolete even before it was published.

Figure 3.8. Westgate water tower, Lincoln, 1910

Whereas cast iron tanks could either be encased within the tower or left exposed and free-standing at the top of the tower, rivetted iron tanks were generally enclosed within the supporting tower. Not only were exposed wrought iron tanks more susceptible to atmospheric corrosion than cast iron but their appearance, like that of a large boiler, could neither be softened nor disguised by ornamentation. Paradoxically, the 'temporary' water tower that Leeds Corporation erected at Moortown in 1907 to supplement a hilltop service reservoir which the rising tide of housing development had reached (it was superseded by the present concrete tower in 1923) was exactly that — a redundant 6000 gallon boiler. Purpose built water towers with exposed rivetted iron or steel tanks are, nevertheless, occasionally encountered, such as the tower at Coleshill (Bucks) built using German prisoner-of-war labour in 1915. What appears to be a spherical rivetted iron tank on Goole's original (1885) water tower is, in fact, a sheet metal dome covering a cast iron tank. The example, given above, of the re-used boiler at Leeds shows that eccentric and unusual structures were not the sole preserve of the small rural water undertaker. Boston Corporation installed an elevated tank in a grain silo on Boston Docks to supplement a conventional 'Victorian' water tower built elsewhere in the town in 1905.

Unlike most modern concrete tanks, very few cast iron or rivetted iron tanks had internal access shafts up through the tank. Access to the top of the tank or tower roof had therefore to be external to the tank. Where the tank was encased within the tower, this was either in the narrow space between the tank and tower or, as in Figure 3.9, by means of a subsidiary shaft enclosing an access stairway up one side or corner of the tower, often terminating in a decorative turret at the top. With the exposed iron tank, access was provided up the side of the tank by an iron ladder or staircase, usually from a doorway and platform near the top of the tower (Figure 3.10). This arrangement was not only

Figure 3.9 (left).Lymm water tower, Cheshire, probably late 19th century
Figure 3.10 (below). Horncastle Road water tower, Boston, Lincolnshire, 1905

unsightly but also less safe for waterworks employees than an enclosed staircase. On the other hand, an exposed iron tank needed a tower only as large in plan as the tank itself. An enclosed tank was inherently more expensive to build as the tower's 'footprint' had to be significantly larger than the area of the tank to permit access for maintenance between the tank and the tower wall, even if a separate staircase turret was provided for normal operational access. With a brick or masonry tower, only a limited amount of oversail could be provided by corbelling out the tank storey.

The last (1890) of the three large Victorian towers grouped together on the same town centre site at Hartlepool (Figure 3.11, now sadly all demolished) had a sectional cast iron tank which not only had two separate compartments but also an internal access shaft enclosing a spiral iron staircase, but this degree of elaboration in cast iron seems to have been exceptional. As can be seen from the illustration, Hartlepool's earliest (c1850) tower had an octagonal cast iron tank, and all three towers had exposed tanks. Perhaps as uncompromisingly industrial a town as Hartlepool did not have aesthetic pretensions. A cylindrical rivetted steel tank with a central access shaft (Tiptree, Essex) is known to exist but this is a 1933 water tower and the present tank may even be a later replacement.

Throughout this chapter it has been implied that the supporting tower, whether of brick or masonry, was a monolithic structure like the castle keep upon which so many were modelled. Although this configuration was not a structural necessity it does seem to have been the norm, though never universal. Apart from the ill-fated Shrewsbury towers, readers will have already noticed that Everton water tower, with its peripheral ring of stone columns, arcaded at the top and at an intermediate level, does not fit the general pattern. Everton's elegance has been much admired but it is very doubtful whether, when building in masonry, such a multi-arched structure would have been as economical as a plain, load-bearing wall. Most Victorian engineers clearly thought not, although a similar structure to Everton, though nearly 30 years later, is to be found in a very different setting at Dorchester. Here the tank is of wrought iron and, once again, the tank and its supporting tower are circular in plan. It should be noted that the arched structure, requiring balanced horizontal forces at the top of each column, is better suited to a circular than a rectangular tower where large columns or heavy buttressing at the corners would be required. Colchester's Balkerne Tower (Figure 3.12) is a square, arched tower but its central shaft and four corner piers are so massive that any out-of-balance forces imposed by arch action will be structurally insignificant.

Two of Ormskirk's three Victorian water towers were of this 'open plan' design. Tower Hill (1850) was similar to Colchester's 'Jumbo' in that the tank was supported on a square grid of nine heavily plinthed red sandstone piers. The later (1879) Scarth Hill tower, known locally

Figure 3.11. Hartlepool water towers, Cleveland, c 1850 (left), c 1870 (right) & 1890 (centre)

Figure 3.12. Balkerne Tower ('Jumbo'), Colchester, Essex, 1882

as 'The Pepperpot' was circular in plan with eight circumferential brick pillars surrounding a central brick shaft, a layout which was to reappear with numerous mid 20th century concrete towers. This was a particularly attractive structure, elegantly proportioned and imposing without being intimidatingly massive. The Romanesque-style arcading above the columns and corbelling beneath the tank, with its conical roof and cupola, gave it an impressive dignity and made it one of the most attractive of Victorian water towers.

There are many fine examples of the 'Victorian' water tower still to be seen throughout Britain (Figures 3.13 and 3.14) but perhaps the most notable is that at Norton, near Runcorn. This tower was built in 1888 as

Figure 3.13 (left). Winshill water tower, Burton on Trent, Staffs, 1907
Figure 3.14 (right). Rockwell Green water tower, Wellington, Somerset, 1885

part of Liverpool Corporation's scheme to bring water from North Wales. Norton is unusual in that it is filled by gravity from the Vyrnwy aqueduct and not by pumping, its purpose being essentially that of pressure regulation in the delivery pipeline. Its 76′ diameter, 650,000 gallon steel tank has an elliptical base. Like many of the larger towers of this type, provision has been made for differential expansion between the tank and the tower, although Norton is probably unique in that the masonry ringbeam which supports the tank is held in compression by bands of high tensile 'plough steel' wire as an added precaution (a very early example of pre-stressing, see Chapter 6). Another very unusual feature of Norton is the use of large ornate cast iron panels to conceal the steel tank, rather than enclosing the tank within an oversize tower.

CHAPTER FOUR

Early Rural Water Towers

T he burgeoning growth of the urban population in first half of the 19th century was boosted by a steady migration from the countryside. If the population in agricultural areas did increase, such increases were relatively modest and villages did not expand to any great extent. Unlike what was happening in the towns, population densities in agricultural villages (industrial or mining villages were themselves becoming small towns) never reached the point where pollution of the traditional domestic water sources, streams, springs and wells, became an overwhelming hazard to public health. No doubt many village water supplies were polluted, but no more than they always had been and, even if the public health implications were not understood, the innate preference of ordinary householders for clean rather than dirty water should not be disregarded.

A study of the spread of piped water supplies to villages in the Craven district of the West Riding of Yorkshire has illustrated the chronology of the process and identified the factors driving it. The relative abundance of surface water in the area, and the tendency of the local topography to favour gravity-fed systems, suggests that the growth of village water supplies in Craven may have been in advance of that which occurred in less well endowed parts of the country. On the other hand, it could be argued that with a natural abundance of springs and fast flowing streams the need for piped supplies was less pressing in Craven than elsewhere. There is no reason to suppose that Craven's water supply history is atypical of rural Britain, and the fact that there seems never to have been any water towers in Craven does not detract from its value as an example of the development of public water supplies in a rural area.

Craven is centred on the Aire Gap, the break in the Pennine Chain which has formed a major east — west communications route across northern England since prehistoric times. It extends westwards from the edge of the industrial West Riding in Airedale to the borders of Westmorland, and includes a small part of Lancashire. Craven covers an area of some 250 square miles within which there are some 70 settlements, ranging in size from Keighley, an industrial town with a population of over 60,000, to small, remote upland villages. The present day population of the area, including Keighley, is now over 120,000.

Not unexpectedly, it was the small market towns in Craven which were the first to see piped water. Local water companies were established in Keighley in 1816, Skipton in 1823 and Settle in 1843. Here the company took over an earlier, rudimentary water supply system provided in 1769 by one Thomas Preston who had laid pipes into a limited number of private houses from existing spring-fed stone troughs used by the general public. Embsay, a village on the outskirts of Skipton, obtained its piped supply in 1854 followed by Crosshills (1856), Sutton Mill (1861) and Grassington in about 1870. By this time industry was spreading up Airedale and villages like Crosshills now found themselves on the edge of the West Riding conurbation.

Although the Public Health Act of 1848 had enabled local boards of health to be established, their powers, which encompassed (*inter alia*) water supplies, were permissive and were mainly taken up by urban authorities. The by far more effective Public Health Act of 1872 imposed duties on local government and gave poor law boards of guardians, whose principal function had until then been the provision of outdoor relief for able-bodied paupers and workhouses for the rest, powers to establish rural sanitary authorities. These, despite their name, had permissive powers to provide public water supplies — possibly seen as a useful form of outdoor relief. Craven's boards of guardians were not conspicuously forward in this respect, for it was not until 1878 that the Settle Union Board of Guardians provided piped water in Ingleton, followed by Bentham and Settle itself in 1883. In Settle the rural sanitary authority took over the town's water company, reflecting the trend to municipalisation that was by that time well established in the larger towns and cities. The Skipton Union Board of Guardians was even less active than that at Settle ('Union' in this context refers to groups of parishes formed to achieve economies of scale in the building and operation of workhouses) and their only water supply venture appears to have been that at Gargrave in 1883. The boards of guardians did not finally disappear until 1929, but by that time their remaining powers were once again solely those relating to the relief of poverty.

Despite the activities of the rural sanitary authorities, local water companies continued to spring up through the 1880s. Hitherto the provision of piped water had been confined mainly to the towns and those larger villages, like Grassington, which, in their provision of the more specialist and professional services to all the smaller villages in the surrounding area functioned, in effect, as small towns. But now we start to see the appearance of piped water supplies in the smaller villages; Sutton-in-Craven (1882), Farnhill (1883), Cowling (1884), Salterforth and Bradley (1888), Hetton (1889) then Linton and Earby in 1891, though once again there is a distinct bias towards villages on the edge of the industrial areas.

Grassington reappears in the list in 1887 when a new water company was formed. Presumably the original company had not been an outstanding financial success, suggesting that, on a purely commercial basis, these small rural water companies were only marginally viable. The publication from which these figures have been taken makes no mention of village water supplies provided by the large landed estates. The Craven district is not known for its landed gentry with their great houses, associated estates and 'model' villages. Nevertheless, there would undoubtedly have been a significant number of villages where most of the property in the parish would have been in a single owner-ship, with the land farmed by tenants rather than freeholders. In such cases it is quite conceivable that the impetus behind the setting up of a company to supply the village with water would have come from the principal landed proprietor — the local squire — since his estate would be the main beneficiary. Even in villages where there was no principal landowner, the more affluent farmers and tradesmen could well have considered it to be in their own personal if not financial interest to com-bine to promote a local water company.

Unlike their larger, urban counterparts, very few of these small local water companies would have been statutory water companies, estab-lished by an Act of Parliament. The cost of promoting and obtaining such an Act would for them have been prohibitive. In any case, they would not have needed the compulsory powers provided by an Act of Parliament since, in a small community, those affected by the works would have been among the immediate beneficiaries of those works. Anyone opposing the project or failing to cooperate with the scheme would have incurred the social opprobrium of their neighbours. Even if the local estate or principal landowners were not directly involved in promoting and financing the water company, their support and coop-eration would still have been essential for the success of the project. Where small parcels of land were required for sourceworks — or water towers — they would be gifted or leased to the company by the estate or local landowners.

Local government, as we know it today, did not reach the rural areas until the creation of county councils in 1889 soon followed by urban and rural district councils in 1894 (many of the 'urban' districts were rural in all but name). The district councils inherited the functions of the old boards of guardians including rural water supplies and, right from the start, the new authorities were far more diligent in this respect than their predecessors had ever been. Village water supply schemes in Craven now spread rapidly; Newby (1896), Kettlewell (1898), Horton-in-Ribblesdale (1900), Austwick, Keasden and Eastby (1902), Airton and Scosthrop (1903), Starbotton (1904), Conistone and Appletreewick (1909), Langcliffe (1912) and Coniston Cold (1913). In 1934 government grants became available to district councils to help meet the capital cost of rural water supply schemes, and from 1934 until its demise in 1974, funding was also made available by the West

Riding County Council. By 1949 a Ministry of Health report on water supplies in the West Riding was quoting figures for the percentage of the population supplied with piped water in the Skipton and Settle Rural Districts as 97.6% and 93.3% respectively. Given that both these districts included large areas of the Yorkshire dales with their many isolated farms and hamlets, these figures are remarkably high. The report did not give comparable figures for boroughs or urban districts. Presumably the proportion of the population supplied with piped water in those areas was so close to 100% as to be not worth reporting.

The story of water supplies in Craven culminates in 1959 with the setting up of the Craven Water Board which was formed from an amalgamation of the six separate local authority water undertakings in the area; Keighley Borough, the Barnoldswick, Earby and Skipton UDCs and the Skipton and Settle RDCs. But even at this late date there were still a few villages served by local water companies or by the local estate. These remnants were, however, steadily 'mopped up' by the Water Board; Carleton in 1961, Kildwick and Salterforth in 1962, Burton-in-Lonsdale and Stainforth in 1967, East and West Marton, Horton-in-Craven and Hawkswick in 1969, and finally Clapham in 1973. By this time the Craven Water Board itself was about to be absorbed within the multi-functional Yorkshire Water Authority which came into being in April 1974 and which, in turn, became the present Yorkshire Water Services plc on privatisation of the water industry in 1989.

This potted history of water supplies in one small part of the country illustrates both the timescale and the pattern of development of rural water supplies in Britain. There are two prominent and noteworthy features of this development, both of which have, by inference, a significant bearing on the construction of rural water towers.

The first point to emerge is the proliferation of small, local water companies before 1894. Britain's rural economy was still deep in the severe agricultural depression which had begun in the mid 1870s and which, with only a brief respite in the late 1880s, was to continue until the end of the century. These companies would, for the most part, have been set up with very limited capital and operated on a financial shoestring. There were, undoubtedly, exceptions. A small but increasing number of country estates were now owned by wealthy businessmen or industrialists, for whom their estate would have been a hobby rather than a livelihood. Such men could well afford to invest liberally in the infrastructure of their estates and the associated villages. This phenomenon is considered in greater detail in a later chapter.

Secondly, even when the district councils assumed responsibility for water supply, the development of rural water supplies was an essentially piecemeal process, a proliferation of small, self-contained distribution networks relying on a single sourceworks. Such systems would require modest storage capacity and were characterised by small water towers. Not much in the way of amalgamation of net-

Figure 4.1. Appleton water tower, Norfolk, 1877

works and interconnection of sourceworks — and larger water towers serving a wide area — would have taken place until water boards appeared on the scene.

Where local topography necessitated a water tower, the implications of these two salient features of early rural water supplies for the design of that water tower are obvious. The early rural water tower would generally be small and built as cheaply as possible. There is a paradox here. Perhaps the most prominent characteristic of Victorian engineering was its solidity and durability. The Victorian civil engineer's design criteria did not include the concept of a finite lifespan (or if it did they were careful not to say so) and, since so many of their structures appear to have been designed and built with posterity firmly in mind, if not to last indefinitely, a certain amount of functionally redundant decoration could be applied. Where the local estate or water company was endowed by a wealthy patron its water tower would reflect this and be built as a miniature version of its municipal cousin. A supreme example of this is Appleton water tower (Figure 4.1) on the Royal Estate at Sandringham. Not only the designer, James Mansergh, but also the resident engineer responsible for its construction in 1877, Robert Rawlinson, were later to become presidents of the Institution of Civil Engineers. An interesting feature at Appleton, apart from the royal shooting lodge on the second floor, is the chimney taken up through the tank as a protection against frost. Another example of the estate water tower as status symbol is shown in Figure 4.2.

The precise status of many estate water towers is now uncertain, given the blurred distinction between the 'private' water supply to an estate and the 'public' supply to the village, especially when the local water company may simply have been an offshoot of the estate. A considerable amount of local historical research would be needed in each case to determine whether a particular tower was a public water supply tower within the definition given in the Introduction and, even where a clear distinction could be made, it might well be that the tower's status was found to vary with time. The categorisation of an estate tower as a public supply tower has inevitably been based on a considerable amount of subjective judgment. It is inevitable that a few of the early rural water towers listed as public water towers in the Appendix have been wrongly included. Conversely there may be others which have been unfairly excluded. On the other hand, an omission may simply mean that that the author was unaware of that tower's existence!

A clear distinction should however be drawn between estate towers and domestic water towers. Many of the country mansions built during the latter half of the 19th century had their own water towers, either free-standing or incorporated into the house itself. Considerable numbers of older country houses had water towers added at this time as their occupants came to regard piped water as an essential amenity. Most of these domestic water supply towers seem only to have sup-

Figure 4.2. Warnham Lodge water tower, West Sussex, 1894

plied the house rather than the whole estate. They are therefore periph-eral to the principal concern of this book, the public supply water tower, and will be dealt with briefly as a separate topic in a later chap-ter. Estate towers can usually be distinguished from house towers by their size and location. Because a tower built to supply an entire estate or village would have been much larger than one intended merely to supply a large house, the former would have been badly out of scale with the house had it been erected adjacent. Estate towers therefore tend to be found at some distance from the proprietor's country house.

Where the village water undertaking did not have the financial sup-port of a wealthy patron the situation would have been very different. The engineer employed by the company, the sanitary authority or the district council would, for a Victorian, have been faced with the uncomfortable dilemma of reconciling his engineering instincts with his client's very limited resources. The results appear to have varied widely, ranging from the uncompromisingly professional, complete with ornamentation, to the crude and primitive, occasionally verging on the 'Heath-Robinson'. By the end of the 19th century a wide variety of types and sizes of water towers could be found within the same dis-trict. Unfortunately for the historian, most of this first generation of economy-class rural water towers have been superseded by a subse-quent generation of modern water towers and few survive. Such is the shadowy nature of those early rural water undertakings that their records have largely disappeared and so, even where their water tow-ers have survived, it is rarely possible to determine with any certainty whether or not they were public supply towers.

Where the engineer opted for a scaled-down version of the munici-pal tower it might be supposed that the less costly 'exposed tank' design would be preferred, and this generally seems to have been the case. A very early and particularly attractive example of this type is the miniature octagonal tower, believed to date from 1855, at Hawkhurst, in Kent. (Figure 4.3) The tank is made up of eight very large cast iron panels, one bearing the inscription 'Carrett, Marshall & Co, Sun Foundry, Leeds', bolted onto a flat iron baseplate. This structure is of interest for two reasons; firstly its unusual shape (though perhaps jus-tified by the perceived market for large numbers of towers of a stan-dard capacity for estates or country houses) and the distance of the site from the foundry, at least 230 miles. This would have incurred consid-erable transport costs in the 1850s when the national rail network was still in its infancy, suggesting that there were relatively few iron-founders producing sectional tanks at that time. By contrast, the cast iron panels of the tank on the 1909 Foredown Tower at Hove bear the name of an ironfounder in nearby Lewes.

Even with the advent of the district councils, the proliferation of rural water tower types remained. It seems unlikely that the new local authorities would themselves have built many unusual or eccentric water towers but they would certainly have inherited a very heterogeneous stock and then in the course of time taken over a wide variety of small private water company or estate towers. Considerable research is necessary to discover the provenance of these small rural towers and in too many cases the records have vanished. The problem is compounded by the considerable number of amalgamations of the original 'urban' and rural districts that subsequently occurred — many of the smallest districts were never destined to be viable administrative units. A nationwide review of district councils was carried out under the Local Government Act of 1929 and a host of mergers followed. This Act also enabled county councils to contribute towards the capital cost of rural water supplies and permitted district councils to spread expenditure incurred on individual schemes across the whole district.

When county councils did begin to take an active interest in water

Figure 4.3. Hastings Road water tower, Hawkhurst c 1855

supply, their findings revealed a remarkably uneven picture. Spurred into action by the severe drought of 1933/4, Huntingdonshire commissioned a detailed report on water supplies in the county which found that, apart from the boroughs of Huntingdon and St Ives and the urban districts of St Neots and Old Fletton (on the southern outskirts of Peterborough) only two or three villages in the county had a piped water supply. If the report is correct, for many villages their only source of supply was a roadside pond, quite probably the same pond they were using at the time of the Domesday Book. No doubt the absence of underground aquifers across most of the county was part of the problem but Huntingdon is, after all, little more than 60 miles from London, hardly the back of beyond

Whether of district council origin or earlier, many ingenious and sometimes incongruous solutions to the problem of providing an effective, minimal-cost water tower appeared. One of the more common and, in retrospect, the most appropriate of these was the installation of water tanks in or on the towers of disused windmills. The growth of rural water supplies coincided with the demise of windmills and, although a few did survive in commercial use as late as the 1930s, their inexorable decline had begun well before the end of the 19th century. Windmills were particularly vulnerable to storm damage and the destruction of sails or cap would in most cases mean the abandonment of the mill. Only tower mills (as opposed to post or smock mills) were suitable for conversion to water towers but considerable numbers of such conversions have been recorded, though once again it is not always possible to determine whether for public supply or private use.

Cottenham (Cambs) water tower (Figure 4.4) was certainly intended as a village supply. The large, exposed, rivetted iron tank does little to enhance the appearance of the brick mill tower in its prominent position in the village. A more interesting but equally unsightly example is the very early reinforced concrete tank perched on the masonry mill tower at Askham Richard, near York (Figure 4.5). This tall, cylindrical tank, erected in 1908, was still in operational use by the York Waterworks Company when that company was taken over by Yorkshire Water in 1999. Undoubtedly such conversions would look much less obtrusive when the tank was enclosed within the upper storey of the mill tower, as at Weatheroak Hill (Worcs.) where the Bournville Village Trust converted the windmill to a water tower as recently as 1948. Unfortunately this form of conversion would considerably limit the size of tank that could be installed. The appropriately named LeTall's Mill in Lincoln, noted for its exceptional height (nine storeys), was converted to a water tower for an industrial water supply in about 1888. This example is unusual in being in the heart of an industrial city; most such conversions were for smaller, rural industries.

It might be thought that the economical and decidedly utilitarian 'Braithwaite tank' type water tower with its pressed steel panel tank supported on a steel framework (described in detail in Chapter seven) would have been a popular choice, although this design did not become common until well into the 20th century. It is difficult to be categorical about this. There is little firm evidence that they were used for early rural water supplies in any great numbers but, on the other hand, we cannot be sure that they were not. Their 'industrial' appearance would certainly not appeal to the aesthetic sensibilities of the late Victorians or Edwardians, but when an all-steel tower is demolished it leaves little trace. Unlike a disused brick tower, a disused steel framework has no obvious alternative use but does have considerable value as scrap metal.

The one material not yet considered is timber. An engineering text-

Figure 4.4 (above). Cottenham water tower, Cambs, c 1903

Figure 4.5 (right). Askham Richard water tower, North Yorkshire, 1908

book had advocated the use of timber for water towers in 1927, albeit in a colonial context, the assumption being that such structures could be erected quickly and cheaply by a pioneer community utilising unskilled labour and locally available materials. Were all-timber water towers ever built in any numbers in Britain? Probably not, but it is not easy to know since they would only have been built by the smallest and poorest rural undertakers whose records have long since disappeared. As might be expected, none has survived. Their life expectancy in Britain's damp climate would certainly not have been great. On the other hand, a number of English railway companies erected timber bridges and viaducts in the mid-19th century in order to minimise their initial capital expenditure, replacing the timber with more permanent materials a few years later when revenues had built up. Did any water undertakers pursue similar financial policies?

What appears to have been a cylindrical iron or steel tank on a timber trestle supplied Selsey in West Sussex as late as 1927, but the only all-wood water tower known to the author was the one at Skelton on Ure, near Ripon, which is said to have survived until the late 1940s when a mains supply reached the village. The elevated tank at Skelton has been described as having the appearance of a giant barrel. It may have been unusual but is unlikely to have been unique. One suspects that the saturated wooden staves would have provided an ideal environment for algae and similar organisms. Ironically, an impressive concrete water tower was erected nearby in the grounds of Newby Hall as early as about 1910 with a capacity greatly exceeding that required simply for the stately home and its grounds, yet it is said not to have supplied the adjacent estate village.

Disappointingly few of the first generation of district council water towers now remain. When an estate tower was superseded and fell into disuse it would often revert to its original owner and be left to a gentle decay, whereas a redundant local authority tower would usually be demolished once it had been replaced by a larger, more modern structure. For some reason, small Norfolk country towns seem to have been an exception to this. Diss and Dereham have both retained their Victorian tower alongside its modern replacement; Fakenham and North Walsham each have two generations of concrete tower on the same site.

Although few, if any, of the more impromptu early rural public supply towers have survived to the present some indication of how widespread they must once have been can still be found. In the years immediately after World War II, apparently in response to a Ministry of Health directive from Whitehall, a series of reports reviewing the provision of water supplies, county by county, was commissioned. Each county seems to have produced one, either published by HMSO or independently, though copies are not always easy to identify or obtain. Unfortunately these soft-bound, lithographed documents have no common format and their contents vary widely in both scope and detail. It is quite obvious that scant guidance was given to the individual local authors who interpreted the Ministry's requirements as they saw fit. Nevertheless, some of these reports give a fascinating insight into the state of rural water supplies at that time, when in some smaller villages their original 'cheap and cheerful' water tower (or, more usually, an 'elevated tank') was still in use. It can be inferred from these reports that 'Braithwaite tanks' may once have been a considerably more common feature of the British landscape than they are today, if only in the years immediately after the second world war. One such report has already been referred to in this chapter and the contents of another are considered in some detail in Chapter 6.

The use of windpumps in connection with private farm water supplies was once, before mains electricity reached even the most isolated farms, widespread. A number of firms manufactured this equipment, notably Godwin Pumps of Quenington in Gloucestershire, who

Figure 4.6. Dorrington water tower, Lincs, 1910

mounted their windpumps above an elevated tank. The galvanised steel sails and fantail were vulnerable to corrosion and storm damage but the gaunt, rusty remains of these devices, often little more than a spindly steel tripod, can still be seen marooned in fields beside an equally derelict Braithwaite tank. Very few are still in use. But wind-pumps were not confined to agricultural use. Examples of small rural water supply systems whose pumps were operated and water towers filled by wind power are surprisingly common.

They were certainly being installed well into the 20th century. A windpump was erected in conjunction with the new concrete water tower built at Barmby Moor in East Yorkshire for the Pocklington UDC in 1909. Nor were windpumps confined to village supplies; photo-graphs of the older (1886) water tower at Southwold on the Suffolk coast show a windpump mounted above the tank. A few miles down the coast in 1923, the developer of the select resort village of Thorpeness went so far as to acquire, re-erect at its new location and modify a traditional windmill to pump water up into his now well known *House in the clouds* water tower. A conventional windpump would have been a far cheaper but less flamboyant option.

The great advantage of wind power is of course the elimination of fuel costs. The problem with any wind powered system is the fickle nature of the wind itself, though with a water supply system this can be ameliorated by providing a greater storage capacity — a larger water tower — than would be needed for an engine-powered system. Even so, there is still a significant and unavoidable risk of failure to meet demand in prolonged periods of calm weather. Perhaps for this reason windpumps were often installed in tandem with an oil or petrol engine driven pump, as was done at Potterhanworth in Lincolnshire.

A typical example of an early district council water tower, built by the Sleaford RDC at Dorrington (Lincs) in 1910, is shown in Figure 4.6. This district council was notably progressive in the provision of village water supplies in the years before the first world war, yet there seems to have been no attempt at standardisation of design in the towers it built and no two of its towers were remotely similar. District councils and small rural water companies were, perhaps rather surprisingly, among the pioneering clients who commissioned the earliest rein-forced concrete water towers before the first world war, but these first concrete towers are worthy of separate consideration and will be dealt with in detail in the next chapter.

CHAPTER FIVE

Early Concrete Water Towers

Coencrete, in various primitive forms, has been in use in Britain since the middle ages, most commonly as mass concrete foundations but it is also encountered as a hearting within masonry walls or pillars. The middle of the 18th century saw a resurgence of interest in concrete. In 1756 John Smeaton carried out experiments on a range of cement mortars to obtain a quick setting concrete for use in the construction of his Eddystone lighthouse and produced the first good quality cement since Roman times. Towards the end of the century a Kentish parson, Rev James Parker of Northfleet, discovered what he patented as 'Roman' cement, so called because he believed that he had rediscovered the material widely used by the Romans. Parker's cement was produced by heating and crushing the septaria nodules embedded in London Clay. These were found in abundance along the beaches of the Thames estuary where a thriving cement industry rapidly developed.

A chance purchase in 1813 by a Leeds bricklayer, Joseph Aspdin, of a copy of a book written by Smeaton with an account of his researches into the properties of cement inspired Aspdin to continue where Smeaton had left off. In 1824 Aspdin patented and four years later commenced production of his *Portland* cement. As the name suggests, he envisaged that the concrete made from his cement would resemble and be used as a substitute for Portland stone. Aspdin's sons, William and Joseph, developed the commercial production of cement which throughout most of the 19th century was widely used for mass concrete, ornamental concrete mouldings for architectural purposes, and for the rendering of brickwork. It was to prove superior to 'Roman' cement and its popularity was established when considerable quantities of cement were used in the mid 1840s in the building of Osborne House, Queen Victoria's country mansion on the Isle of Wight. Osborne House incorporated a water tower in which concrete was used, though it cannot by any stretch of the imagination be described as a concrete water tower.

The origins of reinforced concrete are considerably earlier than is generally realised. The idea that concrete could be reinforced with iron rods, wire or mesh to give a material that would combine the compressive strength of concrete with the tensile strength of a metal dates back to at least 1822 when a patent was granted to a James Frost though it was never put to practical use. The world's first reinforced concrete boat was exhibited at the Paris exhibition of 1855 but it seems that such early examples of reinforced concrete were designed empirically and not based on any coherent theory of the combined action of the two materials. In 1854 a Newcastle builder, William Wilkinson, obtained a patent which suggests that he understood the basic structural principles involved and he is now regarded as the originator of reinforced concrete design. In about 1860 Wilkinson built a concrete house using discarded wire ropes from a colliery to reinforce the floor slabs. The building was found to be still structurally sound when it was demolished in 1954.

For the reasons outlined in Chapter 2, any water tower utilising concrete as its principal construction material would have to be built of reinforced concrete in order to withstand the tensile stresses in the walls and base of the tank. The initial development of reinforced concrete in Britain was a surprisingly hesitant and piecemeal affair. It appeared in individual buildings and structures here and there, where enthusiastic entrepreneurs attempted to generate by example an interest in the new material but even where concrete was used it was still, as often as not, in the well-tried forms of mass concrete, mouldings or rendering.

The lead that Wilkinson had given Britain in the field of reinforced concrete design was not followed up and was therefore short lived. Six years before Wilkinson took out his patent a French engineer, Joseph Monier, had constructed a number of garden plant tubs in reinforced concrete simply by coating an iron mesh with cement mortar. This process was wholly empirical and involved no quantitative analysis or design, but Monier was fascinated by the possibilities offered by reinforced concrete and gradually continued to develop his ideas, and reinforced concrete design theory. Over the following two decades his concrete plant tubs evolved into progressively larger water tanks. It was inevitable that, sooner or later, he would design and construct an elevated tank — a water tower. This seems to have occurred at some time in the 1860s when Monier erected a simple, cylindrical concrete tank supported on six rustic 'tree-trunk' pillars for what appears to have been a domestic or garden water supply at a house in Nizza, in northern Italy.

By the 1870s what had begun almost as a pastime had become a commercial operation. In 1868/70 Monier constructed a 5500 gallon tank at Fontenaible; in 1872 he erected a 29,000 gallon tank at Bougival, then a 40,000 gallon tank at Alençon, a 44,000 gallon tank at Fontenay sous Bois, culminating in 1880 with a pair of 220,000 gallon tanks at Sèvres aux Bruyères. It is uncertain which of these tanks were elevated. The final pair were ground level service reservoirs but photographic evidence shows that the Alençon tank was a trackside railway water tower — a plain, cylindrical tank on a marginally wider circular shaft. By this time other notable names in the early history of reinforced concrete had emerged. Back in 1867 François Coignet had built a concrete water supply aqueduct in the Forest of Fontainebleau, near Paris, though its appearance suggests that it may have been essentially a mass concrete structure with the reinforcement performing a secondary role.

Also in France, Hennebique built his first concrete water tower at Dinard in 1895 and Coignet's son, Edmond, erected his first water tower at the Toulon naval dockyard in 1898. With 110,000 gallon capacities, these were both sizeable structures. The German pioneer, Eduard Zublin, had built his first water tower at Scafati (Italy) in 1897 although Wayss and Koenen had designed a 72ft tall reinforced concrete tower for the municipality of Landshut in southern Germany in 1885. Despite its modest 13,000 gallon capacity, the design drawings show a surprisingly sophisticated structure. The tank has an access shaft up through the centre and is supported on splayed concrete columns connected by curtain walling and with intermediate-level bracing. Regrettably the tower was not built to this design, the authorities playing safe and opting for a conventional 'Victorian' water tower.

It is difficult to say how long concrete, reinforced or otherwise, would have continued as little more than a structural curiosity in Britain had it not been for the initiative and enterprise of François Hennebique who had pioneered the design and development of reinforced concrete in his native France. Hennebique had set up in business as a public works contractor but in 1892 devised and introduced a system of reinforcing concrete with steel bars and strips (*béton armé*). His system was based on sound structural design principles and rapidly gained acceptance in France. At this time reinforced concrete was more commonly known as 'ferroconcrete' and it was not until well into the 20th century that this term would be supplanted by 'reinforced concrete'. The Hennebique house journal named *Ferroconcrete* commenced publication in 1909.

In 1897 Hennebique established an agent in Swansea, Louis Mouchel, in an attempt to create a market for his reinforced concrete design system in Britain. The choice of Swansea was no doubt influenced by the fact that Hennebique had lived for some time in South Wales where he had served as the French consul. Mouchel's first contract was for a seven storey flour mill in Swansea itself, for Weaver & Co. Completed in 1898, Weaver's Mill became Britain's first multi-storey concrete framed building. The Hennebique system of reinforced concrete design gained rapidly in popularity as its reputation spread and Mouchel went on to design and construct a succession of 'firsts' in reinforced concrete. His and Britain's first reinforced concrete water tower was built at Meyrick Park, Bournemouth for the Borough Council in 1900. It is nevertheless worth noting that Weaver's Mill, demolished in 1984, incorporated a 20,000 gallon water tank in the roof.

Meyrick Park's 15,000 gallon capacity water tower does not look particularly dated, much less so than many of its immediate successors. Its general layout, a cylindrical tank with a scalloped skirt and prominent lower ringbeam supported on six columns which were circumferentially braced at three intermediate levels, could have been designed at any time before the second world war (Figure 5.1). It is claimed that in the first 25 years of its life a mere £5 had been spent on maintenance, and that on painting the central iron staircase. Meyrick Park water tower was not built for public water supply purposes but for watering a cricket pitch, golf course and bowling greens, and it may well be that Bournemouth Council's bold and pioneering choice of material for what was to be Britain's first reinforced concrete water tower was encouraged by the knowledge that it was intended for a non-essential purpose. Sadly this historic structure, despite being a listed building, was demolished in 1994.

Meyrick Park was followed spectacularly in 1904/5 by what was at the time the world's largest water tower, Newton-le-Willows in Lancashire (now Merseyside), standing 117 feet high and with a 300,000 gallon capacity, a whole order of magnitude greater than Meyrick Park. Newton-le-Willows had a central shaft within a concentric arrangement of columns, 28 in all (Figure 5.2). It was constructed by the well known firm of contractors, Cubitts. It was an ambitiously large and bold design for its time but this tower had a less trouble free life than Meyrick Park. The tank gave trouble from the start and had to be repaired at least three times, in 1910, 1933 and again in 1962, to deal with leaks but its problems persisted. Newton-le-Willows was declared redundant in 1966 and eventually demolished in 1979.

The popularity and success of Mouchel and the Hennebique system was meteoric. By 1910 over 40,000 reinforced concrete structures had been built to Mouchel's designs, although Mouchel himself died in 1908. A contributory factor in this was undoubtedly the protection conferred by patent rights and for the first decade of the 20th century Mouchel and the Hennebique system had an effective monopoly of the market for reinforced concrete in Britain. Mouchel's British patent was taken out in 1892, though there had been earlier attempts to patent techniques for reinforcing concrete with steel. Mouchel's patent was by no means comprehensive — it concentrated on concrete beams — and the various loopholes in his patent were readily exploited by others, as firms offering alternative reinforcement 'systems' had been established and were winning contracts before the first world war. Hennebique's activities were not confined to Britain and France; by 1909 the firm and its associates boasted 62 offices worldwide and over 20,000 concrete structures completed. Mouchel was just one of many, although a significant one, for by 1911 he and his British successors had already

Figure 5.1. Meyrick Park water tower, Bournemouth, Dorset, 1900

undertaken 1073 projects.

In 1921 L G Mouchel & Partners (the firm is still a thriving and well known civil engineering consultancy) published a list of all their successfully completed projects to that date, arranged by categories of

Figure 5.2. Newton-le-Willows water tower, Merseyside, 1905

structure. The list of Mouchel/Hennebique water towers and 'elevated reservoirs' erected up to the end of World War I is given at the end of this chapter. The original text has, apart from a few necessary abbreviations, been reproduced verbatim. The dates given in Mouchel's *Blue Book* are taken to be the year of construction. This seems to be so in most cases but there is a suspicion that some are the year in which Mouchel was engaged to undertake the project. A number of interesting points emerge from this list. After a relatively slow start, there was a surge of activity between the years 1908 and 1913 followed, as would be expected, by a dearth of commissions during the war. The slow start can be explained by the caution with which clients and their engineers or architects would have approached the new material — was it suitable for the demanding task of retaining water at an elevation at which any leak would be instantly apparent?

There is strong circumstantial evidence that its reputation spread by word of mouth, as can be deduced from the local clusters of water towers that appear in the Mouchel/Hennebique list, South Yorkshire being perhaps the most obvious example. The rapid acceptance of the concrete water tower at about this time may well have been due to the publicity which was generated in 1909 by the new YMCA building in Peter Street, Manchester. Despite its conventional appearance and terracotta facing, the building had a reinforced concrete framework and a concrete swimming pool on the top floor, a dramatic demonstration that reinforced concrete could confidently be used for elevated water retaining structures.

The range and variety of Mouchel's clients is intriguing. It is not possible to determine the precise use for which the tower was required in every case but the 49 towers on the list are divided as follows: 15 public water supply, 11 industrial (including two firefighting), eight private or estate water supplies, six railways and docks, three hospitals and workhouses, three amenity, two schools and colleges and one military. Local authority water towers are assumed to be public water supply unless there is evidence to the contrary (eg, Meyrick Park, Belfast and Portsmouth are classified as 'amenity' and Burton on Trent under 'workhouses'.) Although public water supply is the largest single category it represents under a third of the total, although if private water supplies are included (at least three of the towers built for private clients — Askham Richard, Ridgmont and East Grinstead (The Placeland) — were later absorbed into the local public water supply system) this proportion increases to nearly half. Even so, industry and transport account for over a third of those early concrete water towers.

The variety of Mouchel's clients has already been remarked on. The names of the engineers and architects involved are equally interesting. From a detailed study of the correspondence relating to specific commissions, it is clear that Mouchel acted as a sub-consultant to the engineer or architect responsible for the larger project. At Maytham Hall in Kent, for example, Lutyens (or possibly his client, as the water tower was built about four years later than the mansion) employed a G J Jenson as engineer for the water supply system and he in turn engaged Mouchel to design the water tower. Until the first world war very few professional engineers would have had the theoretical knowledge, let alone the experience, to undertake the detailed design of a reinforced concrete structure or supervise its construction. Jenson, described like many others on the list merely as 'engineer', was not a member of the Institution of Civil Engineers (ie AM or MInstCE). Equally surprising is the number of architects involved with water tower construction at that time. This can be explained as a legacy of the Victorian era when the architectural input to the design of the water tower itself could be of at least equal prominence to the engineering component. This would certainly be the case if a proprietary sectional iron tank was used, enclosed within an ornate masonry tower. Reinforced concrete water towers, which require a much more sophisticated and specialised structural analysis, were soon to upset this balance of professional responsibilities.

For most applications, L G Mouchel & Partners produced a plain, utilitarian design, essentially a cylindrical tank on slender vertical columns, the number of columns and the configuration of the bracing between the columns determined by the size and height of the tank. Hatfield, a public water supply tower near Doncaster (Figure 5.3) is typical of these. It is unlikely that this design would have appealed to Mouchel's more aesthetically conscious clients for whom Mouchel produced a variety of individual designs. Sandsend water tower, in the vicinity of Mulgrave Castle near Whitby, was designed to resemble a castellated tower. Maytham Hall's water tower, although closer to the utilitarian, was designed as a square concrete tank on four columns but with a steeply pitched and hipped tiled roof over the tank, in keeping with the style that Lutyens had adopted for the estate. The most elegant of these 'one-offs' was the tower designed for the Duke of Bedford's estate village at Ridgmont (Figure 5.4). Other designers found themselves faced with the same concerns; the half-timbered exterior and tall, complicated tiled roof of the 'mock Tudor' water tower built in 1916 for a private estate at Milton Hill, Oxfordshire, were necessary to conceal a pair of square concrete 'double decker' tanks.

Right from the start — we see it at Meyrick Park — cross-bracing was used at one or more intermediate levels to stiffen the vertical columns and provide an element of resistance to buckling, a sensible precaution as the ability of slender concrete columns in compression to resist buckling was not then fully understood. This bracing took the form of concrete beams linking the columns and, if present, the central shaft in a wide variety of patterns and configurations. Bracing was almost invariably in the horizontal plane, as any bracing in the vertical plane would involve diagonal members and be very awkward to construct. A tower with 29ft unbraced columns had been built at Topsham (Devon) in 1917 but tall, unbraced columns did not begin to appear until the late 1920s and then only in conjunction with a substantial central shaft. Eventually unbraced peripheral columns such as those erected at Cantley (Doncaster) in 1958 would reach 105ft.

Mouchel's near monopoly was gradually whittled away by rival firms who found ways of circumventing his patents with their own systems of reinforced concrete design. Even before 1910, reinforced

Figure 5.3 (left). Hatfield water tower, South Yorkshire, 1912

Figure 5.4 (above). Ridgmont water tower, Bedfordshire, 1912

concrete water towers not on the Mouchel/Hennebique list begin to appear. The years immediately prior to the first world war are regarded as the 'golden age' of proprietary reinforcement systems, though many of them never got much beyond the drawing board. Clients were wary of them and usually insisted that specialist designers submit their designs to an established independent engineer for verification. A 1920 reinforced concrete textbook noted that there were 'over seventy systems in use today in Europe and America.' An indication as to the speed at which Mouchel's massive early predominance was being eroded can be gauged by an analysis of the company's records. These show that the ratio of the numbers of contracts won to the numbers of tenders submitted fell from a third before World War I to around one in ten thereafter. Since a considerable proportion of their earliest tenders would have been submitted in competition with designs utilising more conventional materials, rather than rival concrete designs, the actual trend was probably even more marked than is suggested by the figures quoted above.

There were other notable reinforcement systems of this era which the reader may encounter. Some of them enjoyed a brief vogue whilst a few endured somewhat longer. They include Coignet (a French family with a long association with concrete and a London office from 1905), Considere (another French firm, with a British patent in 1902 but not used until 1907), the Trussed Concrete Company ('Truscon', who used the American Kahn system in Britain from 1903), the British Reinforced Concrete Company (established 1905), the Indented Bar Engineering Company (an American company with whom one of Britain's most outstanding civil engineers of the 1930s and 50s, Sir Owen Williams, was associated), the similarly named Patent Indented Steel Bar Company (utilised by the British Concrete Steel Co) and even more ephemeral names like Monier (Armoured Concrete Construction Co), Johnson, Moss, Wells, Ridley-Cammell and the Chain Concrete Syndicate of Leeds. Most of these firms, unlike L G Mouchel & Partners, have been lost in the mists of time. Expanded Metal reinforcement, a steel mesh produced from thin sheet steel, was being used from 1890 and three concrete water towers are known to have been built in Ireland using this type of reinforcement but this form of construction is not regarded as reinforced concrete in the now generally accepted meaning of the term. The only known example in Britain was a square tower at Holsworthy (Devon) built in the early 1920s.

Even from the earliest days of concrete water towers a variety of types was apparent, especially as regards the supporting structure. As we have seen, the second concrete tower was designed with the hybrid combination of a central shaft within a ring or concentric rings of columns. The hollow shaft has a number of advantages; the supply and delivery pipework is protected from the elements and effectively insulated against frost, and it affords security from unauthorised interference to valves. A shaft also provides an enclosed and therefore a safe means of access to the tank, and onto the tank roof if the core of the shaft is continued up through the centre of the tank, which is usually the case. Central cores have been a feature of cylindrical concrete tanks from their beginning, though some early access shafts were claustrophobically narrow; a pair of water towers built for the North Eastern Railway at York in 1911 had an internal diameter of less than thirty inches, if the published drawings are to believed.

At its simplest, access from the shaft to the tank roof can be through a trapdoor or cupola at the top of the shaft, then down inside the tank through manholes in the tank roof. The extended access shaft also serves as a central support to the tank roof. Occasionally this shaft terminates above top water level inside the tank, giving access to the interior of the tank without the need for manholes in the tank roof. Although this arrangement is more convenient for maintenance staff it has a number of disadvantages; there has to be considerable headroom — dead space — between top water level and the tank roof, some form of access to the tank roof is still needed, the simple central roof support is lost, and the benefits to hygeine of a 'sealed' tank are also forfeit unless a trapdoor is placed at the top of the shaft. The tank must of course be ventilated to maintain atmospheric pressure inside it.

Where the shaft through the centre of the tank emerges onto the tank roof it has long been customary to erect a small cupola, almost invariably in concrete. Newton-le-Willows had one, another example of how both Meyrick Park and Newton-le-Willows established a particular configuration of structural elements that was to be repeated in almost endless variations for over half a century. Cupolas come in a host of shapes and sizes, the only common element being a doorway, though many have windows or at least skylights to allow daylight into what would otherwise be a narrow, dark and claustrophobic tube at the very top of the shaft, hemmed in by the inner walls of the tank. The cupola also affords a welcome shelter from the elements for those working on the tank roof. Cupolas are not, strictly speaking, entirely necessary. Many water towers manage with a mere trapdoor although, unless counterbalanced, this can be awkward for someone at the top of a vertical ladder to open. Often the cupola is an excuse for a little light relief, even a flight of fancy by the designer. Gawthorpe water tower near Wakefield (Figure 5.5) has a particularly ornate example. This tendency is a little odd when it is realised that many cupolas cannot be seen (or photographed) from ground level unless the observer is some distance from the tower, in which case any detailed ornamentation can no longer be clearly distinguished.

The reader will have noted the assumption in the preceding paragraphs that the tank either has an integral roof slab or is covered by a roof. It is, however, known that some concrete water towers were built without roofs, despite the obvious risks that this would have presented to a potable supply. As late as 1927 a water supply textbook used a photograph of an unidentified tower as an example of a ferroconcrete water tower, describing it without adverse comment as 'open to atmosphere' and merely adding that the tank had an inward cantilevered rim to prevent spillage under windy conditions. As any open-topped public supply towers have long since been demolished or roofed over it is now almost impossible to know how

Figure 5.5. Gawthorpe water tower, West Yorkshire, 1928

common such towers were. Even where early concrete towers have been abandoned but still survive, it is very difficult to ascertain whether or not the tank is open because any access ladders have long since rusted away. Since nearly all Victorian municipal water towers seem to have been roofed it is surprising that any open-topped concrete towers were built at all. On the other hand, it may simply have been assumed that small rural water supplies were less vulnerable to airborne pollution.

Newton-le-Willows was followed by a series of towers built without any form of shaft, supported merely on columns. Access to the tank was by means of vertical steel ladders, continued up the side of the tank. Larger towers might have inclined stairways linked by intermediate platforms leading to a hollow core through the centre of the tank. Workmen and pipework were still exposed to the elements and the latter would require lagging, often of asbestos, for insulation. The shaftless water tower could very easily present a stark and utilitarian appearance (Figure 5.6). A public supply tower of this type can usually be dated fairly reliably to the 1920s although the type enjoyed a brief resurgence during the second world war. The reason why Mouchel & Partners reverted to this type of tower can only be guessed at, but it was almost certainly economic. With the emergence of competition Mouchel found itself having to offer clients a cheaper product, both as regards its own design fees and the cost of construction. A water tower with a shaft might be a more convenient tower to operate but it was significantly more expensive. Until the disadvantages of not having a shaft became overwhelmingly apparent, the client would choose the cheaper option. Fortunately this was not always the case and some remarkably attractive towers were commissioned, such as the exuberant Rimswell in the otherwise bleak Holderness landscape (Figure 5.7). The rectangular equipment cabinet is an insensitive

Figure 5.6. Boundary Tower, Woodville, Derbyshire, 1926

Figure 5.7. Rimswell water tower, Humberside, 1916

modern accretion.

The circular concrete tank established itself as the industry standard right from the start, and even when in later years engineers forsook the cylindrical drum for more adventurous shapes the tank remained determinedly round in plan. Towers with square or rectangular concrete tanks were built but they have always been a comparative rarity, though a number appeared in Glasgow. Multi-sided tanks are however not uncommon but anything with eight or more sides can for structural purposes be considered circular. Often only the external face of such tanks is polygonal, and for aesthetic reasons. The attraction of the circular tank to engineers is easy to understand. In the first instance, the ratio of circumference to area is smaller for a circle than for any other shape and a cylindrical tank will therefore require less concrete than a square or rectangular tank to contain the same volume of water. The circular tank is symmetrical about a single axis and the forces, both internal and external, acting on the tank and indeed the whole tower are virtually independent of the orientation of those forces. This structural symmetry is preserved by the use of concentric chambers where a twin-compartment tank is required. Stresses in a square tank, by contrast, have to be analysed in two separate planes. There are also awkward stress concentrations at the corners to contend with, and a more complex arrangement of reinforcement. The circular tank's only drawback is the need for curved shuttering (the temporary moulds into which the concrete is poured) on opposed faces. That is the contractor's, not the designer's problem, though it would inevitably be reflected in the tendered price.

There are basically two ways to design a concrete tank. The engineer can treat it as a barrel, depending on hoop action and the tension in the horizontal reinforcement in the walls to hold the tank together or, alternatively, rely on cantilever action between the walls and floor of the tank, treating each strip of wall as an independent vertical cantilever with the maximum tensile stress in the inner, vertical reinforcement at the junction between wall and floor. As analytical techniques developed during the 20th century it became possible using Reissner's method to design concrete tanks utilising a combination of hoop and cantilever action but the analysis was, until computers became available, fairly complex and time consuming.

By designing the tank in the hoop mode there is, in theory, no *prima facie* requirement for a structural connection between the tank walls and the floor. The tank can be thought of as a round cheese dish with a large lid, no steel reinforcement crossing the construction joint between wall and floor. The joint would, of course, be sealed by a thin layer of bitumen to permit thermal movement, the dead weight of the tank walls and roof keeping the concrete 'lid' in place on the 'dish'. Some early tanks are believed to have been built to this design, though the horizontal joint at the point of maximum water pressure could prove troublesome and prone to leakage. In practice, engineers normally played safe and inserted nominal steel reinforcement across the angle between tank floor and walls. The ring beams round the top and bottom of the tank which are seen on so many early concrete water towers are generally more an architectural than a structural feature, though in some cases the upper ring beam may serve to constrain the outward thrust of a domed tank roof.

Despite Newton-le-Willows, the great majority of early concrete water towers were of modest size as can be seen from the list at the end of this chapter. Capacities of around 50,000 gallons were typical, with overall tank diameters ranging generally between 20 and 35 feet and depths from ten to 16 feet. On the other hand diameter-to-depth ratios varied widely, from one and a half up to three. Since 35.9 cubic feet (224 gallons) of water weigh a ton the contents of a modest 50,000 gallon tank represent a 223 ton load on the supporting structure, plus of course the weight of the tank itself. Depending upon the configuration of the tower and the efficiency of the design, the water within a concrete tower, when full, will contribute from a third to a half of the total weight of the structure and its contents. For towers without shafts and supported only on columns this ratio could even exceed half.

By the start of the first world war the concrete water tower had established itself as a viable alternative to the traditional 'Victorian' tower. During the 1920s there was a relative lull in the building of water towers, but with the start of the rapid expansion of piped water supplies into the rural areas in the 1930s the rate of construction of water towers accelerated rapidly and the great majority of this new generation of water towers were of concrete. Despite the lull, by the 1920s reinforced concrete had proved its worth as a construction material and concrete structures could no longer be regarded as unusual or idiosyncratic. The period when an engineer, even a consulting engineer, would as a matter of course sub-contract the reinforced concrete design components of a project to a specialist was drawing to a close. It had ceased to be a slightly esoteric activity. Although firms specialising in the design and construction of reinforced concrete structures still flourished and were to do so for some years to come, any engineer wishing to make a name for himself now had to be able to undertake reinforced concrete design as a matter of course. Furthermore, by the mid 1920s the economic balance had tipped in favour of concrete, and it was then being claimed that the capital cost of a concrete water tower was comparable with that of a pressed steel panel tank and considerably less than that of a cast iron tank on a steel framework.

There followed a relatively brief period when the natural caution and restraint exhibited by engineers handling a new material and unfamiliar design concepts would result in unambitious, even timid designs. Familiarity, if not exactly breeding contempt, certainly pushed the pendulum hard in the opposite direction. This in the 1920s had a certain resonance with the spirit of the age and gave rise to a number of remarkably bold reinforced concrete structures, in Britain and elsewhere. Water towers were certainly no exception and the decade produced a number of towers which it is doubtful would have been built at any later date.

The water tower built circa 1924 for St John's Hospital on Bracebridge Heath, south of Lincoln, combines a remarkable slenderness with elegance of form (Figure 5.8). The 22ft 8in diameter tank is supported on six slightly splayed legs, their base circle diameter of 23ft being only marginally wider than the tank. The structure is 125ft high overall, and although the tower is built on limestone the base of the 26ft diameter, three foot thick concrete raft foundation is a mere five feet deep. Ironically, whereas all the worthy but unremarkable Victorian hospital buildings are listed, the most noteworthy building on the site, the water tower, is not. An even more remarkable structure, of unknown vintage but probably also from the 1920s, is the industrial water tower at Blackburn Road in Sheffield (Figure 5.9). In this case the design has crossed the boundary from the slender to the spindly, from the impressive to the disconcerting.

The 1920s saw water towers feature in design competitions. In 1915 the Royal Institute of British Architects had set the design of a water tower as the subject for their annual Grissell Gold Medal award but

Figure 5.8 (above). St John's Hospital water tower, Bracebridge Heath, Lincoln, c 1924
Figure 5.9 (right). Industrial water tower, Blackburn Road, Sheffield, South Yorkshire, date unknown

because of the war the competition was deferred until 1920. A 50,000 gallon tank was stipulated and entrants could design their tower in any material. The winner opted for reinforced concrete, though other competitors chose 'reinforced concrete with brick facing, reinforced concrete structure with steel tank, and dressed stone.' Not only did the winning entrant, an architect, submit a considerable amount of detailed engineering analysis but the appearance of his water tower was such that it could have been built at any time between 1930 and 1960. It was certainly in an entirely different class to the starkly utilitarian concrete structures then being built. Entrants in the Institution of Structural Engineers' annual Brenforce Travelling Scholarship competition in 1927 had to submit a design for 'a water tower in reinforced concrete to be erected in an exposed, commanding position on an eminence in moorland country and provided with a balcony open to the public.' In this case the tank was to have a 250,000 gallon capacity at a height of 100ft above the ground — a large tower. Perhaps inevitably, the three winning entries were all rather intimidatingly monumental in scale, though by no means unattractive. Paradoxically, the structural engineers' designs appear considerably more self-consciously 'architectural' than the winning entry in the RIBA competition and, to modern tastes, distinctly dated.

The 1920s also saw something of an obsession with concrete, as if its practitioners had to demonstrate to the world that there was nothing that concrete could not do. Hints of this exuberant and all-embracing use of concrete were occasionally seen before the first world war, as at Cleethorpes in 1908 where the ornamental concrete frames for the new water tower's entrance door and mullioned windows with their crude 'Gothic' tracery were precast on site. Just up the coast at Immingham, the top of the contemporary (1909) tower's octagonal tank was embellished with a concrete balustrade, a pinnacle at each angle and a matching pinnacled cupola but, by and large, pre-1920 towers were essentially cautious, utilitarian structures. After this date things changed. Hertford's Bengeo water tower was topped off with a 15 ft reinforced concrete flagpole though even this was exceeded in 1927 by Goole's new concrete tower which boasted a 40 ft concrete flagstaff. Even more extreme, Blackpool's Warbreck Hill water tower was fitted with reinforced concrete doors, precast on a bronze mould. Would it have been that much more expensive to have had bronze doors? These may have been exceptional but many examples can be found of tanks surmounted by elaborate concrete balustrades (a feature that appears as early as Newton-le-Willows) when simple economics might have suggested steel handrailing or a plain parapet wall. Yet at the same time the 1920s are regarded as a decade of indifferent construction standards. Increasing numbers of concrete structures were being built but not until the universal adoption of mechanically vibrated concrete (first introduced circa 1924) were contractors able to guarantee a consistent, uniformly dense concrete free of air pockets and voids.

Paradoxically, Warbreck Hill (1934), apart from its doors, exhibits a strange lack of confidence on the part of either the client or the architect. Despite being designed as a reinforced concrete structure, it was disguised to appear as a masonry tower. The ashlar facing blocks used for the main body of the shaft are of precast concrete, and the heavily rusticated courses of 'stone' blocks at the base of the tower were obtained by splitting precast concrete blocks in half and laying them with their broken faces exposed.

The first textbook on reinforced concrete had been published in Paris in 1899 and English language textbooks started to appear in Britain from 1904 onwards, but while these were undeniably sound on the fundamental principles they were all fairly basic and, like the designs of those early structures, exhibited a wide range of approaches, particularly in matters of detail. A technical journal entitled *Concrete & Constructional Engineering* was established in 1906 and continued publication until 1966. Another explanation for the bold designs of the 1920s was undoubtedly the lack of constraints imposed on engineers by formal Codes of Practice. As early as 1907 the Royal Institute of British Architects (RIBA) had drawn up what was, in effect, a code of practice for reinforced concrete design, stealing a clear march on the engineering institutions in doing so. The Institution of Civil Engineers considered that the introduction of regulations and codes would be premature when there was still so much that was not yet fully understood, and to do so would place undue constraints upon its members.

Not everyone agreed, and the Concrete Institute (which in 1923 became the Institution of Structural Engineers) was created, largely by the enthusiasm of a young architect, Edwin Sachs, in 1908. Sachs was an interesting character. An Anglo-German, educated both in Germany and England, widely travelled and as an associate member of both the Institution of Mechanical Engineers and the Institution of Naval Architects he must have been something of a polymath. His early death in 1919 at the age of 49 cut short a promising career. It should not be assumed that the Civil Engineers were complacent, for the Institution had set up an internal committee on reinforced concrete which issued its *Preliminary and Interim Report* in 1910 and it was not until 1918 that the Concrete Institute followed up with its *Recommendations to Clerks of Works and Foremen Concerning the Execution of Reinforced Concrete Works* (reissued in 1934) but this was, in some respects, a reshaping of the original RIBA design code. In 1917 Mouchel issued its *Standard Specification for Reinforced Concrete* but this was intended for internal use.

None of these codes had the force of law. The London County Council (General Powers) Act of 1909 contained statutory powers (Section 23) for the Council to introduce byelaws governing reinforced concrete design and construction standards, but it was not until 1915 that the London County Council issued its *Regulations .... with respect to the Construction of Buildings wholly or partly of Reinforced Concrete*, reflecting the same concerns that had across the Atlantic impelled Chicago to produce its own local regulations in 1906. Despite this early flurry, no further regulations of any significance appeared during the 1920s. The London County Council regulations were strengthened by the 1930 London Building Act, and although this had no application outside London it would undoubtedly have been seen as a benchmark of sorts by engineers elsewhere in Britain.

The first edition of C E Reynolds' evergreen *Reinforced Concrete Designers Handbook,* familiar to generations of civil engineers (and still in print) appeared in 1932. In 1933 the Reinforced Concrete Committee of the government's Building Research Board produced its report on reinforced concrete design, following it up with an explanatory handbook in 1934. This was the first formal and nationally applicable Code of Practice. For water towers, probably the most significant, if perhaps overdue, advance was the publication in 1938 by the Institution of Civil Engineers of its comprehensive *Code of Practice for the Design and Construction of Reinforced Concrete Structures for the Storage of Liquids*. This Code of Practice addressed those aspects of design specific to water towers outlined in Chapter 6. From now on the scope for bizarre and idiosyncratic water tower designs was severely limited and any engineer wilfully disregarding one of the Institution's Codes of Practice did so at considerable risk to his professional standing in the event of structural failure.

We have seen that concrete water towers followed the example of their iron and steel predecessors in having the base of the tank sitting on a grillage of beams. It is of course perfectly possible to design the base of a reinforced concrete tank as a simple, flat slab and do away with the supporting beams, the slab bearing directly on the heads of the columns and shaft. The analysis of the stresses in a load-bearing flat slab, compared with a beam, is relatively complex, especially when the slab itself is subject to non-uniform loading and support patterns. Until the 1930s, structural design theory had not developed sufficiently far to enable most engineers to feel confident enough to design their tank bases as flat slabs. A raft of beams was the simpler, and safer, option.

But the end of the beginning, as far as concrete water towers were concerned, had occurred by the end of the 1920s. By the 1930s, well before the publication of the ICE's landmark Code of Practice in 1938, the teaching of reinforced concrete design in universities and colleges had become an established part of the civil engineering curriculum. It was now reasonable to assume that senior engineers responsible for the tutelage and supervision of trainee engineers in drawing offices would themselves be proficient in reinforced concrete design. A common and increasingly standardised corpus of experience of the design and, of equal importance, the detailing of the steel reinforcement had been developed in the decade since the end of the first world war. The next chapter on modern concrete water towers will therefore take up the story from where this chapter draws to a close, at the start of the 1930s.

List of Water Towers Designed on the Hennebique System to 1918

The four 'elevated reservoirs' may have been service reservoirs, but as this description has been encountered as recently as 1959 to denote a water tower, these entries are included for completeness. The superscript numbers refer to the explanatory notes.

Date	Locality	Description	Owner/engineer or architect
1900	Bournemouth[1]	Water tower, 45 ft high, 15,000 galls capacity	Bournemouth Borough Council; F W Lacey, MInstCE, FRIBA
1904	Newton-le-Willows	Water tower, 300,000 galls capacity	Newton-in-Makerfield UDC; Read & Waring, AMMInstCE.
1905	Heaton[2]	Water tower, 40,000 galls capacity	North-Eastern Railway Co; W J Cudworth, MInstCE
1905	Cahir (Mayo)	Water tower for sprinkler installation	Going & Smith Ltd
1906	Belfast [3]	Water tower, 18,000 galls capacity	Belfast City Council; H A Cutler, MInstCE
1907	Fareham	Water tower, 20,000 galls capacity	Fareham UDC ;Walter Butler, MInstM&CE
1907	Queenborough [4]	Water tower, 80,000 galls capacity	Queenborough UDC; Horatio Small, engineer
1907	Gascoigne Wood [5]	Water tower, 60 ft high, 60,000 galls capacity	North-Eastern Railway Co; W J Cudworth, MInstCE
1907	Pocklington [6]	Water tower, 34 ft high, 20,000 galls capacity	Pocklington UDC; H A Johnson, MInstCE
1907	Milford Junction [5]	Water tower, 37 ft high, 20,000 galls capacity	North-Eastern Railway Co; William Bell, FRIBA.
1907	Edinburgh	Elevated reservoir, 100,000 galls capacity	North British Railway Co; James Bell, MInstCE
1908	Roydon [7]	Water tower, at Briggins, 10,000 galls capacity	Herbert Gibbs; Woodd & Ainsley, FFRIBA
1908	Gopsall Hall Park (Leicester)	Water tower, 20,000 galls capacity	The Earl Howe
1908	York	Water tower at Askham Richard, 25,000 galls built in old windmill	Maj W T Wailes-Fairbairn

1908	Athenry (Galway)	Water tower, 45 ft high, 15,000 galls capacity	Department of Agriculture and Technical Instruction; A R Robertson, engineer
1908	Trim (Meath)	Water tower 50,000 galls capacity	Trim UDC; F E Bergin, BE, CE
1909	Great Marlow	Water tower, 20,000 galls capacity	Great Marlow Water Co.
1909	Much Wenlock	Water tower, 20,000 galls capacity	Trustees of the Lady Forester Hospital
1909	Barmby Moor [8]	Water tower, 26 ft to bottom of reservoir	Pocklington UDC; H A Johnston, engineer
1910	High Wycombe	Water tower, 61 ft high, 60,000 galls capacity	Wycombe Borough Council; J T Rushbrooke, engineer
1910	Burton on Trent [9]	Water tower, 64 ft high, 20,000 galls capacity	Burton on Trent Borough Council; T Jenkins, LicRIBA
1910	Ross [10]	Elevated reservoir, 7000 galls capacity	The Lord Tredegar; Blethyn T Rees, engineer
1910	Manchester	Water tower, 60ft high, 25,000 galls capacity	Manchester Ship Canal Co Ltd; H Congreve, MInstCE
1910	Doncaster	Water tower at Thorne Colliery, 60 ft high, 30,000 galls capacity	Pease & Partners Ltd; H Greener, engineer
1911	Forth (Lanark)	Water tower, 40,000 galls capacity	The Forth & Wilsontown Supply Bd; Warren & Stuart, MMInstCE
1911	Marsden (Durham)	Water tower, 14,000 galls capacity	The Marsden Paper Mill Co; Lt Col J M Moncrieff, CBE, RE, MInstCE
1911	Marsden (Durham)	Water tower, 9000 galls capacity	Ditto; Ditto
1911	Drax [11]	Water Tower	The Grammar School
1911	Sleaford [12]	Water tower, 27,000 galls capacity	Sleaford RDC; W B Marsden, engineer
1911	Sandsend (Yorks)	Water tower, 12,000 galls capacity	Southcliffe Water Co; Thomas Dowson, engineer
1911	Prestwood (Bucks)	Water tower, 100,000 galls capacity	Rickmansworth & Uxbridge Valley Water Co; T D K Restler, AMInstCE
1912	Ridgmont	Water tower, 40,000 galls capacity	Duke of Bedford; D Balfour & Son MMInstCE
1912	Sharpness docks	Elevated reservoir, 5000 galls capacity	Sharpness New Docks and Gloucester &

			Birmingham Navigation Co; A J Cullis AMInstCE
1912	Hatfield (Yorks)	Water tower, 150,000 galls capacity	Thorne & District Water Board; Fairbank and Sons, MMInstCE
1912	Hooton Pagnall	Water tower, 12,000 galls capacity	The Rev J W France; E Bernard Wilson, architect
1913	East Grinstead	Water tower, 91'6" high at 'The Placeland'	A H Hastie; Strachan & Weekes, engineers
1913	Rugby [13]	Water tower, 20,000 galls, capacity at Southam Works	Kaye & Co Ltd
1913	Stockton [13] (Warwickshire)	Water tower, cap 25,000 galls, 40ft above ground	Charles Nelson & Co Ltd
1914	Portsmouth [14]	Sea water tower, capacity 60,000 galls, height 50 ft	Portsmouth Borough Council; A W Ward, AMInstCE
1914	Dursley [15]	Elevated tank and filter at Cam Mills, 100,000 galls cap	Hunt & Winterbotham Ltd; E J Cullis, AMInstCE, MSE
1914	Nuneaton	Water tower at Arley	Nuneaton RDC; Maj F C Cook, RE, AMInstCE
1914	Doncaster [16]	Water tower at Speech House	Dean Forest Water Supply Co; H A Cooke Yarborough, engineer
1915	Manchester	Water tower at Withington, cap 60,000 galls, total ht 114 ft, ht to bottom of reservoir 84 ft	Guardians of the Poor, Sth Manchester; F H Overmann, engineer
1915	Cranbrook [17]	Water tower at Maytham Hall, capacity 20,000 galls	Proprietor, Maytham Hall Estate; G J Jenson, engineer
1916	Pelaw-on-Tyne	Sprinkler tower	Co-operative Wholesale Soc; L C Ekins, LicRIBA
1916	Beverley	Water tower	The War Office
1916	Manchester	Water tower at Trafford Park	British Oil & Cake Mills; Gelder & Kitchin, FFRIBA
1917	Port Talbot	Water tower	Baldwins, Ltd; D Roberts, engineer
1918	Port Talbot	Water tower	Ditto

Notes:

1 Meyrick Park water tower.
2 Newcastle upon Tyne.
3 In connection with a swimming pool.
4 Isle of Sheppey, Kent.

5 Railway water towers in the South Yorkshire coalfield.

6 It has not been possible to identify this tower but it is though to have been located at either Shiptonthorpe or Londesborough, some five miles SE of Pocklington, Yorkshire.

7 Near Harlow, Essex.

8 Filled by a windpump from an adjacent borehole.

9 Erected to serve a workhouse.

10 Ross-on-Wye assumed. The location of this tower has never been identified.

11 Near Goole, South Yorkshire.

12 It is possible that this may be the existing water tower at Clay Hill, Sleaford.

13 Southam Cement Works is located at Stockton, 12 km SW of Rugby. Have two towers been conflated here? Both clients are understood to have been cement manufacturers.

14 Used for sewer flushing and street cleaning.

15 Is 'E J Cullis' the same as the 'A J Cullis' who was the engineer for the nearby Sharpness Docks water tower two years previously?

16 This must be a misprint. There is a Speech House at a high point in the centre of the Forest of Dean, but nothing of that name can be identified in the Doncaster area.

17 The Architect at Maytham Hall (which is some distance from Cranbrook) was Edwin Lutyens.

CHAPTER SIX

Modern Concrete Water Towers

T he modern, concrete water tower is, by and large, a rural phenomenon. By the end of the Victorian era every town of any size had its own piped water supply and, if circumstances demanded, its water tower. Even where the subsequent 20th century expansion of the suburbs, often up the hillsides of the valley in which the town had originated, rendered the original, Victorian water tower inadequate, the new service reservoirs or water towers needed to supply the suburbs were built on the fringes of the town, on the edge of open country. The town's original water tower was, like so much Victorian engineering, solid and durable, and continued to serve a useful function well into the new century. Relatively few new water towers therefore appeared within towns and cities in the 20th century.

The early development of rural water supplies has been outlined in Chapter 4, and although the steady consolidation of water undertakers into progressively larger units began with the formation of the district councils in 1894, the process was slow and the provision and administration of water supplies in country areas remained fragmented right up to the establishment of the Regional Water Authorities in England and Wales in 1974 (in Scotland the regional water boards had come into being in 1968). This process has been studied in detail in the East Riding of Yorkshire and the results of that study are summarised below. They are of interest as they illustrate the rate and timing of this process of amalgamation and the corresponding effect this would have had on the building of water towers in the area.

The East Riding is predominantly rural with a population in 1961 of 525,300, but this included the city of Hull on the southern edge of the area which had at that time a population of 300,790. Hull and its suburbs apart, the area is one of large scale arable agriculture though with considerable livestock farming in the earlier part of the 20th century. The East Riding's towns are either expanding market towns with some light industry or modest coastal resorts. Although Hull lies on the southern edge of the East Riding it is obvious that the city will exert a major influence on the development of water resources and the pattern of water supplies within its hinterland. Since there are few rural areas in England so remote as to be wholly outside the sphere of influence of a large town or city, the relationship of Hull to the East Riding in this respect is not atypical.

As recently as 1933 the East Riding was still being served by a plethora of water undertakers. These were dominated by 13 large or medium sized public undertakers, of which three were corporations (Hull, Bridlington, Beverley), five were water companies (York, Pocklington, Market Weighton, Driffield, Elloughton & Brough) and five urban district councils (Filey, Hornsea, Withernsea, Selby, Norton). The gaps in between were filled by 15 small, village-sized public undertakers and 15 estate water supply systems. It is of note that none of the East Riding's rural district councils were water undertakers at this time. The York and Selby undertakings, although based outside the East Riding, both had areas of supply that extended into the East Riding.

By 1959 the number of undertakers had been reduced by amalgamations and takeovers from 43 to 17 — four corporations, two water companies, five UDCs and six RDCs. The emergence of the rural district councils as water undertakers and the complete disappearance of the small local undertakings are clearly linked. In 1962, a mere three years later, the total had shrunk to 12 — three corporations, one water company, four UDCs, one RDC and, quite suddenly, three water boards had appeared. This situation remained largely unchanged until all 12 undertakers were absorbed into the newly created Yorkshire Water Authority in 1974.

The influence of Hull was felt from an early date by all its neighbours. Hedon Corporation took a bulk supply from Hull as early as 1914 as a precursor to their subsequent takeover. The small coastal undertakers in Holderness, Hornsea and Withernsea, found that their plans for the development of the water resources of their natural hinterland were being opposed and blocked by Hull Corporation, forcing them to look to Hull for their future water supplies. Hornsey took a bulk supply from Hull as early as 1926 and although the two small coastal resorts retained responsibility for their local distribution networks they had effectively lost their independence, although Withernsea's water undertaking was not formally absorbed by Hull until 1963.

The 1945 Water Act is generally regarded as a legislative watershed in the provision of a comprehensive, nationwide water supply system, yet even as late as 1960 a survey by the Beverley RDC revealed how far some country areas were from this ideal. The results are surprising. Of the 6996 dwelling houses in the district in 1960:

> 6,207 had a mains water supply with their own taps,
>
> 122 had a mains supply, but with a common supply pipe, and
>
> 78 had a mains supply, but with a street supply pipe.

Of the remainder not served by the mains:

> 326 took their water from their own well,
>
> 168 took their water from a shared well, and

3 took their water from a public well in the street.

And finally a miscellany comprising:

19 who drew their water from a spring,

23 who drew water a rainwater cistern, and

50 who were recorded as having 'no water supply.'

It is intriguing to speculate who this last, not inconsiderable, category might have been and how they managed to subsist! Nevertheless, over 90% of the dwelling houses in the rural district enjoyed a mains water supply and by the end of the 1950s the spread of piped water into the rural areas can be regarded as substantially complete. Many of the 'wells' would, in fact, have been private boreholes equipped with electric or diesel-engined pumps.

There is no reason to suppose that the process of consolidation of rural water undertakings in the East Riding was significantly different in its timing and duration from that which took place in other parts of the country, and the implications of this process for the construction of water towers can therefore be assumed to be countrywide. The principal feature of this process was not, as is often now assumed, the widespread provision of first-time water supplies in rural areas but the absorption of considerable numbers of small, local undertakings initially into larger, district council-run undertakings and subsequently, by the amalgamation of the district-based undertakings, into water boards. The process was, by and large, concentrated in the two or three decades straddling the second world war, with the first stage of the process occurring in the 1930s and the latter stage in the the 1950s and the early1960s.

The start of the 1930s marks a transition, not only from early to modern concrete water towers but also in the way in which rural water supplies were financed. The Rural Water Supplies Act of 1934 made government loans and grants available to local authorities to provide or improve village water supplies. In the following year an article in a professional journal commented that the Act, 'has done much to relieve the situation' and that as a result of the allocation of a million pounds by the treasury, 'out of 2000 parishes which were in need 1600 have already been dealt with and the work is in various stages of completion.' The writer's definition of need must have been decidedly narrow for, judging by the situation in many areas well over a decade later, the benefits of the 1934 Act had still clearly failed to reach hundreds of smaller villages. Even in the 1930s, a million pounds did not go far and it was not until the 1944 Rural Water Supplies & Sewerage Act made over £21 million available from the exchequer that substantial advances became possible.

In some of the more remote rural areas of Britain the provision of modern piped water supplies came surprisingly late. This pattern is well illustrated across Shropshire. A survey published in 1946 found that in Shifnal Rural District on the edge of the Black Country only three of the 14 parishes were without a piped water supply. Two parishes had an estate supply and all the rest were supplied either by the District Council or from neighbouring urban areas. By contrast, in Ludlow Rural District over towards the Welsh border, 31 of the 45 parishes had no piped water supply at all. The district council supplied a mere five parishes, an adjoining RDC supplied two, and five parishes were supplied by a miscellany of private or estate undertakers or, in one case, by a local cooperative. Two parishes took a supply direct from Birmingham Corporation's Elan Aqueduct which ran through the district.

It should not be assumed that a rural district council supply was necessarily modern or reliable. Of the two parishes supplied by Bridgnorth RDC, Alveley (population 822) had a 700 gallon 'elevated tank' fed by a hydraulic ram, while at Stottesdon (population 948) a windpump, supplemented by a petrol/paraffin standby engine, filled their elevated tank through a two inch rising main. Since 25 of Bridgnorth RD's 34 parishes had no piped supply at all, Alveley and Stottesdon should perhaps have been thankful for small mercies. One of the Bridgnorth RD parishes was supplied by the local mining company and, here again, we find one parish supplied from the Elan aqueduct.

In each of the three Shropshire rural districts instanced above, the eponymous town was a separate borough or urban district with its own small municipal water supply system. This pattern, a small country town administratively separate from its surrounding rural area, was quite common throughout Britain during the first half of the 20th century despite a slow but steady process of amalgamations of rural and urban districts throughout the period. It is quite probable, given the economic disparity between the modestly prosperous country town and a countryside still recovering from the agricultural depression of the 1930s, that this rather odd separation worked against the interests of the relatively impecunious rural district and contributed to the remarkably slow development of rural water supplies in such areas.

By the early 1930s the design of reinforced concrete water towers in consulting engineers' drawing offices was becoming routine. Mouchel had produced a handbook of water tower designs for internal use which covered a range of styles and sizes, with tank capacities from 2 to 750 thousand gallons and heights to base of tank from 6 to 125 feet, though most were in the 20 to 50 foot height range. Despite all this, as wide a range of water tower types as ever was still being built, with little apparent convergence towards a standard configuration. The inter-war years saw two significant developments in concrete water tower design although both seem ultimately to have become evolutionary cul de sacs. Each had its heyday in the 1930s and 1950s.

The first of these was the Intze tank. In Britain the Intze tank is invariably thought of in the context of concrete structures but the concept originated towards the end of the 19th century when it was initially applied to iron tanks. Whilst a flat-bottomed tank of whatever material is easy to construct, the flat base, unless made uneconomically thick, will need to be supported on a grid or raft of beams. If the tank is of concrete the problem can be resolved by making the supporting beams integral with the tank base, and the undersides of concrete tanks exhibit a seemingly infinite range of configurations of radial, circumferential and latticework beams.

But if the tank can be made sufficiently rigid, the need for these beams — and the cost of providing them — disappears. The use of dished bases with rivetted iron tanks was one way to achieve this, although a heavy circumferential ring beam round the rim of the dish would still be necessary to maintain the rigidity of the tank. By 1883 Professor Otto Intze of the Technische Hochschule at Aachen (Aix-la-Capelle) had solved the problem by designing a circular tank floor the central portion of which consisted of a shallow dome (or inverted dish) and the outer part an inverted, truncated cone. The cone and dome converged on a ringbeam, but since the dimensions were carefully calculated to ensure that the outward forces at the base of the dome balanced the inward forces at the base of the truncated cone the resultant force on the ring beam was vertically downwards. This meant that the ringbeam could be relatively modest in size and, moreover, since the ringbeam was only about two thirds the diameter of the tank the supporting structure below the ringbeam could also be relatively narrow. With Intze's design, unlike flat-bottomed tanks, reversals of stress in the tank base between the empty and full states were eliminated.

Although Professor Intze initially developed his design with iron or steel tanks in mind, the principle was extended to reinforced concrete almost immediately. Wayss & Koenen's proposed concrete water tower at Landshut in 1885 (see Chapter 5) incorporated an Intze tank and Edmond Coignet's reinforced concrete tower at the Toulon naval dockyard in 1898 was built with an Intze tank. A further advantage when used with concrete was that the Intze tank's uniform floor and wall thicknesses reduced the risk of cracking.

Like all good engineering, Intze's design (sometimes referred to as the 'balanced design') was not only elegant in concept but also in appearance (Figure 6.1). Concrete water towers with Intze tanks started to appear in Britain in the early 1920s and there are two good examples from this period in the Doncaster area, Armthorpe (1923) and Cantley No.1 (1925). The distinctive shape of the Intze tank can most clearly be seen when it is erected on a ring of columns; when it surmounts a shaft the inner dome is hidden and only the characteristic sloping base of the outer cone is visible. The Intze tank's principal drawback was that it required complex shuttering to form the base. So long as the material savings exceeded the extra labour costs involved the design was viable, but as the cost of skilled labour rose relative to the cost of concrete the point was reached when the Intze tank could

Figure 6.1. Waltham on the Wolds water tower, Leicestershire, c 1960

no longer be economically justified. In Britain this seems to have occurred at some time during the 1950s, although as late as 1963 a plea for the retention of the Intze design was made by a distinguished engineer in a professional journal.

Intze's design is not limited by size. Great Yarmouth's 162 foot high Caister-on-Sea water tower has a massive 784,000 gallon twin-compartment Intze tank, claimed to be the largest of its type in the country when it was built in 1933. Steel formwork was used in its construction, an early example, but necessary to support the 570 tons of concrete required for the 14 foot slanting overhang of the tank floor which was poured in a single lift. Iron and steel Intze tanks were erected in considerable numbers on the continent from 1890 to 1920, in Belgium and northern France in particular, where some extravagantly ornamented examples appeared, but none have been recorded in Britain.

The other inter-war development, known rather confusingly as 'reinforced steelwork' was due to H C Ritchie of Ritchie & Partners, a firm of consulting engineers specialising in reinforced concrete water retaining structures. Reinforced steelwork, despite its name, was essentially a form of reinforced concrete, but in which a light steel framework took the place of the usual mild steel reinforcing bars, though bars were still used as secondary reinforcement. The concept, patented in 1925, was not of course confined to water towers but was found to be particularly suitable for water towers because the steel framework could be used to support the considerable weight of the formwork needed for the tank and thus do away with elaborate and expensive temporary supports. A further advantage claimed was that the main steel reinforcement is effectively pre-stressed under construction loads as the concrete sets around it. The ultimate tensile stress in the concrete is thus considerably reduced and the risk of cracking and hence leakage correspondingly diminished. Reinforced steelwork was also claimed to lend itself to more accurate setting-out and more rapid construction than conventional reinforced concrete.

The first 'Ritchie' water towers appeared in the late 1920s and half a dozen had been built by 1930. Harpenden's Shakespeare Road water tower (1930) is a notable early example. The concept, though it proved entirely satisfactory in practice and had an extended vogue in the 1930s, never gained widespread acceptance. The main reason was probably because 'reinforced steelwork' was considerably more expensive than the equivalent reinforced concrete structure, a drawback accentuated by the acute shortage of structural steelwork in the years immediately after World War II. Another reason could well have been that, despite the same underlying design principles, a 'learning curve' would have been necessary for an engineer schooled in conventional reinforced concrete design to make the transition to 'reinforced steelwork' design which, if it was merely for a single structure, might not have been worth the effort. Unlike Intze tanks, there is no particular feature by which 'reinforced steelwork' towers can be readily distinguished from more conventional concrete structures. It is likely that in many cases reinforced steelwork was used for the supporting structure rather than the tank itself, particularly if the latter was designed to resist hoop stresses rather than as a vertical cantilever. Two of the last 'Ritchies' to be built were the imposing 750,000 gallon Chatterton Tower at Spalding, Lincolnshire in 1955 and York's million gallon Siwards How water tower in 1956.

Notwithstanding the popularity of the Intze tank and the introduction of 'reinforced steelwork' a majority of water towers continued to be constructed to traditional reinforced concrete designs. During the 1930s there was a noticeable consolidation in the variety of types and styles, an increasing consensus on what a water tower should look like. For public supply towers the central shaft became the norm, though in two distinct forms. In the one there would be a relatively narrow shaft surrounded by one or sometimes two concentric rings of columns (Figure 6.2). The alternative would be for the tank and shaft to be of almost equal width (Figure 6.3). In this case the shaft could either be a load bearing concrete cylinder or designed as a ring of columns, the spaces between them infilled with concrete curtain walling. It is often not easy to distinguish one from the other. The use of brickwork infill for the curtain walls was common on the continent but, unless others have been rendered to appear as concrete, the only example known in England is the ex-RAF tower at Bircham Newton, Norfolk. There is said to be a cluster of such towers dating from the start of the 1960s on the Isle of Lewis in the Outer Hebrides.

As time went on, engineers became sufficiently confident to design their supporting columns as a single, unbroken pillar but the majority of water towers up until the 1960s continued to be built with horizontal cross-bracing between the columns at anything from one to a half dozen intermediate levels. This bracing, inserted to stiffen the structure

Figure 6.2 (left). Billinghay water tower, Lincolnshire, c 1950s
Figure 6.3 (above). Wheldrake water tower, North Yorkshire, c 1960

and prevent buckling of the slender columns, can be seen in an almost infinite variety of combinations of radial, circumferential or latticed beams, generally repeating the pattern of the supporting beams beneath the tank. The cross-sectional dimensions of the concrete beams used to form the cross bracing are almost always comparable to those of the columns, though occasionally the columns themselves may diminish in size above an intermediate bracing stage. Even where the shaft has been designed as a ring of columns infilled with curtain walling it is not uncommon to find cross-bracing inside the shaft, despite the stiffening effect of the curtain walling itself or, with some larger towers, to encounter a secondary ring of columns enclosed within the shaft.

The pattern of this bracing would usually be the same at each level but close observation sometimes reveals subtle differences in layout or orientation between levels. Some tall towers exhibit a graduation in vertical spacing between their bracing stages. Bracing is almost invariably in the horizontal plane. This is because of the difficulty of casting the diagonal beams that would be necessary for bracing in a vertical plane. There are few examples of vertical bracing on existing concrete water towers known to the author, the most accessible being Burnham Green (Herts) and Pontefract's Park Hill tower. Ipswich's Park Road tower has vertical bracing but hidden behind the curtain walling. Leverburgh water tower, in the Outer Hebrides and exposed to the full force of Atlantic storms, has full-height vertical plane bracing. At some locations such as Lytchett Matravers (Dorset) the vertical bracing is reduced to mere gussets between columns and horizontal bracing. Vertical plane bracing of the supporting structure is of course an almost universal feature of all-metal water towers.

With the traditional configuration of a simple drum-shaped tank supported on columns, or on columns and a shaft, a small water tower can be designed with a limited number of columns, as few as four. As the required storage capacity increases, in order to maintain variations of pressure in the supply network within operationally acceptable limits the floor area of the tank must increase as the volume. Although the number of columns can be limited to some extent by increasing the size of the beams immediately beneath the tank floor it is clear that ever greater storage capacity must inevitably result in a proliferation of columns. One has only to compare Newton-le-Willows with Meyrick Park for this to become apparent. At the limit, we end up with a broad, flat tank on a veritable forest of legs. Ely's Tower Road water tower with its 36 free-standing columns (plus another 12 forming the shaft) illustrates this all too clearly. Though this tendency does not have any particular economic disbenefit — in fact the capital cost per column probably decreases as the number increases — the visual effect is an unhappy one. A further complication arises with a broad, flat tank. The roof span becomes excessive and intermediate roof support becomes necessary. This can be provided by the dividing wall between concentric compartments but in some instances internal columns have had to be inserted in the tank for this purpose.

A straightforward solution to this problem would be to achieve increased size merely by scaling up the simpler, less cluttered small tower design but, even with some adjustment to restrict tank depth, this would still produce a water tower far taller than necessary or, more important, than operationally desirable. The rather bleak conclusion that must be drawn from this is that as the water tower's capacity increases it will inevitably become progressively more difficult to design an attractive structure.

Although always a tiny minority, square or rectangular water towers keep appearing until the 1950s, randomly scattered throughout the country though with a cluster of four in Glasgow. It is likely that the use of a square tower may have been prompted by the need for uniformity of style when, as sometimes happened, a water tower was designed and built integrally with a rectangular service reservoir, the shape of the reservoir being determined by the shape and size of the site. This appears to have happened at Kimberley, near Nottingham (Figure 6.4). Conversely a circular tower would naturally be designed in association with a circular service reservoir where the two were structurally integrated, as at Southall. If a tower is erected directly above a reservoir its heavily loaded columns must be extended down through the base of the reservoir, giving rise to potential problems with differential movement between columns and reservoir floor. Many water towers have been built on service reservoir sites but as a subsequent development and in these cases, especially if the reservoir is partially buried, the aesthetic requirement for uniformity of appearance does not arise.

One design motif, which originated with Meyrick Park and then reappeared two decades or more later and had a remarkably prolonged popularity, was the scalloped skirt that appears as a series of miniature arches (arcading) between the heads of the columns around the base of the tank. It is perhaps best described as a motif because

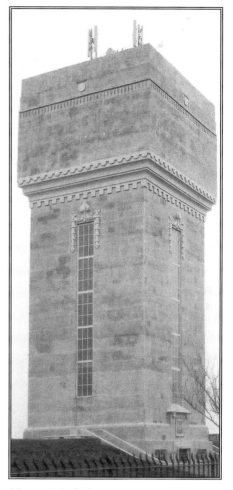

Figure 6.4. Swingate water tower, Kimberley, Nottinghamshire, 1950

although it would undoubtedly have added stiffness to the structure a simple circumferential beam would have achieved the same end. Nevertheless, it has to be conceded that the aesthetic effect of the scalloped skirt is an oddly pleasing one. A similar affectation sometimes found round the base of the columns is a dwarf wall or ring of concrete balustrading enclosing a slightly raised ground level plinth.

Concrete water towers are not always what they seem. Another design of water tower which appeared in small numbers in the 1930s and early 1950s is not, strictly speaking, a concrete tower but is included in this chapter because it appears outwardly to be one. These were towers which enclosed a cylindrical steel tank at the top of a full-width concrete shaft, similar in concept to the 'enclosed tank' version of the 'Victorian' water tower except that there could never be any doubt that the 'Victorian' tower would contain an iron tank. Without detailed local knowledge it is not easy to ascertain whether a particular concrete water tower contains a steel tank since it is natural to assume that the concrete 'tank' at the top of its concrete shaft is what it appears to be and not merely a protective screen for an internal steel tank. In some instances the slightly wider top section and decorative banding appear deliberately intended to suggest a concrete tank.

The reasons for this now rather curious structural timidity can only be guessed at, and it would be interesting to hear the justification for this design. There can be no clear economic advantage, as the relatively small additional expense of providing a concrete tank base and designing the concrete walls at the top of the shaft as part of a water retaining structure would surely be outweighed by the cost of the separate steel tank, leaving aside questions as to the relative maintenance costs and longevity of concrete and steel tanks. At Corby (Northants) three pre-World War II towers were of this type but here the reason is obvious — Corby was a new town established together with its steelworks, the town's *raison d'être*, in the early 1930s and the local water undertaker was a subsidiary of the company which owned the steelworks. Corby's Rockingham water tower is shown in Figure 6.5. Small clusters of this type of water tower have been identified elsewhere; one such is known in Bedfordshire and another is understood to exist in north east Suffolk. There may be others elsewhere. It has been reported that some steel tanks are actually composite 'cheese dish' type structures — a steel cylinder on a concrete base with a sliding joint at the interface — but it has not been possible to verify this.

The earliest occurrence of this composite type seems to have been at Cleethorpes in 1908, but here there was no attempt to disguise the steel tank, though cladding was used to protect the tank from corrosion in its exposed seaside location. Perhaps its considerable size, upwards of 220,000 gallons, discouraged the use of concrete in this case. The cylindrical steel tank was eventually replaced with a concrete tank in 1962.

Figure 6.5. Rockingham water tower, Northants, c 1940

In 1943 the distinguished civil engineer, G Howard Humphreys wrote that 'it would be hard to name an engineering structure more difficult to design than a water tower' and he suggested to his fellow engineers that they obtain an architect's advice on external appearance if they had any misgivings as to the suitability to its environment of the tower they were designing. Howard Humphreys' advice was prophetic for, with the introduction of stricter town and country planning controls after the second world war, water engineers, their clients and the public at large became more aware of the aesthetic aspects of water tower design and their potential for visual impact on the landscape. Since the mid 1960s architects have played a much more prominent role in the design of water towers, almost certainly as a response by water undertakers to an increasing public sensitivity towards environmental issues and a corresponding difficulty in meeting the concerns of local authority planning committees. The results of this closer collaboration between engineer and architect have, on the whole, been fruitful as evidenced by the number of visually dramatic towers erected in recent decades. Even so, the results have not been universally successful and there are certainly a number of modern water towers in which form appears to have taken precedence over function, giving rise to a self consciously 'artistic' — even a pretentious 'look at me' — appearance achieved, one suspects, at considerable expense to the client.

Apart form its overall design, the public face of a concrete water tower is also determined by the nature of its external finish. By the early 1960s it was recognised that this need not be limited to a coat of paint on bare concrete, although colour is often specified by planning authorities as a consent condition. Shuttering specifically intended to give a textured finish to the exposed faces of the concrete came into use. Precast concrete panels with textured surfaces produced under factory conditions can be used as permanent shuttering (Ramsden Heath, Essex) even where the water tower itself is not of precast concrete construction, and a technique known as 'exposed aggregate' had a limited popularity. Here the inside face of the normal timber or steel shuttering would be coated with a decorative aggregate which would transfer to the outer face of the concrete as it set (Mountnessing, Essex). Permanent precast shuttering panels became more widely used with the proliferation of the strutted tank and 'wineglass' designs described later in this chapter. The designer should not, however, lose sight of the fact that unless the water tower is close to a public road or housing it can plausibly be argued that the provision of an expensive finish is of questionable benefit.

Since the water contained within public supply water towers was almost invariably treated water en route to the consumer, increasing care was taken to prevent contamination of water in the tank. There was no longer any question of having open-topped tanks. At one time it had been common for the roof drainage to be discharged into the tank overflow pipe but the possibility, however remote, of cross-contamination of potable water by rainwater now dictated entirely separate roof drainage systems. During the 1970s many water undertakers modified the pipework in their older water towers and provided lengthy downpipes exclusively for roof drainage. At some locations ultra-violet 'electrocutors' are installed to attract and kill any stray insects which have found their way into the airspace above the tank.

Mention was made in the previous chapter of Mouchel's in-house handbook of water tower designs. During the rapid expansion of rural water supplies in the 1950s many of the larger water undertakers such as the newly formed water boards built a number of towers within a relatively short time and would develop a distinct 'house style' for that purpose. Even though the individual towers might vary significantly in height and capacity the same overall design features and motifs would be readily apparent. The East Anglian Water Company was noteworthy in this respect (despite its name this company's area of supply covered little more than Great Yarmouth and North East

Suffolk and on the formation of the Anglian Water Authority in 1974 it changed its name to Suffolk Water.) An example of its standard 1950s water tower is illustrated in Figure 6.6. Some consulting engineers also developed their own house styles as it made sound economic sense for them to be able to offer smaller water undertakers 'off the peg' designs. Markedly similar water towers can sometimes be seen at very diverse locations, clearly the products of the same drawing office, though it can now be difficult to discover the designer of many older water towers without lengthy and often frustrating investigations.

When water towers were still being built in considerable numbers in the early 1960s it was claimed that statutory ('private') water companies were more likely to erect imaginatively original or aesthetically attractive water towers than their

Figure 6.6. Shadingfield water tower, Suffolk, 1955

public counterparts. This was, it was suggested, because the former were not subject to the same financial constraints as water boards and local authority undertakers who had to obtain loan sanction for capital works from the Ministry of Housing and Local Government.

The concept of prestressed concrete — the introduction of a degree of initial tensile stress in the steel reinforcement — is almost as old as reinforced concrete itself. Prestressed concrete enables elegant, slender structures to be built with an economy of material but because of its inherent technical complexity, the need for ducts and anchorages, a means of creating the initial stress and a high degree of quality control, it did not achieve commercial viability until the late 1920s. Here, once again, the French led the way. Prestressed concrete did not really become commonplace in Britain until the 1950s, its acceptance hastened by the shortage of constructional steel in the years immediately following the war.

Prestressed concrete has two principal variants. It is 'pre-tensioned' if, as the name suggests, the steel reinforcement is held in tension while the concrete is poured round it, the tension being released when the concrete has set thus putting the surrounding concrete into compression, and 'post-tensioned' if the steel is tensioned after the concrete has set. In the latter case, the steel is enclosed within ducts in the concrete or is external to the concrete. By inducing a prestress in the steel reinforcement the tensile stresses in the concrete surrounding the reinforcement can be minimised, thus inhibiting the hairline cracking in the concrete which occurs on the tensile face of a conventionally reinforced concrete beam (or floor slab or wall) subject to bending stresses. The benefits to water retaining structures are immediately obvious; eliminate this cracking and you are well on the way to eliminating leakage. It is reasonable to assume that prestressed concrete would rapidly have become the material of choice for the design of water towers. Britain's first prestressed concrete water tower, designed by Sandford, Fawcett & Partners, was erected at Meare in Somerset for the Wells RDC in 1953 (Figure 6.7) yet for the next eight years it was still the only prestressed concrete water tower in Britain. In 1961 the Higham Ferrers & Rushden (later Mid Northants) Water Board built the next prestressed concrete water tower at Manton on the outskirts of Rushden and this, too, remains an isolated example. It is interesting that both Meare and Manton were built by the same contractor, The Vibrated Concrete Construction Company.

Prestressed concrete water towers were already being built in Scandinavia and the USA so Meare was not breaking new ground. Why then the almost total failure of prestressed concrete to be adopted for water towers in Britain? They appeared occasionally; Sapley (Huntingdon) is said to have a prestressed concrete tank and the relatively recent (1987) Mannings Heath water tower in Dorset is of a prestressed design, but they never became common. Appleby Parva on the Leicestershire/Warwickshire border, although not strictly a water

*Figure 6.7. Meare water tower,
Somerset, 1953*

tower because the base of its tall (59ft) cylindrical tank is at ground level, was built in 1972 with 15 parallel but unequally spaced bands of external prestressing. The prestressing wires were set in recessed grooves and protected by a thick coating of grey resin paint, but this did not prevent recurrent corrosion and the structure has recently been demolished.

The technique was being used successfully for concrete service reservoirs, so its neglect cannot be blamed on an innate conservatism or a failure of nerve of British engineers. Water towers are, by their very nature, relatively small 'one-off' structures, often at remote locations, rendering the setting up and use of the specialist equipment needed for tensioning the reinforcement uneconomic. Secondly, the degree of quality control essential for prestressed concrete construction is not easy to achieve perched on scaffolding 100 feet off the ground in all weathers. Prestressed concrete comes into its own either on large projects with repetitive design elements, or in a closely controlled factory environment, mass producing relatively small items such as railway sleepers or standardised bridge beams.

It is, nevertheless, worthwhile looking at Meare water tower in some detail. The layout is conventional enough, a circular 122,000 gallon tank, 37ft in diameter and 24ft deep supported on eight circumferential columns and a central shaft. The outer wall of the tank, 6in thick, is prestressed both vertically and circumferentially on the Freyssinet system. The vertical prestressing consists of 48 cables, each comprising twelve 0.2in high tensile steel wires, enclosed within steel sheaths and anchored at the upper and lower ringbeams. The circumferential prestressing is by means of two-wire cables set in grooves on the outside of the tank, closely spaced at 2.5in (base) to 3in (top) centres . Each cable passes only half way round the tank and is anchored at four of the pilasters (The other four pilasters are for aesthetic purposes only, to match pilasters with columns.) A half inch layer of concrete was then sprayed on to the outside of the tank (*Gunite*) to protect the cables. The tank's inner (shaft) wall is prestressed vertically with four 12-wire cables at the quarter points. The tank floor was also innovative in design, consisting of eight conoidal sections radiating out from the central shaft and spanning like jack-arches between eight radial beams. The tank roof, walls and floor are all of a uniform six inch thickness. Meare water tower is now disused. A slightly earlier (1950) tower, Bloxworth in Dorset, has been reported to have an externally prestressed tank but it has not been possible to confirm this.

Meanwhile other, more conventional advances in design had been taking place. A keen observer may have noticed that, unlike pre-World War II towers, a considerable number of post-war towers have flat tank bases or, to be more precise, no supporting grillage of concrete beams beneath the tank. In some instances this is due to the beams protruding upwards through the tank floor but this creates problems when cleaning and draining the tank, the aesthetic benefits of having a smooth, uncluttered underside to the tank being achieved at the expense of operational convenience. Most such flat tank bases are, however, achieved by configuring the floor of the tank as a flat slab, designed to span in two dimensions simultaneously, thus obviating the need for a supporting raft. Hitherto, until the appropriate two-dimensional structural analysis and design theory had been developed, reinforced concrete 'slabs' had been designed by considering them simply as broad, flat beams. For tank bases, such 'slabs' were used merely to span the relatively narrow gaps between the supporting beams.

If the circle of columns under the tank is interlinked by curtain walling then there is no need for a central shaft, and *vice versa*. Where the cylindrical tank is carried only on a circle of columns, the bending moments in the beams which make up the supporting framework under the tank can be reduced by making the diameter of that circle somewhat smaller than the diameter of the tank. The optimum ratio of the two diameters is around 0.7 to 1 but will vary according to the shape and configuration of the tank and its platform. The resulting tower profile, with the tank oversailing a relatively wide shaft, can give the structure a decidedly squat and potentially unattractive appearance. The designer is also aware that construction costs can be reduced by making the shaft smaller, even if this means having to strengthen the tank platform or the connection between the tank and the shaft. For this type of tower (ie, where the circle of columns and its curtain walling forms the shaft) a narrower shaft can therefore be both aesthetically and economically beneficial, and over the years a variety of methods have been employed to achieve this objective.

The first of these was the use of pilasters up the side of the shaft, formed by recessing the curtain walling slightly (Figure 6.8). These

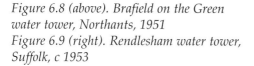

Figure 6.8 (above). Brafield on the Green
water tower, Northants, 1951
Figure 6.9 (right). Rendlesham water tower,
Suffolk, c 1953

pilasters were often cranked out at the top and bottom, but were of architectural rather than of any structural significance. The overall diameter of the shaft remained virtually unchanged. In the 1950s, pilasters developed into load-bearing fins, slab-like columns which extended radially back towards the centre of the tower (Figure 6.9). These fins could be vertical or inclined outwards, either towards the top or, more rarely, the base of the shaft.

Another approach was simply to reduce the diameter of the shaft to the minimum required for operational purposes. The storage or equipment space within the shaft might be useful but was rarely utilised to the full, so why incur unnecessary expense in building a shaft larger than required to fulfil its essential functions; those of supporting the tank, providing a safe and secure access to the tank, and protecting the pipework and controls from the elements and human interference? As a result, the 1960s saw shafts becoming progressively narrower than the tanks they supported (Figure 6.10) but with a conventional drum-on-shaft water tower there comes a point where, as the shaft becomes increasingly narrow relative to the diameter of the tank, the stresses in the structure in the right angle between shaft and tank (and between shaft and base slab) become unacceptably high. It is

Figure 6.10 (above). High Acres water tower, Wordsley, West Midlands, 1968
Figure 6.11 (right). Baydon water tower, Wiltshire, 1974

notable that many of these drum-on-shaft towers were now being designed with uncluttered flat-slab tank bases to achieve a fashionable and starkly functional appearance.

This problem can be resolved by inserting brackets or struts between the tank base and the shaft, or by enlarging and extending the struts up the outside of the tank and designing the latter as an inverted, truncated cone — the strutted tank or 'bowl-in-hand' water tower (Figure 6.11). The struts have to be tied together and this is done by placing a ring beam or collar round the struts, or by radial extensions linking the struts beneath the tank. Alternatively the problem can more elegantly be overcome by building a tower of a 'wineglass' design with the tank as a simple inverted cone blossoming out from the top of its ultra-narrow shaft. The rationale behind the wineglass design is thus fairly straightforward. Britain's first wineglass was erected by the Newcastle & Gateshead Water Company at Morwick (Northumberland) in 1963.

In many respects the 1950s were the end of an era, not least for water towers. The 1960s brought with them the 'white heat of technology' and a sea-change in social attitudes. It is hardly surprising that the sixties also heralded the appearance of the single-stem or wineglass water tower. Some might even regard the origins of this radically new design in Sweden in the late 1950s as significant. There is no doubt that the wineglass water tower (sometimes called a 'mushroom') has a dramatic visual impact on its surroundings (Figure 6.12), though the public response generally seems to have been favourable — or at least they have not, as a class of structure, provoked any notable outcry.

The wineglass did not, however, render the strutted tank obsolete. The bowl-in-hand design, perhaps more so than the wineglass, lends itself to prefabricated construction methods using large precast units and these two modern types have proved

Figure 6.12. Upton Beacon water tower, West Yorkshire, 1972

equally popular since their introduction. Although the bowl-in-hand has an undoubtedly striking appearance, the cleaner, uncluttered lines of the wineglass make it the more aesthetically pleasing of the two. This assumes a conventional, single-stemmed configuration. A wineglass on five squat shafts exists at Scarth Hill, Ormskirk, transforming what ought to be an elegant and potentially graceful design into something verging on the brutal. This is all the more regrettable because it replaced three fine Victorian water towers (and a large Braithwaite tank) which graced the skyline on a ridge east of the town, notable landmarks in the West Lancashire plain and visible from ships entering the Mersey. Unfortunately all four of the old towers had been erected by different undertakers and had different top water levels, rendering them incompatible in any amalgamated supply system. As soon as the Scarth Hill wineglass had been completed the 1879 and 1897 towers were promptly demolished, almost as if to avoid unflattering comparisons, and the 1850 tower, a Grade II* listed building, survives only as a tank-less stump. In contrast, the wineglass at Thorne (South Yorkshire) has its shaft divided vertically into six closely spaced curved columns and its appearance is not harmed in the least by so doing. Minor differences in shape and proportion can make all the difference between an attractive and a downright ugly structure.

The inverted cone is not the ideal shape for a tank. If the angle is too acute the water level in the tank, and pressure in the distribution network, changes rapidly with change in storage volume, increasingly so as the water level falls. Conversely, as the cone is flattened the storage volume becomes diminishingly small and the design, although undeniably impressive, is inherently uneconomic. In many cases a compromise is reached, the tank extending above the cone with a shallow cylindrical section (Figure 6.13). The intersection of a cone with the vertical sided shaft tends to produce a rather stark profile and various attempts have been made to ameliorate the effect by curving the transition between tank and shaft or by the use of splayed ribs between cone and shaft. (Figure 6.14). The roof of the wineglass may be either domed or flat, usually with a small cupola in the centre, though this is often obscured from view by the protruding rim of the tank.

It is readily apparent that the wineglass is not the easiest or cheapest of water towers to construct *in-situ*. Not only is curved shuttering required (though this can be overcome by adopting a polygonal shape) but there is a real problem of supporting the shuttering and concrete until the concrete has set. The Austrian RSB ('Rundstahlbau') shuttering system was developed to address this problem and has been used successfully for a number of recent towers, including Castle Syke near Ackworth in West Yorkshire (1989). Another approach, pioneered in Sweden in 1956 (though there are reports of its earlier use in French West Africa) is to build the shaft, construct the tank round the base of the shaft at ground level and then jack the completed tank up the shaft to its final position. Ludham (Norfolk), built in 1980, is

Figure 6.13 (left). Headless Cross water tower, Hereford and Worcester, 1973

Figure 6.14 (below). Garthorpe water tower, Humberside, 1967

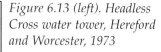

believed to have been the first British tower erected using this technique. Raising the tank took a total of 22 hours spread over three working days. On a subsequent tank jacking project however, considerable difficulties arose in achieving a watertight joint between the tank and the shaft.

An alternative method of construction is the use of precast concrete tank units, usually with prestressed reinforcement. These can be produced to high dimensional accuracy off site, though it should be noted that the use of precast tank slabs does involve some risk of leakage along the joints between adjacent units. As with all wineglass designs the shaft is carried up through the tank and the precast units are tied back to the top of the shaft using steel rods. An early (1965) and impressive example of a prefabricated wineglass is York University's water tower (Figure 8.11, page 143). It is a remarkably bold structure; the 68 foot diameter 50,000 gallon tank is carried on a shaft a mere seven feet wide, its extreme slenderness emphasised by the exaggerated oversail of the flattened cone above. The cut-out formed by the access doorway in the base of the shaft must result in extreme local stress concentrations at the base of the shaft. The shaft itself springs from a 3ft 6in thick reinforced concrete slab founded on 26 bored concrete piles in a 28ft diameter ring round the edge of the slab. Because the 87 foot high tower is set in the centre of a courtyard and surrounded by other buildings it is not easy to appreciate what is a remarkable piece of engineering design. Unfortunately the precast tank units have not withstood the test of time and are deteriorating badly and at the time of writing the university authorities are contemplating demolition as their only feasible option. A visitor to the site might wonder why this tower, erected within shouting distance of York Waterworks' taller Siwards How water tower, was deemed necessary in the first place. Apparently a constant head of water was needed for the University's chemistry laboratories but was this the most cost effective means of achieving it?

Such were the proportions of the York University tower that an analysis was undertaken at the design stage to confirm that the natural frequency of any wind-induced oscillations would not coincide with those of the water in the tank and that no uncontrolled 'sloshing' would occur. A model of the water tower was tested in a wind tunnel to determine the simple static bending moments imposed on the structure by high winds and those due to wind-induced oscillations, which were found to be of comparable magnitude. Lightly tensioned radial ties in the form of aluminium alloy wires were therefore added during the detailed design stage to avoid the rim of the tank vibrating like a bell. In November 1965, a few months after commissioning, the tower was subject to the full force of a severe gale with gusts of up to 108 ft/sec (74 mph). It was reported that 'there was no apparent effect' on the structure, but the report then rather contradicted itself by adding, 'although (its) in-wind deflections were observable from the ground.'

A variation of the wineglass design which has appeared in Europe but not in Britain closely resembles a coal-fired power station cooling tower. Seen in profile, the outline of its tank, waisted shaft and splayed base forms a continuous hyperbolic curve. Another highly unusual design which appeared in the mid-1960s is the concrete tower with an angular, multi-lobed tank, a complexity of intersecting lines and planes, rather like a snowflake in plan. Only two examples are known, at Arkley (Greater London) and Horstead (Norfolk), which appear to have originated from the same drawing board (Figure 6.15). Undoubtedly impressive, but whether this bravura design with its heavily cantilevered lobes was cost effective is open to question. It could be argued that York's Siwards How tower was the first to have a lobed layout. Its massive square concrete tower, one of the last 'Ritchies', was built with full-height octagonal lobes at each corner to

Figure 6.15. Horstead water tower, Norfolk, c 1970

give the impression of a medieval castle keep.

One Victorian concept to make a minor comeback in recent years has been the semi-detached access shaft. An isolated example was constructed at Featherstone (West Yorkshire) in 1952 with a rectangular concrete shaft abutting two of the very spindly columns and the side of the cylindrical tank, and extending above the top of the tank with a doorway onto the tank roof. In the late 1960s at least four large towers of this type were built in Cambridgeshire to a design which used a

Figure 6.16. Highflyers water tower, Ely, Cambridgeshire, 1968

lightweight rectangular glazed shaft, offset to one side of the tower and with an enclosed walkway from the head of the shaft onto the top of the tank (Figure 6.16). A variation on this theme followed in the 1970s in which one of the ring of rectangular columns supporting the tank was enlarged to form the access shaft as, for example, at Earls Barton in Northamptonshire.

The number of new water towers erected in recent years has dwindled rapidly, though refurbishment of existing towers is commonplace. The latest concrete tower to be built for public water supply in Britain, a bowl-in-hand type, is Church Langley at Harlow in Essex (1993), though one or two impressively large towers have subsequently been completed in Ireland. As with many other classes of civil engineering structures, there has been a trend in the last two decades for an almost ingratiating attempt (born, perhaps, of a loss of confidence by the profession at large?) to ensure that almost every new water tower is visually distinctive. Whereas the later Victorian municipal water tower was sometimes subject to excessive and over-elaborate detailing and ornamentation the late 20th century equivalent seems to have been a tendency to over-elaborate layout and design.

This has resulted in some rather self-consciously 'architectural' designs, typified by Cockfosters (North London) water tower as early as 1968 (Figure 6.17). The result in this case is undeniably impressive and not displeasing. A careful inspection of the hyperbolic lattice of interlaced concrete struts will reveal that each inclined member is in fact straight, though twisted through 120 degrees over its full length from ground to tank. Other recent 'one-off' designs are Honingham and Bowthorpe on the western outskirts of Norwich, Rushmere Heath near Ipswich, and the water tower linked to Leeds University's Henry Price Building. Honingham and Bowthorpe are intriguing in a variety

Figure 6.17. Cockfosters water tower, Greater London, 1968

of ways, though it is a moot point whether the former is actually a water tower. Honingham has three tall, cylindrical tanks in parallel, interlinked at top and bottom and grouped round a central, independent shaft. At each location the shape of the tanks (height nearly three times the diameter) seems to negate the need to keep water level fluctuations to a minimum, but does the cluster of tanks echo the continental concept of grouped towers, discussed in Chapter 1? At Bowthorpe (Figure 6.18) the tanks are elevated, albeit only by 26ft, but in response to a planning condition that the tanks should be clear of the ground on a supporting structure. This requirement may be compared with that of a neighbouring local authority which in almost the same year (1980) insisted that a second water tower pro-posed for a site at Fram-ingham Earl should replicate the existing tower. The result was a 'retro' 1950s design, right down to the tank's scalloped skirt and concrete balustrading.

With so few concrete water towers having been built in Britain in the final years of the 20th century it will be interesting to discover how long it is before we see the first concrete tower of the 21st. At the time of writing that honour seems likely to go to a projected replacement for the old 'Expansion Period' water tower at RAF Cottesmore, in Rutland.

Figure 6.18. Bowthorpe water tower, Norwich, Norfolk, 1979

CHAPTER SEVEN

All-metal Water Towers

*Figure 7.1.
Pirton water
tower,
Hertfordshire,
mid
20th century*

For most people the all-metal water tower is synonymous with what is commonly referred to as a 'Braithwaite Tank;' a decidedly utilitarian structure consisting of prefabricated, pressed - steel panels bolted together to form a sectional tank, supported on a steel lattice framework. Even if the term 'Braithwaite' is not familiar, the reader will nevertheless immediately recognise the seemingly ubiquitous structure illustrated in Figure 7.1.

The Braithwaite tank was made possible by the introduction of structural steel in the late 19th century and the development of the technology necessary to mass-produce standardised pressed-steel panels to acceptably close dimensional tolerances. The precursor of the pressed-steel plate tank was of course the sectional cast iron tank, an essential element in the majority of Victorian water towers. The production of cast iron panels to close tolerances to ensure easy assembly and subsequent watertightness represented a considerable technological achievement but the great disadvantage of the cast iron tank was its great weight. If a cast iron tank was to be supported on a massive masonry or brick tower this was not a serious drawback since the labour and materials required for the tower were both relatively inexpensive. The vast majority of cast iron tanks were therefore erected on such towers. Cast iron is also a brittle material and, even though the bolted and sealed joints may introduce a modicum of flexibility, the cast iron tank is an essentially rigid structure and requires equally rigid support. Even a minor differential settlement of the supporting structure could result in fracture of the cast iron panels and failure of the tank. A massive masonry tower on solid foundations would provide this support.

As the railway engineers were fully aware, large masonry structures, whilst they might be economically competitive with iron structures, could take years to build, brick by brick or stone by stone. The attraction of an iron bridge or viaduct was that it could be erected in a fraction of the time. This saving could be particularly significant where the construction site was at a remote or awkward location. Piers consisting of clusters of cast iron columns, bolted together in sections and cross-braced in three dimensions with wrought iron tie-bars, replaced the massive and laboriously constructed masonry piers and, being only a fraction of the weight, required much lighter foundations. Even so, the iron piers still had to carry very heavy compressive loads and cast iron columns were essential to support them as wrought iron, unlike steel, could not be rolled to the heavy sections necessary to form stanchions which would not buckle under such loads.

Engineers such as Thomas Bouch with his Belah and Deepdale (1861) viaducts in the northern Pennines pioneered this form of construction. Other notable examples of this type of structure were the Severn Railway Bridge (1879) and the Crumlin (1857) and Bennerley (1878) viaducts. Of all these only Bennerley survives. The main practical difficulty with these all-iron structures was in ensuring that the cross-bracing remained correctly tensioned. Cotters worked loose; bottle-screws on the ties rusted solid; movement and then wear took place between the ends of the tie-bars and the lugs on the cast iron columns to which they were attached. Once the tie-bars lost their tension the piers would tend to lose their rigidity, bending moments could then be imposed on the cast iron columns and failure occur. The hapless Thomas Bouch's final and greatest work was the Tay Bridge, opened in 1878, failed 1879. The Forth Railway Bridge (1890) was of course an all-steel structure.

The problems confronting an engineer designing a composite cast and wrought iron tower to support a cast iron water tank were essentially the same as those faced by the engineer designing a tall iron pier for a railway bridge or viaduct. Both structures carried heavy, concentrated, cyclical loads although the live load carried by a railway viaduct might be more widely distributed than that supported by a water tower. Differential settlement would be less of a problem for wrought iron bridge beams than for a cast iron tank, but in other respects the bridge pier was subject to a more punishing regime. The frequent dynamic loading imposed on railway structures by a moving train on indifferently maintained track could be severe and the water tower would not have been subject to the vibrations which would inevitably have hastened the loosening of the bridge pier tie-bars.

This chapter is titled 'all-metal' rather than 'all-steel' so as not to exclude the Victorian all-iron water tower. (The evolution of the cast iron or rivetted iron tank itself has already been described in Chapter 3.) It is not easy to estimate how many all-iron, as opposed to all-steel, water towers were constructed for, like iron viaducts, hardly any have survived. It may well be that all-metal towers were uncommon, if not rare, in the pre-steel era, but we know that they existed. It is difficult to be precise as to numbers because by its very nature a redundant all-metal water tower is, when compared with its masonry counterpart, easy to dismantle and economically advantageous to do so. Once the all-metal tower has been demolished and the material salvaged and recycled, little or nothing remains above ground to indicate where it once stood. The type seems to have originated as early as 1843 when one was erected in Portsmouth naval dockyard, primarily for firefighting purposes. This tower will be described in another context in the next chapter.

During their lifetime the best known all-iron water towers were undoubtedly the spectacular pair built by Brunel at the Crystal Palace. Joseph Paxton's Crystal Palace had originally been erected in Hyde Park for the Great Exhibition of 1851. This was a temporary location and when the exhibition closed the Crystal Palace itself was dismantled and re-erected, considerably enlarged, on a new site south of London at Sydenham Hill where it was reopened by Queen Victoria in 1854 as a 'winter park and garden under glass' — in effect a massive greenhouse. Paxton had, after all, begun his career as a gardener at Chatsworth House. The surrounding grounds were landscaped with terraces and fountains. These changes required a heating system and a copious water supply and this led Paxton to envisage two massive towers which would serve both as chimneys and elevated reservoirs.

Paxton's assistant, Charles Wild, was given the task of designing the two great iron water towers, one at each end of the Palace. Construction of both towers had reached an advanced stage but Paxton must have had reservations about Wild's design for he turned to Brunel for advice. Brunel confirmed Paxton's concerns and expressed the opinion that Wild's towers were too slender, as well as making a number of more detailed criticisms. Robert Stephenson's opinion was also sought and he concurred with Brunel. Work was halted and Wild's structures were completely dismantled — a crushing humiliation for the man — and Brunel was engaged to design the water towers in his stead, the opportunity being taken to increase the capacity of each tank from 112,000 to 290,000 gallons.

Wild's cast iron tanks and his proposal to utilise the hollow cast iron supporting columns as pipework were abandoned. Brunel supported each of his wrought iron tanks on twelve pairs of 12in diameter cast iron columns, every pair yoked together with narrow cast iron panels. His towers were braced at nine intermediate levels by annular wrought iron diaphragms and with horizontal and vertical plane tie-bars. The 9ft 4in diameter brick chimneys which passed through the centre of the 35ft deep tanks were ringed with six 12in inlet/outlet pipes and acted as newel posts for the spiral iron access staircases. A gallery, cantilevered out on ornamental brackets, ran round the base of each tank and was reached by an oval iron tube through the tank's domed base. Glazed panels served as curtain walling between each pair of columns and the tanks themselves were capped with a conical glazed 'ridge and furrow' roof through which the cast iron rim of the chimney protruded, thus emulating the design of the Palace itself.

The two towers, commissioned in 1856, were an immensely impressive 284ft tall overall, the supporting structure some 48ft in diameter. As with so many of Brunel's projects, he was never scared or shy of building on a hitherto unattempted scale if the need and opportunity arose. The two towers were interconnected, giving a common water level in both tanks. Water was pumped up to the tanks by a pair of condensing beam engines housed at the foot of the north tower — hardly advanced technology when they were installed in 1853, but they were still at work as late as 1901. The towers' great height also enabled them to power hydraulic lifts and the bellows of a concert organ. The Crystal Palace itself was destroyed by fire in 1936 and though the water towers survived they were now redundant and were demolished in 1940, partly to meet the wartime demand for scrap iron and partly to avoid them being used as a landmark by enemy bombers. Only the foundations remain.

It is fortuitous that any such towers remain at all, let alone in their original state. The once impressive structure at the Great Western Railway's carriage works in Swindon has had its cast iron tank replaced by a smaller, more modern glass reinforced plastic one. The few known survivors of this class of water tower all date from the late 19th or early 20th century. The most notable is the fine example at Chilton Foliat on the Berkshire/Wiltshire border. There are actually two towers here; the smaller one, dated 1891 on the tank, was presumably part of a private supply to a country house so it is reasonable to assume that its much larger counterpart nearby (Figure 7.2) must have fed an estate water supply to the local village. The Chilton Foliat towers are unusual in having cylindrical cast iron tanks. Equally

Figure 7.2.
Chilton Foliat
water tower,
Berkshire,
1891

unusual, the larger tower 's eight cast iron columns are splayed and surround a central tubular steel shaft.

Two all-metal public water supply towers survive from this period, but neither has a cast iron tank. One is the public supply tower at Cargate, near Aldershot (1906/7), which has a rivetted steel tank on six cast iron columns, though these are cross-braced with steel. (The tank does not appear to sit comfortably on the column heads so may not be the original.) The other, a big all-steel tower dating from 1902, originally one of a pair, is to be found at Dovercourt in Essex. Since large structural steel beams and stanchions had been generally available since the mid-1880s it is somewhat surprising that cast iron was still being used for the principal members of the supporting structure 20 years or more later. A remarkably late example of the all-iron water tower, *circa* 1920, exists at RAF Digby (Lincolnshire). It stands adjacent to a cast iron tank on an all-steel lattice framework, erected only two years later, a type which continued to appear until the second world war. Digby's 1920 water tower is not, strictly speaking, 'all-iron' as steel rods have been used for the cross-bracing between the cast iron stanchions used to form the columns.

The widespread adoption and commercial success of the all-metal water tower was made possible when steel became readily available for the production of prefabricated pressed-steel panels for tanks. This was inevitable when a cast iron tank could weigh up to five times as much as a steel tank of equivalent capacity. Indeed, this is implicit in an early advertisement for steel panel tanks which boasted that 'one hundredweight of tank plates store one ton of water.' If the advent of mild steel made possible the pressed steel tank panel it simultaneously made possible the steel lattice tower to support the steel tank. The strength in both tension and compression of rolled steel stanchions and beams enabled supporting structures to be designed which were at once more economical, more resilient and of course much lighter than those utilising cast iron.

Their main disadvantage was the vulnerability of steel, compared with cast and even wrought iron, to corrosion. Despite its far smaller capital cost, the all-steel water tower requires regular repainting to keep rust at bay and its maintenance costs were inevitably much greater than those of the traditional iron tank/brick tower type, let alone the concrete water tower which was very soon to make its appearance. Unlike concrete, the design of the all-steel water tower leaves little scope for aesthetic enhancement. It is an essentially and uncompromisingly utilitarian structure with no pretensions to beauty, and is often criticised and disliked on that score. In many respects it is the antithesis of the Victorian concept of the water tower as an expression of civic pride. Nevertheless Braithwaite tanks, as they came to be widely known, rapidly gained popularity and by the start of the first world war were starting to become almost ubiquitous as a 'cheap-and-cheerful' means of providing elevated water storage quickly and economically for applications where asset life and appearance were not prime considerations. Although these applications were principally with industrial and agricultural users, they were soon also to become popular with the armed forces. Even some of the smaller public water undertakers started to erect the occasional Braithwaite tank, though they did not come into anything like common use in public supply systems for another 40 years or so.

Much to the irritation of the other manufacturers, 'Braithwaite tank' is now virtually a generic term for this type of water tower, though Braithwaite was merely one among a number of companies who produced them, their design stemming from a 1901 patent. The credit for introducing the steel panelled tank is claimed by Thomas Piggott & Co of Birmingham, whose original patent was obtained in 1880.

Despite its obvious advantages, the all-steel water tower did not, by and large, become popular with public water supply undertakings. Initially this would undoubtedly have been due to the persistent Victorian ethos that demanded that public buildings should be ornamental as well as functional and built to last indefinitely, but it is interesting to speculate as to how long this ethos would have stood firm against the Braithwaite tank had it not been for the arrival on the scene of the concrete water tower at the start of the 20th century. Increasing numbers of the smallest and impecunious rural water undertakings would have erected all-steel water towers but it was through industrial users that their success was established, combined with an almost limitless market in Britain's rapidly developing dominions and colonies. Clayton Son & Co of Leeds, another of the principal manufacturers of pressed-steel tanks, boasted in 1926 that their products 'have been made and erected in places varying as widely as Stockholm in the North, Falkland Islands in the South, India and Singapore in the East, and Winnipeg in the West.' From 1910 to at least 1932 Clayton's advertisements carried the claim that they were the 'Makers of the largest elevated steel water reservoir in the world. Nine million gallons capacity.' This referred to the monster all-steel water tower supplied to the Calcutta Corporation, 110 feet high with a tank measuring 321 feet square by 16 feet deep (ie 80 x 80 x 4 panels) and divided into four separate compartments. The 7000 ton structure carried a 40,000 ton load. An even larger sectional steel tank water tower, a 19,600,000 gallon, 12 compartment monster, was reported to be in existence in Buenos Aires in 1964.

As will be seen in Chapter 8, the second world war saw a massive expansion in the construction of military installations, especially airfields, throughout Britain. Airfields, by their nature, were established in open country in areas of relatively gentle topography. At the end of the war the operational need for the great majority of these airfields disappeared and the Ministry of Defence was left with the problem of disposing of the now redundant infrastructure and the surplus land upon which it stood. The buildings erected in connection with most of the wartime airfields (as opposed to the pre-war aerodromes) were of an essentially temporary and utilitarian nature — the ubiquitous Nissen hut and, of course, Braithwaite tank water towers.

Although a few airfields had their own independent source of water, many received a bulk supply from the local water undertaker, even if they were not connected directly to the local mains network. In many instances the airfield may well have had a more modern and more reliable water supply than many of the surrounding villages. After the war the presence in an area of a redundant water tower, if only a Braithwaite tank, represented an opportunity for the local water undertaker to extend or improve its water supply system with relatively little effort and at minimal cost. In an economically straitened post-war Britain this was not an opportunity to be missed, even though an airfield site may not have been the most appropriate location within the supply network. Scores of ex-military water towers were taken over by public water undertakers throughout the country during the late 1940s. Not all of these World War II water towers were

Braithwaite tanks, as a small but significant number of cast iron tanks were erected at military installations. It must be assumed that there were still firms manufacturing cast iron tanks and that, faced with widespread wartime shortages, the War Office would have obtained tanks from whatever source could readily supply them. All these later cast iron tanks seem to have been of the internally flanged type and erected on steel lattice towers (Figure 7.3).

Many of these ex-military Braithwaite and cast iron tank towers performed an unobtrusive but vital public water supply role for 30 years or more. Without unusually careful maintenance this is about the asset life of a lightweight steel structure in an exposed location. In some instances these towers were replaced by larger and more permanent structures, often on the same site. Others were superseded by pump-pressurised systems and not replaced at all, as will be seen in Chapter 11. A few have been refurbished, their operational life extended by the substitution of the corroded steel tank by a similar lightweight, prefabricated tank of a modern, low-maintenance material on the original steel lattice tower (Figure 7.4).

In Chapter 4 it was assumed, reasonably enough, that as the production of cast iron tanks proliferated it would make sound economic

Figure 7.3 (left). Honington water tower, Suffolk, c 1940s
Figure 7.4 (below). Ashton Wold water tower, Northamptonshire, 1941, with modern grp tank

sense for anyone building a water tower to purchase the tank locally, given the inherently high transport costs involved. Yet this was by no means universally the case, and some strange anomalies can be found. The tank installed at Poole's Parkestone water tower in 1884 was manufactured by John Abbot & Company of Greenhead-on-Tyne, a small village on the Northumberland/Cumberland border. Even so, by the end of the 19th century, at a time when cast iron was still a commonplace engineering material and industrial production still unconsolidated, virtually every British town of any size would have had an iron foundry or an engineering works with that capability. It is therefore not surprising that cast iron tank panels would have been produced by a host of small local ironfounders as the demand arose whereas, from the start, pressed steel tank panels were manufactured by a small number of relatively large firms marketing their products nationally, even globally.

At some time in the early years of the 20th century the production of cast iron tanks seems to have followed the same trend. The tank for Hartlepool's 1891 tower was supplied by a nationally known albeit locally based firm, the Whessoe Foundry Company of Darlington and by the second world war only a handful of names are associated with cast iron tanks, most notably Mather & Platt of Manchester. Spittals of Newport is another name which crops up in this context. Unlike the earlier, externally flanged cast iron tanks which often had their maker's name and date obligingly embossed on one or more of the castings, the later, internally flanged ones tended to be frustratingly anonymous.

Mather & Platt was a large engineering conglomerate manufacturing, *inter alia*, textile and food processing machinery, electrical motors and generators, centrifugal pumps and, from the 1880s, industrial fire protection systems. Their manufacture of sectional cast iron tanks was initially associated with their sprinkler systems, but the market for such tanks was clearly much broader and by the 1920s Mather & Platt's tanks were being supplied to a wide range of commercial and industrial customers. London's County Hall, completed in 1922, contained no fewer than 14 elevated tanks with an aggregate capacity of 70,000 gallons. Mather & Platt mainly used a small 2ft standard panel, reflecting perhaps the confined roof spaces within which so many of their tanks were installed. Mather & Platt tanks were, nevertheless, supplied to water undertakers, not only for water towers but also for service reservoirs, and they continued to appear in the company's advertising brochures until the 1960s.

The external appearance of a steel panelled tank gives no clue as to the presence of the internal steel tie-bars that are essential for these relatively flexible structures to maintain their shape under load, though some stiffening is imparted to the structure by the flanges and the pattern embossed on each panel. Neither does their external appearance readily indicate the presence of internal dividing walls within the tank, creating two or more separate compartments, though this can be detected by noticing the duplication of inlet, outlet and overflow pipework beneath the tank. A characteristic feature of the Braithwaite tank is the cross-shaped indentation embossed onto every panel. This is intended primarily to stiffen the panel but since, for copyright purposes, each manufacturer has adopted a slightly different shape of indentation they can also be used to identify the maker of any tank.

These internal features are made possible by the *Meccano*-like nature of the Braithwaite tank and its interchangeable component parts. The design is based on a standard, four foot square panel, though its one metre square equivalent is now also available. The fundamental design, although it has evolved over the years, is still essentially the same as it was when first introduced in the late 19th century. The standard panel is flanged on all four sides. Each flange has an intermediate section, bevelled at 45 degrees, and an outer edge at right angles to the face of the panel. All four flanges are drilled for bolted connections. There are three principal variants; panels with all four flanges drilled at 90 degrees to the face, edge panels with one of the flanges drilled on the bevelled section at 45 degrees to the face, and bottom corner panels with two adjacent flanges drilled at 45 degrees. Tanks may be assembled either externally or internally flanged. The former configuration is recommended for ease of assembly, maintenance, emptying and cleaning, although the latter is employed where a tank is to be installed in a constricted space, usually within a building. The thickness of the steel plate used for the panels varies between $^1/_6$in (4mm) and $^1/_4$in (6mm) and panels can be supplied either galvanised or painted with a bituminous enamel primer. More recently, sprayed metal (zinc or aluminium) sealed with an epoxy resin or an epoxy zinc phosphate primer are also offered.

Butyl rubber strip gaskets are used to achieve a watertight seal between adjoining panels, though bitumen and even lead have been used in the more distant past. Inside the tank, small pressed-steel joint plates are bolted across the points where four panels meet. These plates take the form of cleats where internal tie bars are to be attached. The faces of the panels are drilled at each corner for a joint plate. Angled joint plates are used along the edges of the tank and at the bottom corners of the tank the joint plate takes the form of a small tetragonal steel cup. The presence of a joint plate or cleat should be apparent from the nuts visible at the outside corners of the panel faces, but close examination of some older Braithwaite tanks can reveal joints without these nuts. Are joint plates a relatively modern development? An engineer with long experience in the refurbishment of these tanks has reported often finding wooden pegs hammered into the bottom corners of older tanks in lieu of joint plates, to good effect. For potable water storage, where it is essential to cover the tank, a sectional, flat-pitched roof of lightweight steel sheets is available, the gable ends being blanked off with triangular panels. Older tanks can sometimes still be found with rounded roofs assembled using 'corrugated iron' sheets. In both cases access into the tank is through hatches in the roof.

Braithwaite tanks of small and medium size are normally supported on a lightweight steel lattice framework consisting of a matrix of slender stanchions braced horizontally and diagonally in the vertical plane, the number of stanchions (4, 6, 9 etc) depending on the size and shape of the tank. With the largest tanks, such as that at Harbury (Warwickshire), the tower may be made up of a number of independent latticework columns, each column consisting of four cross-braced stanchions. Harbury is also of interest for the unusual metal skirt round the base of its tank. Larger Braithwaite tanks will sometimes have a walkway round the base of the tank and their towers will be erected with inclined stairways between intermediate level access platforms, rather than vertical ladders.

An externally flanged Braithwaite tank, even when erected as a service reservoir at ground level, must have a minimum clearance between the tank and the ground for its assembly. This is achieved by means of dwarf concrete cross-walls from 18in to 24in high with a standard cross-section stipulated by the manufacturer. These are set at panel-width spacing beneath each row of bolted flanges and run the full width of the tank. This results in a tank supported clear of the ground — a water tower by definition — but can this really be considered a water tower (Figure 7.5)?

The modular nature of the design means that tanks of a wide range of sizes and shapes can be assembled. Braithwaite tank water towers as

large as 12 by 12 by 4 panels high have been recorded in Britain (an industrial tower at Bletchley) and as small as a miniature 3 by 3 by 2 panels. The maximum height for which these tanks are designed is four panels. One advantage sometimes claimed in manufacturers' brochures is the ability to dismantle and reassemble a Braithwaite tank on another site, an advantage perhaps more potential than actual though there is one recorded instance of this happening with a public supply system. A water tower erected in the 1940s at Willoughby Waterless in Leicestershire was re-erected at Sewstern in the same county by Severn Trent Water in 1970, presumably as a temporary expedient as it had gone by the beginning of the 1990s.

Figure 7.5. Settrington Beacon tank, North Yorkshire, 1981

Despite the 'all-metal' in the

chapter heading, consideration must be given to what may well be the successor to the traditional steel panelled tank, in which steel has been partly superseded by modern synthetic materials, particularly grp (glass-reinforced plastic). The design and often the appearance of these modern plastic-panelled 'Braithwaite tanks' is very similar to that of the older, steel panel tank water towers. The grp panels are produced to a range of standard sizes, both Imperial and metric, from 2ft x 1ft to 4ft x 4ft or from 1m x 1m to 1m x 2m, for a maximum tank height of 4 metres (13ft). Panel thickness varies between 4mm ($1/6$ in) and 10mm ($2/5$ in) depending upon size of the panel and depth of tank. Although they are significantly lighter than their steel equivalents — a typical 6mm ($1/4$ in) 4ft x 4ft grp panel will weigh only 26kg (58lbs) — grp panels are inherently less strong and an external steel framework ('corseting') as well as internal stainless steel tie-rods were initially provided to ensure a rigid structure. More recent designs have, however, been able to dispense with the external stiffening. Pre-insulated grp panels are available, incorporating a 25mm (1in) or 50mm (2in) polyurethane foam outer layer. Like steel tanks, grp tanks are normally assembled externally flanged.

To their credit, tanks of these new materials are being offered as an alternative to steel by the same manufacturers, though the traditional steel tank continues to be available. Indeed, in recent years a new design of prefabricated steel tank has appeared. This consists of heavily corrugated ('profiled') steel wall units, 1.5 metres (4ft 11in) wide and up to 6.1 metres (20ft) high, welded to each other and to a flat baseplate. Up to 5 metres (16ft 5in) high, the rigid tank so formed needs no internal stiffening. An example of this design is shown in Figure 7.6. There is as yet no British Standard specifically for profiled steel water tanks. Whatever the tank is made of, the supporting lattice framework is still usually of steel. Although the overall numbers involved are still relatively small, these new types have in the past 20 years contributed to a minor revival in the use of prefabricated sectional tank water towers for public water supply use, as many of the recently privatised and keenly cost-conscious water companies see them as a cost effective means of maintaining supplies to small, remote rural communities.

This chapter cannot be concluded without mention of another type of all-steel water tower, one which will be familiar to readers from Hollywood films and what seems to be a prominent feature of almost every mid-western town in the United States. This is of course the spherical or cylindrical steel tank on its tall, splayed steel columns. Impressively large examples were already being built in America at the turn of the century (eg, a million gallon, 50ft diameter cylindrical tank on a 135ft high trestle, giving an overall tower height of 234ft in 1905) though at that time with rivetted rather than the welded plates of today. In America the steel columns are frequently braced with diagonal tie-rods tensioned by turnbuckles and the central inlet/outlet pipe is sometimes designed as part of the load-bearing structure.

Figure 7.6. Crowle water tower, Hereford and Worcester, with modern profiled steel tank, 1947

Alternatively an expansion joint is inserted into the pipe below the tank, although this has been reported to be a potential source of trouble in icy weather.

It is a type which has never found much favour in Britain, though a handful of examples are to be found in this country, mainly at industrial sites where the influence of an American parent company can be felt. There is a prominent one at the USAF base at Chicksands, in Bedfordshire. A similar transatlantic design, this time a welded steel ovoid tank supported on a ring of tubular steel columns (the 'Horton tank'), appeared in Britain in the mid 1950s (Figure 7.7). Horton tanks can be seen at Dunstable (Vauxhall Motors) and Glasgow (Caterpillar Tractors), where the tank was fabricated at ground level and raised in three stages using gin poles as the supporting columns were erected. There is a single public water supply example of the Horton tank, at Motherwell, the location of which can hardly be coincidental as the Motherwell Bridge & Engineering Company is credited with the introduction of the American-style steel water tower into Britain. It has not been possible to discover when this was, although since an engineering textbook noted in 1927 that there were 'not many' in Britain it can be deduced that they had already crossed the Atlantic by the mid-1920s.

The Motherwell Bridge Company obtained a licence from the Chicago Bridge & Iron Co to manufacture and erect ellipsoidal and spheroidal tank water towers to the American company's designs in 1954. When it was erected in 1955, Vauxhall claimed that theirs was 'the only one of its kind in the country', presumably referring to its

Figure 7.7. Vauxhall Motors water tower, Dunstable, Bedfordshire, 1955

Horton design. About a dozen were erected by Motherwell Bridge for industrial clients, mainly at sites across Scotland's central lowlands, in the early and mid 1960s but this late burst of activity proved to be their British swansong.

A solitary but much earlier trans-Atlantic immigrant had appeared some 60 years earlier with the construction of the Metropolitan-Vickers water tower at Trafford Park in Manchester in 1902. This steel structure was designed by a Pittsburgh engineer and was typical of the

American water towers of its day in style and appearance. Here too, the use of an American design may well have been influenced by the fact that Metropolitan-Vickers was an offshoot of an American-owned company, British Westinghouse. The supporting framework consisted of a ring of eight ornately interlinked steel girder legs round a 4ft diameter tubular steel shaft to which was attached an external spiral staircase. The 179ft tall legs, which extended up the outsides of the pair of superimposed cylindrical steel tanks, were splayed at the base, producing an effect vaguely reminiscent of the Eiffel Tower.

The M-V tower, as it became known, served the Metropolitan-Vickers works and had a dual purpose; to power the hydraulic lifts and to supply the fire sprinkler system. Its latter function permits its inclusion as a water tower, but it is interesting to note that half a century after Armstrong had abandoned simple elevated tanks in favour of hydraulic accumulators, we have a return to the old technology, no doubt the reason for the M-V tower's great height. Despite its height (210 ft), the tower supported a pair of very modest 27,000 gallon cylindrical tanks. These were capped with a copper-clad dome surmounted

Figure 7.8. Wittering water tower, Cambridge-shire, 1965

by an eight foot raised arm, the gilded hand clutching an array of three 15 ft long 'thunderbolts', free to revolve like a weathervane. The ornate balcony around the tanks was subsequently decorated with a garland of electric lights. This impressively tall water tower was a prominent feature of the Manchester skyline until World War II when it was reduced to a 100ft stump to prevent it from becoming a landmark for enemy aircraft. What remained was finally demolished in 1954.

A recent and more elegant version of the steel spheroid is one where the tank is supported on a single tubular shaft. There is one at the Ford tractor factory at Basildon and another, the lone public supply example in Britain, at Wittering in Cambridgeshire (Figure 7.8) though even here there is an American connection — the married quarters at the adjacent RAF station have been used to accommodate USAF personnel. There is even an all-steel version of the concrete 'wineglass' design which was described in Chapter 6. This is to be found serving what was once a lead-mining village, Greenhow Hill, perched incongrously high on the Pennine moors between Pateley Bridge and Grassington and, at 1320 feet above sea level, probably the highest public supply water tower in Britain. Although its 12mm steel plate tank is externally insulated, it was built to an Australian design as there was no appropriate British Standard.

CHAPTER EIGHT

Water Towers for Other Purposes

A lthough this book is primarily concerned with water towers built by water undertakers in connection with public water supply systems, it is recognised that many hundreds of water towers were built by other bodies and for a wide variety of other purposes. Not only is this range of uses and users which water towers have served of interest, but some of these towers are themselves of considerable significance, whether technically, architecturally, historically or merely as curiosities, and it would be inappropriate not to mention them. The principal categories of use, apart from public water supply, for which water towers were built in substantial numbers have been identified as industry, railways, hospitals, military establishments, schools and universities, and private houses. Each of these categories will be dealt with under a separate heading below.

Industrial Water Towers

The use of water by industry is as as old as industry itself, both as a source of power and as part of the industrial process. Apart from sanitary use, a factory may require a water supply for a wide variety of reasons; washing, rinsing, soaking, pulping, diluting, dissolving, heating, cooling, raising steam, or merely to have on hand for firefighting. Water power is an entirely separate subject and one, with a single notable exception, that does not involve the use of water towers and so need not concern us further.

Many industrial users take their water from the public mains but many others, where a convenient source of water is available, prefer to have their own private supply. Economic considerations may be involved, or water quality may be the deciding factor. This may sound surprising, but many chemical or textile processes, particularly those of a continuous nature, are very sensitive to any variability in the amount and constituency of the mineral content of the water they use, far more so than the domestic consumer. On the other hand, the domestic consumer must have water of a far higher biological purity than is necessary for most industrial processes.

As was noted in Chapter 3, the unsuitability or inadequacy of urban water supplies for industrial use was a significant force behind the improvement of public water supplies in the mid 19th century. In industrial applications, twin compartment tanks are sometimes used to store water of different hardness or chemical characteristics required for different processes. Corby steelworks, for example, has a tower with the conventional arrangement of a cylindrical tank with concentric chambers whereas Scunthorpe had a more unusual 'double decker' tower.

The factory with its own private water supply will have very similar operating criteria to any public water undertaker, with water towers playing a comparable role in each case. Even where the public water supply is utilised, it may not always be available at the required peak rate or pressure and a separate water tower at the factory may still be found necessary. A substantial consumption of water is a notable characteristic of the heavier end of the industrial spectrum and water towers are therefore associated with Britain's older, traditional industries. Since these industries are the ones which have seen severe contraction and widespread plant closures in the past quarter century, it follows that the attrition rate for industrial water towers, especially free standing ones, has been much greater than for public supply towers. Early examples of industrial water towers are very rare and the water tower at Scremerston Old Mine, just south of Berwick-upon-Tweed, dating from 1840 is an exceptional survivor.

Many Victorian and Edwardian mills and factories were constructed with a large water tank as an integral part of the building (Figure 8.1), the tower upon which the tank was supported often being made

Figure 8.1. Facit Mill, Whitworth, Rossendale, Lancashire, 1905

into a prominent architectural feature. Because many of the more attractive of these industrial buildings have subsequently been 'listed' the chances of survival of such towers have been considerably enhanced, but as these water tanks were incorporated into a building intended primarily for a wider purpose they cannot, strictly speaking, be regarded as water towers. Where a separate water tower was constructed, often as a later addition to the factory because of changing industrial requirements, it tended to be a relatively unadorned version of the typical Victorian municipal tower; an exposed cast iron tank on a plain rectangular brick or stone shaft. Until the end of the 19th century the sectional cast iron tank was almost exclusively used for industrial applications as it could be readily obtained from stock and its rectangular footprint combined well with the rectilinear shapes of the surrounding mill or factory buildings. Constricted urban industrial sites may also have influenced the choice.

Cotton spinning mills, because of the nature of the processes involved, presented a particular fire risk. Sprinkler systems were introduced from the mid-1880s and by 1900 most mills were equipped with them. Such systems required a substantial water storage capacity with sufficient head to supply all parts of the building. In practice this involved extending the staircase tower to create a water tower. With older mills a tank would be installed on the roof of the existing staircase tower, heightened if necessary. New mills were designed from the start with a dual-purpose tower. Mill architects designed these towers to be a prominent feature of what might otherwise have been a relatively featureless facade. They were often elaborately detailed, sometimes ornately decorated, and usually bore the name of the mill or its owner. They thus became a notable characteristic of Lancashire's industrial landscape.

Industrial users were quick to see the potential of reinforced concrete towers and a significant proportion of the earliest Mouchel/Hennebique water towers was built for industrial clients (see Table 5.1, Chapter 5.) A particularly striking example of an industrial water tower in concrete was shown in Figure 5.8. Not so far away, but right at the other end of the scale, the Staveley steelworks near Chesterfield was supplied by a massive 1,500,000 gallon concrete tower. This was a squat and singularly unattractive structure with a flat, disc shaped tank on a forest of short, thin, unbraced legs, 77 in all, giving the impression of a biscuit being carried away on the back of a giant insect. Despite its aesthetic shortcomings, Staveley water tower was noteworthy. When completed in 1945 it was believed to have been the world's largest elevated cylindrical tank. It was also innovative. A concrete pump was used for pouring the tank's wall panels and the central portion of the tank floor was designed as a flat slab, though the deeper floor slab between the two outer rings of columns was designed as a ring beam. A sliding joint between wall and floor was contemplated but not implemented because of doubts as to the durability of the mastic jointing materials then available. A more typical industrial tower in reinforced concrete is shown in Figure 8.2.

For smaller and more modest installations Braithwaite tank towers became commonplace throughout the 20th century, though in recent years the pressed steel panels have given way to glass-reinforced plastic (grp) or similar modern materials. At a limited number of large factory sites established in Britain by American multinationals, especially in the 1950s and 60s, American-style steel water towers were erected and these have been described in Chapter 7.

Since large industrial sites usually include chimneys, combining a chimney and water tower in the same structure has obvious attractions. The chimney can be designed as a load-bearing shaft, supporting the weight of an annular tank at some intermediate height up the chimney although, for obvious reasons, the shaft cannot now be used for

Figure 8.2. Western water tower, Corby steelworks, Northamptonshire, 1938

access purposes. If the water in the tank is to be used for an industrial process the heat exchange between flue gasses and water can provide a useful energy saving. Water towers incorporating chimneys were not confined to industrial use and, apart from the Crystal Palace pair, examples could be found on the railways and, more recently, at schools and at least one hospital. At one time a particularly fine example could be found at an oil refinery on the Isle of Grain (Kent), with an annular, hyperbolic profile, prestressed concrete tank 36 ft up a 220 ft concrete chimney. Another industrial water tower at the adjacent South Eastern Gas Board installation had two cylindrical prestressed concrete tanks one above the other, though it cannot now be confirmed whether or not the lower tank was elevated.

The great majority of Victorian factory chimneys, even when embellished with architectural detailing, are unmistakable for what they are, but a few were designed to resemble Italianate towers. Two fine examples can be seen from trains entering Leeds station from the south.

Such a dissimulation could be remarkably effective, until smoke began to billow from the top of the tower. Nowadays these disguised chimneys can readily be mistaken for rather narrow 'enclosed tank' water towers. Ironically one such chimney was erected by the then Nottingham Waterworks Company at their Bestwood pumping station in 1871. The site in Bestwood Park was owned by the Duke of St Albans who insisted that the pumping station should be designed in keeping with his home at Bestwood Lodge. This resulted in an elaborate mock Gothic engine house with an Italian Renaissance campanile for a chimney — 'tall and tasteless' according to Pevsner but a striking local landmark and, given its waterworks location, difficult at first sight to accept that it is not actually a water tower. It is not inconceivable that some of these chimneys may indeed have incorporated elevated water tanks.

Industrial water towers have covered a wide range of industrial uses, not least within the water industry itself. Water towers have occasionally been erected at waterworks to provide process water for specific treatment processes, such as dechlorination at Bournemouth's Alderney Works and filter backwashing at Davy Down (Stifford) in Essex, both between the two world wars. London's Crossness sewage treatment works even had its own water tower, also dating from this period. Both Blackpool and Portsmouth built sea-water towers in the late 19th and early 20th centuries respectively to enable an unlimited resource to be used for street cleansing and sewer flushing. At Blackpool the sea water was also used to supply hydropathic (spa) hotels and an aquarium and the 67,000 gallon capacity tower remained in use until 1983. Other municipal purposes for which water towers have been erected include the water supply to public swimming baths (Portobello, Edinburgh) and to parks and playing fields. Bournemouth's historic concrete water tower in Meyrick Park has previously been mentioned, but the resort already had a small Victorian tower for a park water supply in the Upper Gardens.

Contemporary technical journals give the impression that significant numbers of concrete water towers were being erected at gasworks during the inter-war years but, if so, these, like the gasworks they served, have all been swept away in the rapid substitution of coal gas by natural 'North Sea' gas which took place from 1967 onwards.

At the start of this section it was stated that the use of water as a source of power does not involve water towers and is thus outside the scope of this book. Whilst this is undoubtedly true of water flowing in rivers and streams it should not be overlooked that water power also includes hydraulic power — the use of relatively small volumes of water under high pressure to operate heavy machinery. Large hydraulic power systems have now been almost entirely superseded by electricity (a network of cables is cheaper and easier to install and maintain than a network of high pressure water mains) but they were once relatively common. Until the 1970s the London Hydraulic Power

Company operated just such a pipe network beneath the streets of London into which their customers could connect to power hoists, lifts or similar machinery.

From about 1850 hydraulic power systems were widely used in commercial docks to operate dock gates and cranes. The high pressures necessary for their efficient operation, latterly up to 1000 lb/sq in, meant that the water had to be maintained under pressure in a device known as a hydraulic accumulator. There was, however, a brief initial period when systems working at lower pressures could be maintained at those pressures by an elevated tank open to the atmosphere — a water tower in all but name. The only system of this type in Britain from which the hydraulic tower still exists is, as far as is known, that at Grimsby where J M Rendel, the civil engineer responsible for the Royal Dock, engaged Sir William Armstrong of Newcastle upon Tyne to design and install the dock's hydraulic power system. The Grimsby system initially operated at the very modest working pressure of 90 lb/sq in but this nevertheless required a header tank 214 feet above the ground. To support this tank Rendel erected a slender brick tower 309 feet high in 1852, designed in the Italian Renaissance style by the architect R W Wild. Though long disused, Grimsby's elegant Dock Tower still dominates the town, a notable landmark for miles around, by far the tallest 'water tower' in the country. This lofty structure was clearly at the limit of economic viability for such towers and greater hydraulic pressures could only be achieved by other means.

Railway Water Towers

Perhaps the largest category of industrial user of water towers was the railways and railway towers merit consideration in a category of their own. Taken as a whole, the railways were a major user of water right up until the end of the steam age in the 1960s. A large steam locomotive can carry 5000 gallons of water in its tender and consume it at a rate of up to 30 gallons a mile. Combined with this was the need to refill a locomotive's tanks as quickly as possible to minimise delays to traffic. Small wayside stations could make do with a lineside water column — typically a cylindrical, rivetted iron tank on a cast iron stanchion, discharging water into the engine's water tanks by means of a rotating horizontal pipe from the end of which was hung a short length of canvas hose. At principal stations or engine sheds, where there could well be a need to water considerable numbers of locomotives in a short time, the large volume of temporary storage provided by a water tower would be essential, even where the water came from a gravity-fed supply.

The explosive expansion of Britain's railways from 1835 would inevitably have involved the construction of a substantial number of water towers, and not only at at principal centres of operation. It is likely, given the limited tender capacity of early locomotives, that railway water towers were initially more widely distributed than they were in the latter years of the steam age though, equally inevitably, most of these original railway towers would have been replaced with larger but fewer towers during later waves of development as the numbers and size of locomotives increased relentlessly.

This is demonstrated by the North Midland Railway, opened from Derby to Leeds in 1840. It was eventually to become part of the Midland Railway's main line between London and Scotland so that by the end of the 1870s almost all of the original stations had been demolished and rebuilt to keep pace with the massive growth in traffic. Fortunately an album of engravings of the original stations was made and these show a remarkably elegant set of stone buildings, largely single storey but in a variety of styles from the severely classical through Italianate to Jacobean, for which Robert Stephenson, the North Midland's engineer, engaged Francis Thompson as architect. From the engravings it can be seen that at least four of the intermediate stations, Clay Cross, Chesterfield (Figure 8.3), Masborough and Wakefield (Oakenshaw) had sizeable water towers. These were substantial and carefully detailed masonry structures with what appear to be exposed iron tanks, all in the same architectural style as the adjacent station building. Each square tower was flanked by a boiler house and chimney on one side and a pumphouse on the other and, apart from the chimney, the arrangement was strictly symmetrical. Thompson was a distinguished railway architect and the North Midland stations were among his best works. Despite this, it is unlikely that these fine water towers were wholly atypical of numerous others being erected elsewhere on Britain's infant railway network in the 1830s and 40s.

Until a few years ago there was still an original London & Birmingham Railway water tower at Blisworth, Northants, and another early one on the Trent Valley line at Tamworth, but hardly any of

Figure 8.3. Chesterfield station with the water tower at left, 1840

Figure 8.4. Curthwaite station water tower, Cumbria, 1843

these early railway towers have survived. Those that do are small, plain examples in out of the way places. This is a great pity, for as has been remarked in Chapter 3, these water towers predated the first generation of municipal public supply towers and it is fairly certain that the key to the origins of the mass-produced cast iron sectional tank can be found with the earliest railway water towers. A clue to the relative importance of public supply and railway water towers at this time comes in a Glossary of Civil Engineering published in 1841. This book makes no mention of water towers but does have an entry for 'Water Station (on Railways)' which it defines as 'a small reservoir of water upon a line of railway consisting of a tank connected with a well.' The water had, presumably, to be pumped from the well to the tank.

The only examples of first generation railway towers known to the author are the modest structure at Curthwaite station in Cumbria, built in 1843 (Figure 8.4), and the even earlier and somewhat larger cast iron tank built in 1839 for the York & North Midlands Railway at the Queen Street locomotive works in York. Here one of the three-foot square panels bears the date and ironfounder's name, John Walker. The recently restored water tower at Haltwhistle (Northumberland) station, also conveniently dated on the tank, is somewhat later (1861) though the water tower further along the same line at Hexham may date from the construction of the line which was open throughout in 1838. John Blackmore who built the Maryport & Carlisle Railway through Curthwaite was also engineer to the Newcastle & Carlisle Railway. The Hareshaw Ironworks, a local (Bellingham) firm, cast the ironwork for the Curthwaite tank and it is more than likely they were also responsible for the original Hexham tank which, if it was contemporary with the station buildings there, could date from as early as 1835. The Hexham station water tower appears to have been rebuilt in the 1850s and has unfortunately lost its original tank. There is a water tower at the south end of Charfield (Avon) station which may date from about 1844 and there is still the masonry stump of a small railway water tower just west of Stamford (Lincolnshire) station (1848) but this has long since lost its tank. Others from this era have been even less fortunate. The towers at Belmont Junction (Co Durham) dating from 1845 and at Blisworth, possibly even earlier (1838?), were both swept away in British Railways modernisation programmes as recently as the 1970s.

In their Victorian heyday, the railways employed a very large workforce, often living in railway housing and occasionally in 'railway towns', from the Swindons and the Crewes associated with the great railway companies to the more modest settlements established by some of the smaller companies. One such was the small town (in real-

Figure 8.5. Melton Constable water tower, Norfolk, 1898

ity more of an industrial village) of Melton Constable in Norfolk, which was the hub and operating centre of the Midland and Great Northern Railway. Here a massive 125,000 gallon cast iron tank (Figure 8.5), erected in 1898, supplied the needs of the locomotives, the railway's engineering works and the town itself — each of its 256 external cast iron panels individually embossed with the company's initials.

Since much of Britain's railway infrastructure is essentially Victorian, most railway water towers were indistinguishable from their contemporary industrial counterparts. Even so, new water towers were added to the stock in the first half of the 20th century and British Railways continued to build water towers as late as the 1950s with good examples at Barking, Cardiff and Ilford, which had a large chimney up the centre though structurally the chimney and water tower were entirely independent. These later towers were of concrete, a tradition established by the North Eastern Railway who pioneered the use of reinforced concrete water towers before the first world war, though not one of their half dozen or so early concrete towers — at Newcastle (Heaton), York and in the South Yorkshire coalfield (Milford Junction and Gascoigne Wood) — survives. Since their *raison d'etre* disappeared with the rapid demise of steam traction on British Railways in the 1960s, large numbers of redundant railway water towers of all types have been demolished. One exception to this trend is the traditional small cast iron and masonry tower at Appleby (Cumbria) recently reconstructed to serve preserved steam locomotives running 'steam specials' on the Settle - Carlisle line.

Hospital Water Towers

From about the middle of the 19th century the large Victorian mental hospitals, erected to serve an entire city or county, began to appear. The numbers of inmates that these hospitals were built to serve often ran into four figures, with a correspondingly large demand for water for sanitary, cleansing and laundry purposes. They often occupied extensive grounds and were therefore sited on the outskirts of towns or in open country where the local water supply infrastructure would be inadequate to meet the hospital's demands or simply did not exist. Such hospitals would therefore need their own water supply and, as often as not, their own water tower. In at least one instance, Hatton asylum near Warwick, the hospital towers (there were two) could be used in an emergency to support the local public water supply system, although here the difference in hardness between the water from the hospital's sourceworks and from those normally feeding to Warwick could give rise to complaints from consumers.

As these hospitals were often built in a single phase, the water tower would be designed in an architectural style consistent with that of the development as a whole, with the result that many of these hospital water towers were as elegant and richly ornamented as their larg-

Figure 8.6. Seacroft hospital water tower, Leeds, West Yorkshire, c 1902

er municipal water supply counterparts. A typical hospital water tower of this type is shown in Figure 8.6. This combination of clock tower and water tower is something which occurs at a number of locations. It is, at first thought, curious that so many of these large Victorian hospitals were mental, rather than general, hospitals. This gives an unflattering impression of Victorian social priorities, but it should be borne in mind that until the advent of the National Health Service most medical patients were treated at home or in isolation hospitals — there was little need for large general hospitals. The mentally ill, on the other hand, could neither be treated at home (if they had a home) nor cured and the 'asylum' was arguably the least inhumane solution then available.

Most large NHS hospitals are generally located within an urban area and date from a period when their water supply could easily be taken from the public mains. Despite their often considerable consumption of water, there is now no real need for hospitals to have their own water tower though occasional exceptions occur as, for example, the combined water tower, boiler house and chimney included in the post-war development at Hereford's County Hospital. Earlier in the century some established hospitals seem to have been provided with their own water tower at a later date. St John's Hospital on Bracebridge Heath near Lincoln (Chapter 5) is one example. Another is the very early (1909) concrete tower at the Lady Forester Hospital at Much Wenlock in Shropshire; this hospital is now an old peoples' home and its abandoned water tower is buried in dense woodland on the hillside above.

Although hospital water towers may be thought of as a Victorian innovation there is one isolated but remarkable exception. This is the octagonal stone tower at Plymouth's Stonehouse Naval Hospital. This structure contained a number of water tanks arranged in a ring at the top of the tower which were filled by a chain pump from a ground level reservoir. These tanks fed water 'into every ward [there were ten] for the use of the patients, cleansing the water closets, filling the baths, etc, every building being furnished with a bath and copper for heating the water to the temperature required.' The tanks' lead linings have disappeared but their wooden supporting structure remains in place. Stonehouse Hospital was completed in 1762. The water tower stands just outside the main hospital compound and is of limestone rubble masonry, in contrast to the ashlar stonework of the other buildings, so it could be a slightly later addition though the water tower can clearly be seen in a view of the hospital drawn in 1780.

Workhouses can be considered in the same category as hospitals, as they were provided to house the destitute and those too handicapped or simply too old to subsist in the world outside. Workhouses were a feature common to both urban and rural areas, and although country workhouses were established to serve a union of parishes, they tended to be relatively small and could easily be supplied from a well like the rest of the village. It is, nevertheless, not unusual to come across larger workhouses which had their own water tower, though these often seem to be a later addition, perhaps because most of the Poor Law workhouses were already in existence by the time the great mental hospitals were established. It is not generally realised that workhouses remained in existence as such right up to 1920 and, in an interesting blend of the archaic and the modern, a reinforced concrete tower was built for the workhouse at Burton-on-Trent in 1910, despite the fact that the workhouse already possessed an imposing clock-*cum*-water tower dating from the original development in 1884. It seems likely that where a new water tower was added to an established hospital or workhouse complex, as at Burton, it was done partly as a firefighting resource.

It might be supposed that prisons would also have had their own water towers, but this does not generally seem to be the case. There are a number of possible reasons for this. First, most of the large 19th century prisons are still in use and, for obvious reasons, information on their layout and facilities is not readily available. Secondly, most of these prisons seem to have been built in the early years of the century, and they predate the large mental hospitals by at a generation at least. They were designed at a time when the sanitary requirements of the prisoners were perhaps not the foremost consideration of those who designed the prisons — it is only recently that 'slopping out' has ceased to be a feature of the daily routine in these older prisons. Perhaps the main reason is that, apart from Dartmoor, they were built within the cities, or were quickly engulfed by the rapidly expanding urban areas, and could readily be served by the city's water supply system.

Military Water Towers

The building of military barracks in Britain as we would recognise them today — purpose built, self-contained, permanent but unfortified accommodation for a large number of troops concentrated on one site — began in earnest at the time of the Napoleonic wars. Weedon Depot in Northamptonshire is a classic example from that era and a water tower, now demolished, is marked on an 1899 map of the area but date and details of the structure can only be guessed at as the complex was occupied and progressively developed by the army until after World War II.

We know that the prisoner-of-war camp at Norman Cross, near Peterborough, opened in 1797 to house up to 7000 of Napoleon's sailors in a 22 acre compound, relied on simple wells for its water supply. Presumably the domestic water consumption of a large concentration of men under military discipline would, in those days, have been relatively modest. The regime at Norman Cross was a humane one, but the deaths of nearly 1800 of the inmates, chiefly from waterborne diseases (1020 from typhoid in 1800-1) during the 17 years of the camp's existence illustrates all too clearly the undesirable combination of shallow wells and pit latrines in close proximity. Conditions within British barracks cannot have been fundamentally better, for in 1857 a Royal Commission report found that the mortality rate among soldiers was 17.1 per thousand, nearly twice as high as the comparable rate of 9.8 per thousand for the civilian male population between the ages of 20 and 40. Considering that soldiers were relatively well fed and exercised and that their recruitment would, by and large, exclude the chronically sick and disabled, these figures reflect badly upon the prevalent sanitary conditions within military establishments. Only in places like Portsmouth or Plymouth, where the naval base functioned as a self-contained industrial complex, would a piped water supply have been regarded as essential.

The Royal Commission led to the formation of a standing Army Sanitary Commission in 1862, with the result that the 1860s saw the gradual introduction of piped water for baths, water closets and kitchens in army barracks. The Militia Act of 1852 had seen the reconstitution of the local militias for which the Lords Lieutenant of the Counties were expected to raise some 80,000 men in two years. This had resulted in the building of barracks for the new militias in county towns throughout the country but, as regards sanitary arrangements, they offered little or no improvement on what already existed.

Not until the implementation of the Cardwell army reforms in the 1870s and the establishment of 'localisation depots' the length and breadth of Britain did the efforts of the Army Sanitary Commission bear real fruit. These depots fulfilled a similar function to the earlier generation of militia barracks, and although they exhibited a wide variety of architectural styles their configuration was essentially simi-

Figure 8.7. Le Cateau barracks water tower, Colchester, Essex, early 1870s

lar. To provide a secure local armoury many were constructed with a prominent 'keep,' a solidly built tower, often located adjacent to the main entrance gate, which incorporated a structural iron framework and an elevated water tank. By the 1870s piped urban water supplies were well established, obviating the need for a large storage capacity within the depot, and such tanks would have been relatively small. These keeps cannot therefore be considered as water towers though, like their industrial counterparts, they often bore a marked similarity in appearance to the contemporary free-standing municipal water tower. Two notable exceptions are the Royal Marine barracks at Eastney, Portsmouth (1862-7) with its own impressively large water tower and the sizeable tower with its exposed octagonal cast iron tank dating from the early 1870s at Colchester's Le Cateau cavalry barracks (Figure 8.7). Both were typically 'Victorian' in their design and orna-mentation.

The 1850s had seen a shift in military thinking with the creation of the 'great camps' at Aldershot, Colchester and Shorncliffe, Kent, to enable large concentrations of men to be trained and exercised over an extensive area, in the field rather than on the parade ground. These large camps, well outside the urban areas, were initially rather primitive affairs, row upon row of wooden huts, but during the 1890s these camps were enlarged, modernised and reconstructed in more permanent materials. The 'great camp' at Tidworth on Salisbury plain followed in the early 1900s. They now required their own piped water supply systems and thus, where appropriate, their own water towers. They were the precursors of what was soon to come.

The heyday of the military water tower begins with the First World War. The numbers of men under arms was of an order of magnitude greater than had ever been known before. Such masses of men could not be accommodated in traditional barracks and an entirely new type of army camp, with its row upon row of prefabricated, single storey dormitories — the Nissen hut dates from 1916 — rapidly evolved to meet this need. Bovington in Dorset, and Catterick Camp in Yorkshire originated at this time. Furthermore, an increasing proportion of these men were conscripts and most would by then have come from homes with a piped water supply and their standards of personal hygiene (or that to which they aspired) would have risen accordingly. All large military bases, even those of an essentially temporary nature, would therefore have incorporated a piped water supply, and by this time the standardised, utilitarian, sectional steel-panelled tank on a steel lattice framework — the Braithwaite tank — was available to meet this need.

Figure 8.8. Howden airship base water tower, Humberside, c 1915

138

From then on, any large military establishment in Britain would be a major consumer of water. There was a general desire by the military to have their own water supplies, independent of the local civilian system, not least because the local, almost invariably rural, water supply would have been unable to cope with the massively increased demands placed upon it. In most cases the military water supply would be obtained from an on-site borehole, and this would automatically necessitate a water tower.

They were not always Braithwaite tanks. The First World War saw a number of decidedly 'one-off' concrete towers appear at military bases, such as the tiny, square and alarmingly unbraced structure at what was once a Royal Flying Corps establishment at Bramham Moor, near Tadcaster, and what is now the only surviving building at Howden airship station on Humberside (Figure 8.8). A small rectangular concrete tower above the ablutions block can still be found at the old coastal defence battery at Seaton Sluice in Northumberland. In each case there is a lingering suspicion that it was used as a fortuitous opportunity for a young engineer to obtain his first unaided experience of reinforced concrete design. Other, more conventional concrete designs appeared in the following decades, some virtually identical in appearance with their civilian counterparts, others starkly utilitarian.

Whilst a Braithwaite tank might have been an acceptable wartime expedient (as it would once again in World War II) the military bases established in the inter-war period demanded more permanent and aesthetically acceptable structures. This was certainly true of the Royal Air Force's 'Expansion Period' aerodromes of the latter half of the 1930s. In response to public concern about the impact of such widespread and large scale developments on the countryside, these aerodromes were built to a common architectural style, approved by the Royal Fine Arts Commission and on which Edwin Lutyens is believed to have had an influence. They almost invariably included a water tower (Figure 8.9). These

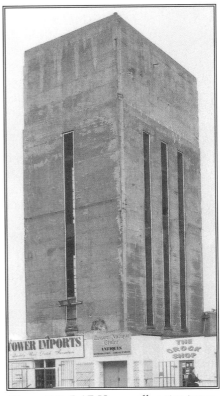

Figure 8.9. RAF Hemswell water tower, Lincolnshire, late 1930s

towers, square in plan, were plain but quite distinctive. Although they were all essentially similar in external appearance they seem to have been built to a wide variety of designs, ranging from entirely of reinforced concrete to a sectional steel panel tank enclosed within a brick tower, strengthened with concrete ring beams. Most of them appear to be of brick but RAF Hullavington's tower in Wiltshire has Bath stone cladding. For reasons that have never been divulged the Expansion Period water tower at the RAF hospital at Ely was built with a prominent Norman-style doorway. A similar structure, what appears to be a scaled-down version of the water tower, is an equally common feature of these inter-war airbases. It is actually a boiler house chimney enclosed in a square brick tower allegedly to enable parachutes (or canvas fire-hoses, according to other informants) to be dried. It is not a water tower. The Expansion Period water towers were not the first standard War Office designs; these appeared as early as the mid-1920s. Reinforced concrete airfield towers from this decade can still be seen at Wittering, Cambridgeshire, and Bicester, Oxfordshire.

The Second World War saw a proliferation of military airfields established throughout Britain, especially in the eastern counties of England, but these were strictly utilitarian in design, erected quickly and cheaply and using prefabricated buildings wherever possible. They were very different from the rather elegant Expansion Period establishments. There was a further, more subtle difference in that whereas the pre-war water towers had been located within the aerodrome's technical site, the wartime structures were erected within the communal site, away from the enemy's main target area. Although water towers seem to have been an integral part of the wartime airfield infrastructure, most appear to have been standard Braithwaite tanks, although small, utilitarian concrete water towers of the circular tank on columns type are occasionally encountered. Sectional cast iron tanks were still being manufactured in the 1940s and these, too, were utilised at some installations. No doubt what was erected at any site would depend largely on what was available under wartime exigencies. The War Office systematically allocated type reference numbers to each building design (eg, 440/42, a twin compartment 8x6x4 Braithwaite tank tower with a nominal capacity of 50,000 gallons), the final two digits indicating the year of the design. Many site layout plans show these reference numbers but unfortunately it is now very difficult to locate the relevant design drawings. The Defence of Britain Project is currently collating information on the design and layout of 20th century military installations and their buildings.

During the Second World War many RAF airfields in Britain were allocated for use by units of the United States Air Force and some of these continued as American bases long after the war. Military hospitals, with their own water towers, also appeared. Other allied forces established bases in Britain. A concrete water tower still stands at what was the Canadian army camp at Thursley in Surrey but it is not possible to tell whether the design was British or Canadian. At most of these bases the infrastructure was provided by the Ministry of Defence and reflects British architectural and engineering styles, but one exception is the USAF base at Chicksands, Bedfordshire, where the water tower, an uncompromisingly transatlantic design, could have been transplanted straight out of the American Mid-West.

It is not widely appreciated that the first industrial complexes to be established in Britain were the Royal Naval dockyards, the principal ones being Woolwich, Chatham, Portsmouth and Plymouth. The building, equipping, arming and repairing of warships, well before the age of steam, involved a wide range of specialist crafts and a considerable degree of technological innovation. Although the various processes involved would not have required great quantities of water they almost all involved large amounts of inflammable or explosive materials within a crowded area. The fire hazard was ever present and the naval dockyard authorities were very conscious of this. From the time of the Napoleonic wars many dockyard buildings incorporated large elevated water tanks at roof level for firefighting purposes and whilst few of these were water towers as such they are among the earliest examples of large elevated tanks.

Two of the first must undoubtedly be those erected by Marc Brunel, father of Isambard Kingdom Brunel, at Chatham and Portsmouth in the first decade of the 19th century. At Chatham the tank was erected above the dockyard sawmill and at Portsmouth in the roof of Brunel's block-making factory. In the age of sail the navy purchased well over 100,000 wooden pulley blocks each year; nearly 1000 being needed to equip a large man-of-war like HMS *Victory*. In what was arguably the world's first industrial mass production process, 45 purpose built machine tools, designed by Brunel, enabled ten men to produce what 110 men had hitherto produced by hand. Unfortunately both Brunel's roof tanks have long gone and it has not been possible to discover whether they were of lead-lined timber, riveted wrought iron, or cast iron panel tanks. If the last, then they would have predated the earliest cast iron railway tanks by at least 20 years.

In about 1810 Samuel Bentham erected what what can certainly be classified as a water tower in Portsmouth naval dockyard, specifically for firefighting purposes and feeding into a ring main serving the major dockyard buildings. Details of its tank do not seem to have been recorded. This water tower was superseded in 1843 by a remarkable structure built by Royal Engineer officers and incorporating a 172,000 gallon sectional cast iron tank, an immense size for its time. The 770 ton tank was supported on a framework of circular cast iron columns braced together by two tiers of horizontal beams with a shallow arched profile. The framework was subsequently clad with corrugated iron sheeting to form the dockyard fire station (Figure 8.10.) Sadly this unique structure has lost its tank although the supporting iron framework has been preserved and the building is still in operational use.

Figure 8.10. RN dockyard water tower, Portsmouth, Hampshire, 1843

Two hundred yards or so to the north, the west wing of the old dock-yard iron foundry, a three storey stone building of 1854, has a massive exposed iron tank covering the whole roof area. This is not particularly early for a sectional cast iron tank and only a single panel high, but a superb example all the same. During World War II this building was for a while used as the centre of operations by the dockyard's Air Raid Precautions unit until they realised that a direct hit from a bomb would result in them 'not only being blown to smithereens but drowned as well.'

Schools and Universities with Water Towers

The rapid expansion of the public school system during the 19th century resulted in the establishment of sizeable, self-contained communities, often situated on 'greenfield' sites in rural areas. The analogy with hospitals is obvious. Even if a piped water supply was available in the area it might not be capable of meeting the needs of a large school, compelling the school to provide its own water supply. This could well involve the construction of a water tower. A particularly fine six storey Edwardian (1902) example of a school water tower can be seen at Christ's Hospital School near Southwater in West Sussex.

Barely a decade later, in 1911, Drax Grammar School (latterly the Read School) in Yorkshire commissioned a reinforced concrete water tower. The school, situated on the outskirts of a small isolated village near Goole, needed its own water supply. Whether or not the pump that fed the tower was motorised, two of the present governors can still remember schoolboys being made to pump water into the tower by hand on Sunday mornings. The inclusion of a water tower into the design of a modern, urban school is less easy to understand, but examples are occasionally encountered. In 1923 a concrete water tower was built for the King Edward School at Witley in Surrey, and as recently as the late 1950s two were built by Staffordshire County Council for secondary schools at Stafford and at Aldridge. In these last two examples a 70 ft chimney was used as the central shaft of a small concrete tower with the circular tank near the top of the chimney. The exposed walls of their concrete tanks were given a timber cladding, a highly impractical and wholly unnecessary affectation. This combination of water tower and chimney in the 1950s and early 1960s is something encountered previously in this chapter, but why a school should need its own

water tower at a time when the public mains network had become almost ubiquitous is unclear.

At least three British Universities are known to have private water towers. York University dates from the early 1960s when a series of what were then termed 'redbrick' universities were built on greenfield site campuses, with close attention being paid to layout, landscaping and architecture. The results were often both attractive and innovative; York University's water tower (1965) is a concrete wineglass, with the design pushed to its limits. The 50,000 gallon 68ft diameter tank is exceptionally, almost exaggeratedly, flat and the supporting shaft correspondingly slender. (Figure 8.11) Any passing civil engineer would be well advised to visit the site and ponder the

Figure 8.11. York University water tower, 1965

concentration and distribution of stress at the base of the shaft, where the access door seems to be nearly as wide as the shaft itself, a mere seven feet. This tower has, unfortunately, been constructed within a courtyard and it is almost impossible to obtain an unimpeded view of its remarkably bold structure. One other question remains; it stands almost in the shadow of York's impressive Siwards How water tower

143

so why was it needed? The tank was constructed of wedge-shaped precast concrete segments and these have deteriorated badly and the future of this tower, now redundant, is currently under review. Sadly, demolition is the most likely outcome.

Also in Yorkshire, Leeds University's large Henry Price Building, a seven-storey student accommodation block has an integral water tower at its north end. The concrete tank is an irregular quadrilateral in shape, oversailing a similarly shaped shaft. An exposed concrete staircase winds round the outside of the shaft, giving access to each floor of the block. In this case it is clear why a private water tower was needed — the university building is significantly higher than the Yorkshire Water service reservoir on the opposite side of the road. Leicester University has a water tower incorporated into its Engineering Building, but this one was erected to provide a supply of water to the hydraulics laboratory. There is no external indication that the tall, narrow, rectangular and utterly featureless brick shaft on the corner of what is otherwise an attractive piece of modern architecture is indeed a water tower.

Private Houses with Water Towers

The role of the country estate water tower in early rural water supply systems has already been dealt with in Chapter 4. This role was always somewhat poorly defined and there were many water towers in country areas whose function was of a purely private nature, invariably associated with a large country house.

The earliest country houses to have their own piped water supply seem to have been a handful of the great country mansions in the first half of the 18th century, although as early as 1695 Celia Fiennes reported that Broadlands, in Hampshire, had '. . . a water house that, by a wheel, casts up the water out of the river just by and fills the pipes to serve all the house . . .' though whether we would have recognised her 'water house' as a water tower is uncertain.' A similar system was in operation at Blenheim Palace from 1706 where 'an engine' pumped water to a 'great wooden cistern at the top of a nearby hill' from which water was fed to a lead cistern above the entrance gateway — something clearly approaching a water tower. A 'water pavilion' was erected in 1719-20 to serve Carshalton House in Surrey. An elegant complex consisting of orangery, saloon, bath house and robing room was surmounted by a brick tower enclosing a cistern supported on a wooden framework which straddled the well and pump.

Possibly the finest, if not the first of the early country house water towers is that at Houghton Park in Norfolk. Much of the original water supply system at Houghton, including the water tower, survives and its historical significance cannot be underestimated, for here we have what may be Britain's oldest purpose-built water tower still standing (unless further research reveals that the mysterious 17th century 'water tower' at Dame Mary Bolle's Well near Heath Common, Wakefield, was built as a water tower and not merely converted to one at a later date). Houghton Hall, the magnificent new mansion he created between 1722 and 1735, was the country seat of Sir Robert Walpole, the then Prime Minister. Walpole is reputed to have 'designed' the water supply system himself, although the amateur architect, Lord Herbert, was heavily involved with the 'water house.' More significantly, Herbert is also known to have had scientific and engineering interests and was friendly with J T Desaguliers, a contemporary authority on hydraulic engineering.

The water supply at Houghton Park dates from about 1732, though construction began in the late 1720s. Its principal features are the well, pumphouse and associated 'water house', the latter an unmistakably purpose-built water tower (Figure 8.12). The pumphouse was built to enclose the well and the horse-driven pump directly above it. It also contained a stable for the pump-horse. The well, 80 feet deep into the underlying chalk, is itself an impressive structure, consisting of five bell-shaped, underground brick chambers, one above the other. Adjacent to the well, a spiral staircase of timber and cast iron within its own parallel shaft gives access to the pump and the intermediate chambers and pipework above. A second well, of similar construction to the first but on the opposite side to the stairwell, was sunk at a

Figure 8.12. Houghton Park water tower, Norfolk, 1732

slightly later date. These two wells, together with a subsequent third well some distance away, are interconnected by adits within the chalk.

A ten foot diameter wooden wheel, like a giant cartwheel, is mounted on a vertical shaft in a courtyard beside the pumphouse. This wheel was turned by the pumphorse and was geared to an overhead shaft which was taken through the pumphouse wall to power the three-throw reciprocating pump with its crankshaft mounted over the well. Unfortunately details of the pump mechanism cannot be ascertained from the published drawings. The water was pumped 500 yards from the well to the water house through a 3 inch diameter lead pipe. In contrast to the plain and unornamented brick pumphouse, the water house is a remarkably elegant building. Scaling 33 feet square in plan the water house, although of only two stories, is 41 feet high overall. Designed in the Palladian style, it is built of Whitby sandstone and stuccoed brick with a slated, pitched roof. It is situated on a slight knoll, some 10 to 20 feet above the level of the pumphouse.

Rather surprisingly, the tank is located at the top of the lower storey, and not in the upper storey. The original 12,000 gallon tank was of wood, lined with lead, and supported seven feet above ground level on internal brick walls. From here water gravitated in lead pipes a further 700 yards to Houghton Hall. There was only enough head of water to supply the ground floor and *piano nobile* of the mansion, where some of the original brass cocks in the dining room walls have survived to the present day. Given the inadequate head of water in the mansion, it is slightly curious that the tank was not mounted at a higher level within the water house. It can be argued that the second storey is a purely architectural feature with no room for a tank of any reasonable size, though one might have been accommodated within the roofspace. The answer may lie in the depth of the well and the distance and height to which the water could reliably have been pumped at that date.

After Sir Robert's death in 1745 the estate was found to be heavily encumbered with debt and for the next 150 years the mansion, gardens and parkland fell into a deplorable state of dilapidation. This may explain the fortuitous survival of so much of the original water supply system which was still in use ('the classic tank or water house into which water is raised weekly by machinery of a past age') in 1865. The system was partially modernised in 1904, when a 'hot air' engine was installed to drive a pump in the second well, and again in 1921 when the system was uprated to provide sufficient pressure to feed all the floors at the Hall, augmented by a mains water supply. Enough remains of the original system to make Houghton Hall's water supply — and its water tower — of considerable historical significance.

The lead lined tank was replaced *in-situ* by a larger Braithwaite tank during the second world war. This has been retained as a back-up for firefighting purposes, although at the time of writing it is planned to be taken out of commission. Nevertheless, Houghton must be in contention with York's Lendal Tower for the longest continuous record of service of any water tower in the country.

The Grade I listed building known as the Summer House on the Grimsthorpe Estate in Lincolnshire was built by Sir John Vanbrugh in about 1720 when he remodelled Grimsthorpe Castle. The listed building citation for the Summer House adds, 'formerly listed as Swinstead Water Tower.' Was this its original purpose? If so, it predates Houghton's Water House. It is, however, a mile and a half from the castle which has a well and donkey-wheel in its cellars, and although the Summer House is sited on the crest of a ridge this seems to have been for the view rather than to provide a head of water. Now a dwelling house, it stands on the southern edge of Swinstead, a Grimsthorpe Estate village, which it served as a water tower in the first half of the last century. It is known that the Summer House was substantially modified in about 1920 and it must be assumed that its role as a water tower dates from that time. The internal water tank which was demolished in 1992 was of reinforced concrete.

For a century or more, such private water supplies remained the preserve of the very rich, but in the early 19th century things began to change. A detailed study of nearly 400 such houses built in England between 1835 and 1914 has clearly shown the changing social status of their proprietors:

	1835-54	1855-74	1875-94	1895-1914
Peers and squires	54%	35%	24%	8%
Manufacturers	33%	28%	38%	38%
Bankers	9%	18%	11%	13%
Professional	5%	10%	9%	19%
Brewers & grocers	0%	5%	13%	13%
Miscellaneous	0%	4%	5%	9%

It is interesting that manufacturers are well represented throughout the period — the industrial revolution was already well established by 1835 — but the most striking feature of the table above is the dramatic decline of the traditional landed gentry and their replacement by the newly moneyed trades and professions. The penetration of the railways into every corner of the kingdom had not only made the countryside easily accessible but enabled the distribution of goods on a national scale. The food people ate and the beverages they drank could be produced anywhere in the country or, increasingly, abroad. The agricultural depression may have brought about the relative impoverishment of the old landowning classes, but their place in the country was being filled by a multitude of others.

But not all those who established themselves as country gentlemen became large scale landowners. Many, perhaps, had no desire to do so. This is illustrated by the diminution in the size of the land holding associated with newly built country houses as the century progressed.

	1835-54	1855-74	1875-94	1895-1914
No estate			37%	66%
Under 150 acres	11%	16%)		
150 to 2000 acres	13%	32%)	34%	24%
Over 2000 acres	76%	52%	29%	10%

At the start of the era, nearly 90% of new country houses were at the hub of an estate; three quarters of them controlled a very large estate. At the end of the 19th century two thirds of all country houses being built were simply large houses in the country; a mere 10% were associated with a large, traditional country estate and all the social responsibilities it entailed. If these later country houses were built with a water tower it was clearly intended to serve the house alone and had no 'public' water supply function.

After about 1840, country houses were almost invariably built with at least one bathroom. This would be for the exclusive use of the master and mistress; if there was a second bathroom it would be in the nursery. These would both of course be in the private wing of the house. It was a long time before bathrooms appeared in guest wings due, allegedly, to the distaste which visitors to country houses felt at the prospect of sharing a bathroom with their fellow guests. Initially these baths had only cold water plumbing — hot water was brought by servants. Water 'on tap' was increasingly seen by Victorian country house proprietors as a highly desirable, if not an essential amenity and from 1870 onwards the provision of bathrooms in country houses became more generous.

Where the house had its own large estate any water tower provided for the estate would also serve the house, or vice versa. Where the new country house was built without its own estate it was quite probable that the nearby village did not itself have a piped water supply. The house would therefore require its own self sufficient supply. This presented no great technical difficulties as the technology was already well established. In the early part of the period waterwheels, hydraulic rams and steam powered pumps were all used. By Edwardian times smaller, more compact oil or gas-engined pumps were available and electricity was making an appearance. Even so, for the more conservative landowner the 1894 edition of the Country Gentleman's Catalogue carried an advertisement by Woods & Co of Stowmarket offering a three-throw well pump capable of being driven by a 'horse or pony.'

A wealthy proprietor building himself a country house wanted it to be both distinctive and impressive, and he expected his architect to achieve those aims. Being wealthy, he could afford to employ an architect of distinction and some famous names have been associated with private or estate water towers, such as Sir Matthew Digby Wyatt at Castle Ashby in Northamptonshire (1865) and R Norman Shaw at Haggerston Castle in Northumberland (1900).

Since the architect was constrained by the range of largely traditional materials available to him the desired effect had to be achieved through style and decoration. Incorporating a tower into the house itself thus became a common architectural practice. It tended to give the building a 'baronial' appearance, afforded fine views over the surrounding countryside and, of course, provided an elevated platform for the tank or cistern needed to support the domestic water supply system. Indeed, architects often used this as a justification for the inclusion of a tower in their design, but in many cases the tower was substantially higher than the plumbing demanded. In others, architects managed without a tower at all. Nevertheless, the domestic 'water tower' became a familiar feature of many of the large country houses of the Victorian and Edwardian period.

CHAPTER NINE

Problems with Water Towers

M odern water towers are, by and large, remarkably durable and reliable structures, reflecting an evolutionary process of development as seen in the preceding chapters, but water towers, like any other civil engineering structure, are occasionally liable to give trouble, ranging from minor but irritating seepage to major structural distress. Undoubtedly the earliest water towers would have been far more troublesome but those utilitarian structures were so often unremarked and disregarded that little is now known of the difficulties their builders and operators encountered. A notable exception is to be found at Shrewsbury.

In 1656 George Hosier, operating under a lease from the corporation, erected a 'wheel' under English Bridge from where a horse-powered pump lifted water from the River Severn to a cistern, effectively a service reservoir, 'upon the town wall near Mr More's garden on Clarimond Hill'. Hosier's water supply cannot have been entirely satisfactory for when Celia Fiennes visited Shrewsbury in 1698 she noted the intention of the corporation to provide 'a new water engine.' Their intention eventually materialised for in 1705 Hosier's lease was taken over by a Londoner, Robert Aldersey, who set about refurbishing Hosier's system, including the replacement of Hosier's horse with an undershot waterwheel. There is no evidence that George Sorocold was involved at Shrewsbury but, such was his reputation, his influence must have been felt there.

Fortuitously, Aldersey's works coincided with the dismantling of the old timber Market Cross — actually a market hall — and the opportunity was taken to relocate the town wall cistern to a more elevated location on the roof of the new stone 'Market Cross', which was designed accordingly. It was a typical market hall; a single-storey, open-sided building to provide shelter for stallholders and easy access for their customers and was described as 'built octagon on stone pillars and thereon a large cistern for the use of the waterworks was then erected.' It collapsed in 1736. This may seem a little surprising for usually a structure either fails fairly soon after completion, if inadequately designed or badly built, or else many years later when neglect and slow deterioration have taken their toll. In this case it is possible that the cistern, almost certainly a lead-lined timber tank, decayed and a sudden rupture of the tank triggered the collapse of the supporting masonry.

Undeterred, Aldersey or his successors rebuilt the Market Cross *cum* water tower but the new structure fared no better than its predecessor. Whether it simply replicated the 1705 building is not known. It was erected on stone and brick arches, but was 'so injudiciously constructed that it soon cracked and showed evident symptoms of speedy ruin,' though that was written with the benefit of long hindsight. In 1755 workmen called in to carry out a structural survey reported that 'the floor of wood plank supporting the cistern was considerably damaged.' The 1736 'water tower' was deemed unsafe and was taken down, and in 1755 (or 1758) another Market Cross, the fourth since the turn of the century, was built to replace it.

Undaunted by their second failure, Shrewsbury's water undertakers tried again. The 1736 cistern had had a capacity of 'six hundred barrels' and this was now increased to a thousand which, taking a barrel as 36 gallons represented a 21,600 gallon tank — a not insignificant size even by modern standards. The 1758 structure (Figure 9.1) was far more robust than its predecessors and approached the Victorian municipal water tower in appearance. Once again a combination of brickwork and masonry was used, but the supporting structure was now designed as a closely spaced five by five(?) matrix of pillars and groined arches.

Figure 9.1. Market Cross water tower, Shrewsbury, Shropshire, 1758

This time the Market Cross water tower stood firm and the proprietors prospered. The undertaking's annual profits were reported to be £300 against operating costs of £80. It was also reported (in 1808) that 13,000 barrels of water were being supplied daily, but this figure is surely an order of magnitude adrift, since the same source also stated that the 1000 barrel cistern was 'filled every day by the wheel, and in eight hours time with ease.' The system was also described thus: 'the cistern then (ie, 1758) served half the town and the engine forced up as much as supplied the other half, and thus was the town alternately served.' This can be interpreted in two ways; either there were two distinct supply zones served alternately by the water tower, or half of Shrewsbury was supplied by a pump-pressurised system in the 18th century.

Shrewsbury, like most large market towns, had a number of separate markets for different commodities and the 'Market Cross' upon which the various cisterns were erected stood on High Pavement (now the upper end of Castle Street) and must not be confused with the old Market Hall of 1596 in The Square, which still stands. Although the 1758 Market Cross water tower was still functioning in 1808 it was unpopular with the townspeople. It protruded into the street, obstructing traffic, and the limited space beneath the arches — it was clearly designed first and foremost as a water tower — was able to accommodate only a fraction of the market traders. A contemporary writer described it as 'the present unsightly edifice' showing that the adverse effect of water towers on aesthetic sensibilities is not a recent phenomenon. This structure had become 'very insecure and altogether incommodious' by 1817 when it was in turn pulled down and replaced. Its 1818 replacement presumably lasted until superseded by Shrewsbury's St Mary's water tower — a typical Victorian municipal tower — on an adjacent site in 1858, though there is another, not entirely clear report of 'a new (market cross) building' being opened almost on the same site in August 1844.

There are no known instances in Britain, at least not since Shrewsbury, of a water tower failing catastrophically; the whole edifice collapsing or capsizing, or the tank rupturing and releasing its contents

in a sudden deluge. (If any such disaster has occurred it has been kept very quiet!) Nevertheless problems do occur, and the two most obvious difficulties to which a water tower might be subject are leakage and structural instability. Minor leakage or seepage is a different matter, and the number of concrete towers exhibiting the telltale signs of efflorescense (Figure 9.2) on their exposed surfaces — typically a white crystalline deposit

Fig 9.2. Edge Hill water tower, Warwickshire, 1956

along a construction joint — indicates that this phenomenon is fairly widespread. In terms of the amount of water lost the problem is insignificant, but leakage of this nature through concrete, however small, is a sign of slow but progressive deterioration which can only get worse unless remedial action is taken.

Judging by appearances, sectional iron or steel tanks seem much less liable to leakage which, when it happens, is almost invariably through the sealant strip between adjacent plates. If leakage does occur through a plate it will only be due to a cracked plate, if cast iron, or a steel plate in a terminal state of corrosion.

In some respects, concrete is not an ideal material from which to build a water retaining structure. All concrete is porous, though the rate at which water percolates through a dense, well compacted concrete is infinitesimal. In practice the quality of finished concrete can fall significantly short of this ideal for a wide variety of reasons — the use of indifferent materials, poor mixing or careless handling and pouring, inadequate compaction (or over-compaction) can all result in a concrete which is porous to some degree. When concreting is carried out in the open, inevitable when a water tower is being built, it is subject to the vagaries of the weather. Frost, rain, even blazing hot sunshine can all, if appropriate precautions are not taken, adversely affect the quality of the concrete and not just the morale of those working with it. With a conscientious contractor employing a skilled, experienced and closely supervised workforce and with proper quality control at all stages of the operation, porous concrete should not happen, but occasionally it does. The problem is exacerbated by the fact that a concrete tank is only as watertight as its most porous area. Even if 99% of the surface area of the tank is watertight the porous 1%, perhaps just a single construction joint, will represent a potential source of trouble for years to come.

There is however another, more fundamental problem with the use of concrete for water retaining structures. When any structural member is subject to an applied load it will deform, and this is as true of reinforced concrete as it is of steel, timber, plastic or any other structural material. This deformation may be so small as to be detectable only by the most sensitive of instruments, but deform it will. In the case of a beam or slab (such as the wall or floor of a tank) the load will cause the beam or slab to bend. In bending, the material of the inner, concave surface of the member will compress and that nearer the outer, convex surface will come under tension — it will stretch. This concept is fundamental to all structural engineering.

Reinforced concrete is a composite material, combining the strength of concrete in compression with the strength of the steel reinforcement bars in tension — a classic symbiotic relationship. When a concrete beam or slab is subject to bending the compressive stresses in the concave side of the member are resisted largely by the concrete; the tensile stresses in the convex side of the beam or slab are resisted almost entirely by the steel reinforcement embedded in the concrete. The steel reinforcement under tension stretches slightly, as does the concrete surrounding it. But since the concrete, unlike steel, is very weak in tension it cracks. Because the deformation of the member is imperceptible these cracks are microscopic and have no effect on its overall strength. They do however, slightly increase the permeability of the concrete and, if the concrete forms the wall or floor of a water retaining structure, this increased permeability is unwelcome. So long as the tank or reservoir is full the pressure of the water inside will constantly be tending to force moisture through the tiny pores in the concrete. There is, or was, a school of thought that maintains that, provided the concrete is sound, permitting water from the tank to saturate the pores within the concrete will actually inhibit cracking.

To address this problem, the 1938 *Code of Practice for Water Retaining Structures* recommended that the maximum allowable tensile stress in the steel reinforcement should be 12,000 lbs/sq in instead of the generally permitted 18,000 lbs/sq in. By reducing by one third the stress in the steel reinforcement in the reinforced concrete used for water retaining structures the strain in the steel — the amount by which it extends under tension — would be reduced by a corresponding amount. The strain in the concrete surrounding the steel, and hence the tendency to cracking and porosity, would be similarly reduced. Looked at another way, to carry the same load as an ordinary reinforced concrete structure the water retaining structure requires 50% more tensile steel reinforcement.

Does it matter if a concrete water tower leaks, when the amount of water lost by the sort of leakage described above is a tiny fraction of that lost through leaking water mains? In the case of a concrete service reservoir largely buried below ground the answer will almost certainly be no, if only because the leakage will almost certainly be out of sight and therefore out of mind. A water tower is a very different matter. The tank is perched high above ground level on a site that is exposed to the full force of the elements, winter and summer, by virtue of its elevated location. In summer any dampness on the outside of the tank quickly evaporates, drawing more moisture through the concrete. In winter the same damp patch may be subject to repeated freezing and thawing which will cause the surface of the concrete to deteriorate. This of itself would be undesirable, but embedded within the concrete and not far below the surface lies the steel reinforcement. If the concrete is permeable to moisture from within the tank it is also permeable to air from the atmosphere. The steel, in the presence of a constant supply of water and air, will rust. As the rust forms it expands within the surrounding concrete, forcing the concrete apart. Small chunks of concrete split off from the rest revealing the rusty reinforcement bars beneath, which, now that they are fully exposed to the atmosphere, rust more freely. This phenomenon is known as 'spalling' and can be identified by even the most casual observer (Figure 9.3). An advance warning of spalling is given by tell-tale rust stains on the exposed surfaces of the concrete.

Spalling, even quite serious spalling, can be repaired. The rather labour-intensive process involves the chipping away of all loose concrete and as much as possible of the rust on the reinforcing bars. If the problem is localised a clearly defined area of surface concrete round the damaged section is cut away and the area patched with a proprietary cement mortar. If, however, the spalling is extensive a layer of new concrete may be applied to the entire exposed surface of the tower by the *Gunite* process. This involves spraying moist concrete onto an existing concrete surface in a jet of compressed air. The sprayed-on concrete will inevitably have perceptibly

Figure 9.3. Ainsworth water tower, Bury, Greater Manchester, c 1940

rougher and less sharply defined outlines than the original poured and shuttered (moulded) concrete but this is a small price to pay for a considerably extended asset life. *Guniting* has been in use for well over half a century. In 1955 the 32-year-old concrete water tower at King Edward's School, Witley, Surrey, which had suffered severe spalling resulting in exposed reinforcement, was successfully repaired using this technique.

The most obvious means of dealing with such leakage (though seepage might be a more accurate description) is to coat the inside of the tank with an impermeable membrane such as a thick bitumastic paint. Any material used will be in prolonged contact with potable water and it must therefore be chemically inert, non-toxic, non-carcinogenic and not in any way taint the water. There are two opposed bodies of opinion here. One takes the view that since seepage through concrete is almost bound to occur the interior of the tank should be coated and sealed at the outset, before the tower is brought into operation. The contrary view is that porous concrete should not be regarded as inevitable as to do so removes the incentive for the contractor and supervisory staff to produce consistently top quality, watertight concrete. An impermeable membrane, it is argued, should be regarded as a remedial measure, not a safety net for sloppy workmanship. Nor should it be assumed that an impermeable membrane is necessarily a complete solution to porous concrete as problems have been encountered with leaking membranes, or membranes which fail to adhere properly to the concrete beneath. In the 1930s *Gunite*, usually between $3/4$ and $1^1/2$ inches thick and sometimes incorporating a light steel mesh reinforcement, was often used to seal the insides of weeping concrete tanks.

It is rare for leakage from a water tower to be so severe that water can be seen dribbling from the tank. The author has been told of one such occurrence at a tower in Scotland, though even in this case the phenomenon was cyclical in nature, only noticeable in strong summer sunlight when temperature differentials between opposite sides of the tank produced variable thermal stresses in the material of the tank and thus variable leakage rates. Some water towers have a long history of seepage problems, though they are rarely publicised. As we have already noted, Newton-le-Willows was one, and Edge Hill water tower (Figure 9.2) in Warwickshire has a similar reputation. At the latter, water could clearly be seen and heard trickling from the concrete walls of the tank at horizontal construction joints as recently as 2001.

Structural instability is a much less common but potentially more serious problem and is almost always associated with a failure of the tower's foundations. This can happen in two ways. If differential settlement of the foundation occurs, with one part of the structure sinking at a different rate relative to other parts, the tower's superstructure will deform and the tank, unless flexible, may crack or rupture. This danger has already been touched on in Chapter 7 in the context of water towers with cast iron tanks on masonry or brick shafts but it is that much greater where a concrete tank is supported on a number of separate columns. Differential settlement can be avoided in various ways. Where solid rock is close to the ground surface the tower may be founded directly onto the rock. If rock is present but at some depth, the tower may be constructed on a piled foundation, the piles being driven or bored down to the rockhead. In many instances, however, there will be no convenient underlying rock upon which to found the tower or it will be too deep to reach by piling. In these cases the tower will be constructed on a monolithic foundation, usually a heavy concrete raft or ringbeam and, provided the monolith itself does not fail, differential settlement will not occur.

But even if the tower's foundations are monolithic, settlement can still occur. The tower will then either subside uniformly or, more likely, sink and tilt at the same time. Whilst such movement may not jeopardise the structural integrity of the tank it can still buckle or fracture the buried pipework below the tower. The engineer will of course try to ensure that the footprint of the raft or ringbeam is sufficiently large to reduce the pressure imposed by the tower upon the underlying subsoil to within limits dictated by the strength of the material of which the subsoil is composed. The strength of the subsoil is determined by drilling shallow exploratory boreholes and testing the soil samples thus obtained in a laboratory. Provided these limiting pressures are not exceeded, settlement should be minimal. The Leaning Tower of Pisa famously illustrates what happens when the engineer over-estimates the load bearing capacity of the subsoil beneath his foundations. Pisa's 14th century builder could reasonably plead that he did not have the modern science of soil mechanics to guide him. The designer of what was to become the Leaning Water Tower of Skegness had no such defence.

Originally no more than a tiny fishing village, Skegness had been developed as a seaside resort by the Earl of Scarborough in the 1880s, complete with its own water supply and sewerage systems. As Skegness grew, the resort's original water tower became inadequate and in 1926 a new 110 ft tall reinforced concrete 'Intze' tower was built at the same location to replace it. As the new water tower, like its predecessor, had to be built on a relatively weak clay subsoil a rafted foundation was clearly going to be necessary. An exploratory borehole was drilled on the site of the new tower, the soil samples analysed and the concrete raft designed accordingly. All went well until the new tower was filled for the first time, when it began to move and a quite perceptible tilt developed. The 200,000 gallon tank was hurriedly emptied and to everyone's intense relief the movement ceased, but Skegness UDC's water committee — and its engineer — were left with was was beginning to look like an expensive and very embarrassing white elephant.

The committee called upon a consulting engineer, Sir Cyril Kirkpatrick, to advise them, though by this time many of the councillors were considering demolition as the only way out of their difficulties. Kirkpatrick suspended a plumb-line from beneath the tank to measure and monitor the tilt (and settlement, for both had occurred). The tower was found to be leaning at an inclination of 1:50 (27 inches out of plumb), clearly visible to the public who were either amused or outraged, depending largely on whether they were visitors or ratepayers. As well as tilting, it was found to have settled an overall 12 inches. The tower was only a mile from the coast and Kirkpatrick's monitoring also revealed that the tower was swaying very slightly in phase with the rise and fall of the tides. A more comprehensive programme of soil investigation revealed the cause of the problem. The original borehole had indicated a 24ft layer of soft, wet silty clay sandwiched between an eight foot thick surface layer of stiff clay and a basal layer of hard glacial clay. What this borehole failed to reveal was that the surface clay layer diminished in depth from eight to five feet from one side of the raft to the other. On the low side of the tower, where the soft clay layer was at its thickest, it had squeezed out from beneath the raft as the tank was filled. Knowing what had caused the problem enabled Kirkpatrick to solve it.

His solution was both bold and ingenious. He drove a ring of interlocking steel sheet piles as close as possible round the edge of the raft until the base of the piles penetrated the layer of hard clay 32ft below the original ground level. Even the vibration caused by the piling caused the tower to move slightly, with the tower tending to follow the piledriver as it progressed round the base. Kirkpatrick then partially withdrew some of the piles on the higher side of the tower to form an open archway in the ring of piles below ground level. The next step was to drill a row of 12in diameter shallow boreholes into the subsoil on the outside of the archway. This is illustrated in the diagram in Figure 9.4. One hundred and thirty tons of sand were brought to the site and used to fill sandbags which were carried into the tower and placed carefully and asymmetrically on the floor of the shaft. As the weight of sand was gradually increased the soft clay in the thinner side of the layer beneath the high side of the raft was squeezed through the archway and into the open boreholes from which it was reamed out as the boreholes filled with clay.

The tower moved, exactly as Kirkpatrick had intended, slowly back to the vertical. At this point the boreholes were backfilled to prevent further material entering them and those piles which had been partially withdrawn to form the underground archway were smartly driven back down to their full depth into the hard clay. Movement ceased almost immediately and everyone present must have felt like cheering. The whole operation had been an almost unqualified success; the raft had remained intact and the tower had been saved, although it had sunk a further four feet in the process. Almost but not quite, for in order to compensate in advance for some residual tilting in the future, Kirkaptrick had deliberately brought the stricken tower back slightly beyond the vertical by an inclination of 1:300 ($4^1/_2$ inches out of plumb). Unfortunately this residual movement never happened — the sheet pile ring was totally effective — and for the remainder of its working life the tower retained its slight lean and a disconcerting tendency to rise and fall slightly as it emptied and refilled. Even then the water committee's problems were not quite over for when in 1930 the tower was finally brought into use it was found to leak, and the inside of the tank had to be sealed. Rather regrettably, given its heroic history, Skegness water tower was demolished in 1981.

Problems encountered by water towers are not always the fault of those who designed or built them. In 1942 the concrete water tower at Hoton in Leicestershire was found to be in a direct line with the main runway of the wartime aerodrome under construction at Wymeswold and was declared by the War Office to be a hazard to low-flying aircraft. It was demolished, and the local villages were then supplied from the RAF's new Braithwaite tank water tower erected on the

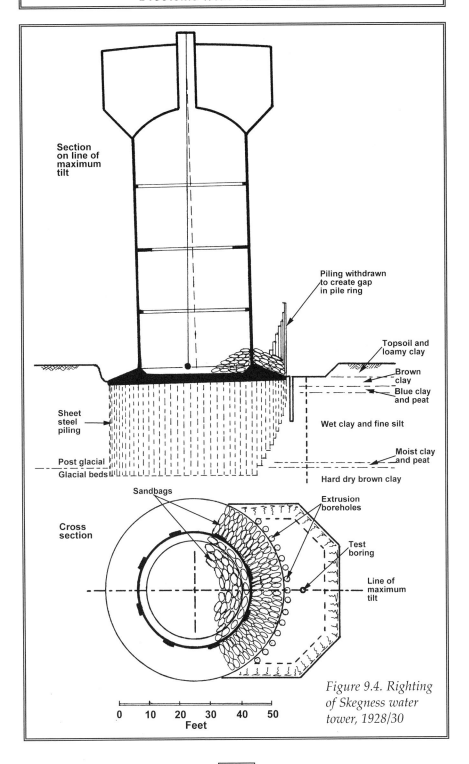

Section on line of maximum tilt

Piling withdrawn to create gap in pile ring

Topsoil and loamy clay

Brown clay

Blue clay and peat

Sheet steel piling

Wet clay and fine silt

Moist clay and peat

Post glacial

Glacial beds

Hard dry brown clay

Cross section

Sandbags

Extrusion boreholes

Test boring

Line of maximum tilt

0 10 20 30 40 50
Feet

Figure 9.4. Righting of Skegness water tower, 1928/30

airfield. Not all water undertakers faced with this situation were as compliant as those at Hoton. A similar situation arose at Milton Ernest in Bedfordshire in 1952, but in this instance the tower's owners, Bedford RDC, were made of sterner stuff and decided that they would simply move their 16-year-old concrete tower out of the way. In every respect, this was just as bold an operation as the remedial work undertaken at Skegness.

The solid design of Milton Ernest water tower, a 12-sided 'tank' on a wide, pilastered shaft, meant that the 79ft tall, 170,000 gallon structure was able to withstand the stresses to which it was likely to be subjected during the move, though the fact that the concrete 'tank' was merely the walling round an enclosed steel tank may have helped. The engineers began by laying foundations for the tower at its new location and excavating a pair of tunnels through the base of the tower. This was followed by the construction of twin parallel concrete runways between the old and new locations on a rising gradient of 1 in 400. The runways consisted of precast concrete blocks laid along 6ft wide concrete slab roadways. A cradle consisting of a pair of massive prestressed concrete beams protruding fore and aft of the tower and aligned along the centre of each temporary roadway was then cast onto the base of the tower. Two closely parallel rows of old fashioned 'bullhead' railway rails, laid on their sides, were fixed along the runways and two corresponding rows of rails were fixed beneath each of the beams forming the cradle. The grooves created by the bullheads and rail flanges were filled with 800, $2^1/2$ inch steel balls, kept at 3 inch centres by perforated spacer plates. The remaining concrete holding the base of the tower to its original foundations was then carefully cut away by controlled explosive charges, allowing the cradle to settle onto the runways.

The empty tower and its integral cradle were estimated to weigh about 1900 tons but the great uncertainty was how much force would be needed to pull the tower the 270 yards along the roadway to its new location. Rather to the surprise of all concerned, a single Caterpillar *D7* bulldozer was all that was needed to tow the water tower (Figure 9.5) and, using a 10:1 ratio block and tackle, a $6^3/4$ton pull was required to get the tower started and $5^1/2$ tons sufficient to maintain movement. At the end of each day the rails, steel balls and concrete blocks now behind the tower were taken up and relaid along the roadway ahead of it, ready for the next day's operation. The whole process took 29 days, though the time taken to travel the 50ft each day was a only a matter of minutes. It can safely be assumed that the world land speed record for water towers established at Milton Ernest in 1952 remains unbroken to this day. On arrival at its destination, the tower was concreted onto its new foundations and the precast blocks and rails lowered and removed by jetting out a two inch layer of sand laid between the blocks and the final section of roadway.

So far as the author has been able to discover, there are no known

Figure 9.5. Relocation of Milton Ernest water tower, Bedfordshire, 1936/1952

instances of civilian water towers in Britain having been badly damaged or destroyed by enemy action during World War II. The water towers at the RAF's 'expansion period' aerodromes were ideal for use as anti-aircraft observation and control posts and many were certainly used for that purpose. It is reported that a *Wellington* bomber aircraft crashed into the water tower at Mursley in Buckinghamshire in April 1943 but detailed corroboration of this is lacking. Another wartime account has a *Whitley* bomber hitting the water tower at RAF Kinloss in Scotland.

On the continent, as might be expected, water towers have been more liable to suffer war damage but seem to have acquitted themselves well. The water tower in the railway marshalling yards at Nuremberg, a large concrete structure of 1910 in a distinctly Teutonic style, survived bombing in both world wars. Less fortunate was the Hennebique structure at Roye in northern France. An unusually large, rectangular tower on 28 columns, four of which formed the corners of the shaft, it changed hands repeatedly during the first 30 months of the first world war, used as an observation post by each side in turn and shelled by the other. It was finally felled by retreating German troops in 1917 but a contemporary photograph shows the tank, still apparently intact, perched lopsidedly on a tangled heap of rubble. Intze tanks were reputed to be particularly robust. In one published account (unfortunately the location and circumstances are not given) also during World War I a small concrete Intze tank was 'blown from its supports by demolition. It fell to the ground but was undamaged, except for a hole about nine inches in diameter. This was repaired and the tank jacked up on temporary timber cribbing and put back into use.'

Water towers are as necessary in coal mining areas as elsewhere but in these areas the potential problems caused by mining subsidence have to be taken into consideration. In at least two cases water towers planned for sites known to be at risk of future subsidence have been specifically designed to allow for the effects of that subsidence. It is, in retrospect, debatable whether the considerable additional cost of these precautionary measures was justified on purely economic grounds, or whether it might not have been more cost-effective to erect a Braithwaite tank tower in advance of the subsidence and replace it with a more permanent structure when the impact of the subsidence had passed and the ground stabilised.

Pye Green water tower, on the edge of Cannock Chase near Hednesford, was erected by the South Staffordshire Waterworks Company in 1935. At the time this tower was planned it was known that a six foot coal seam 900 ft underground would, sooner or later, be mined and the 60,000 gallon concrete tower was designed accordingly. Its external appearance (Figure 9.6) is entirely conventional. The concrete tower consists of an octagonal, parallel-sided tank and shaft, which is formed by eight peripheral columns with screen walls between them. The dimensions of the tower, 50 ft to top water level, 35 ft wide overall, give it a relatively squat but not displeasing appearance.

Any bracing afforded the columns by the screen walls was coincidental. An exceptional degree of structural

Figure 9.6. Pye Green water tower, Staffordshire, 1935

stiffening, not apparent from outside, was provided by five tiers of heavy circumferential bracing, closely spaced at a mere 6ft 8in apart. The tank, although itself of conventional design, is stiffened by eight radial bracing struts sloping diagonally downwards from the edge of the tank to meet below the centre of the tank, in the form of an inverted cone. The tower was founded on a monolithic concrete raft from which rise eight stub columns capped by steel bearing plates. These support the eight columns which form the shaft, continuity between the stub columns and the columns above being achieved by means of sliding steel dowel bars. Three jacking stools were built onto the raft, allowing for hydraulic jacks to be inserted between the stools and the lowest and heaviest tier of circumferential bracing which is only 3ft 5in above ground level. Jacking (and insertion of packing pieces above the bearing plates) would be used not to counteract settlement but to maintain the tower vertical during the active phase of subsidence.

In 1950 the National Coal Board advised the Waterworks Company of the approach of underground coal working and monitoring commenced. Settlement began when the coalface was 370ft from the tower, initially at $^1/_2$ in per month but increasing to a maximum monthly rate of $5^1/_2$ in after 11 months. Subsidence ceased in 1954, by which time the tower had settled a total of 2ft 8in. In the event the tower settled almost vertically and the tilt never exceeded 1in130. Although the jacks were held in readiness they were never needed. The tower remained in service throughout and no structural defects appeared.

Some years later, Heanor UDC was confronted by a very similar problem though in a very different setting, a small industrial town in the Derbyshire coalfield. The council's service reservoir at Tagg Hill in Heanor had already been damaged beyond economic repair by mining subsidence on a site under which further workable coal seams remained. It was decided to replace the reservoir with four identical dwarf water towers, each of 250,000 gallons capacity. The 36ft diameter, 13ft 3in deep cylindrical concrete tanks, like that at Pye Green, were of a conventional design but were only 16ft 3in above ground level. Here conventionality ceased, for each tank was supported on a vertical shaft, triangular in plan, formed by three load-bearing concrete walls. The base of the shaft, slightly above ground level, was carried on three structurally independent stub columns, one below each corner of the shaft, capped with a 5in square steel bearing plate.

The floor of each circular tank was supported on a dense grillage of concrete beams but there was, of course, a large overhang above each wall of the shaft. To avoid cantilever action and thus minimise stresses in the grillage beams, six radial, diagonally raked concrete struts connected the outer edge of the tank to the base of the shaft, two to each face. The base of the shaft was horizontally braced between the walls to take the loads imposed by the diagonal struts. Provision was made for a pair of hydraulic jacks to be inserted between each stub column and the angle between the bases of the two shaft walls above. As at Pye Green, the use of three jacking points would enable levelling to be carried out with a constant load on each support and with maximum precision and control. It is understood that working of the coal seams underlying Tagg Hill recommenced in 1958 but it is not known whether the provision for levelling the four towers was ever used or whether their unique design proved successful. All four of the 'Tagg Hill Tanks' have long since been demolished.

In contrast, Nottingham's Bestwood pumping station, mentioned in the previous chapter, had subsided nearly four feet by 1930 due to colliery workings beneath the site, but such was the massive construction of the beam engine house and its wells and water tower-like chimney that the operation of the pumping station continued uninterrupted until closure in the early 1960s.

The difficulties associated with building water towers in mining areas have not always been overcome. Early in 1927 work began on a concrete water tower on a site, a corporation depot, in the middle of Ilkeston but excavations for the foundations revealed the presence of an abandoned mineshaft. Detailed investigations by the Borough Council's consulting engineer and a mining engineer concluded that the risks involved were too great and the project was abandoned. No alternative water tower was ever built and it would be of interest to discover how the Borough Surveyor dealt with the problem of low mains pressure in the high level town centre supply zone that the abortive water tower had been intended to resolve. Twenty years later a service reservoir was successfully erected on the site.

More recently, Castle Syke water tower near Pontefract, a 52ft high 130,000 gallon concrete 'wineglass', was constructed in 1988 with jacking points at the base of the shaft and, since there is a minor geological fault near one of the points, foundations which incorporated a 3ft layer of reinforced granular fill to cushion the effect of any differential settlement. Given the subsequent rapid contraction of coal mining in South Yorkshire it is unlikely that the efficacy of this system has ever been tested in earnest.

In retrospect, were the elaborate precautions at Pye Green, Tagg Hill and Castle Syke really necessary? No special measures were taken to counter the effects of mining subsidence when Cantley No 2 water tower — one of the tallest in Britain — was built on the southern outskirts of Doncaster in 1958, even though it was expected to tilt three inches and settle by four feet as the subsidence wave passed. If this 143 feet high, 500,000 gallon tower was subsequently undermined, it is still in service and shows no signs of any structural distress.

A less obvious problem facing water undertakers is when the capacity of an existing tower becomes too small to meet increasing demands. The usual solution is to build a larger tower on the same site, either to supersede the older tower or to supplement it. There are however at least three instances where the capacity of an existing tower has been increased.

At Barming (Kent) the then Maidstone Waterworks Company had built a 35,000 gallon reinforced concrete tower in 1926, but by 1950 not only was its capacity becoming seriously inadequate — at least 100,000 gallons was now deemed necessary — but leakage was also causing concern. Despite this, the old tower, a circular tank on a narrow central shaft within a ring of eight slightly inset columns, was still structurally sound. A supplementary tower was considered but rejected on aesthetic grounds. Various other options were looked at but in 1955 it was finally decided to provide the additional capacity by building an annular tank round the existing one (Figure 9.7). The new tank was carried on eight radial fin-walls protruding from a wide octagonal shaft constructed under the new tank. The top water level in each compartment and the overall height of the tower, about 40ft, remained unchanged, though the overall diameter of the structure was increased from 30ft to 47ft. The tank was internally lined with asphalt and coated externally with sprayed concrete (*Gunite*). The old and new parts of the enlarged tower were kept structurally independent, the free joints between the wall of the old tank and the floor and roof of the new tank being appropriately sealed.

At Hunstanton engineers had been faced with the same problem two generations earlier, but here the original water tower was a typical Victorian structure, a rather small one, with an iron tank enclosed within a brick tower. The increased capacity was achieved by erecting a large new water tower around the old one, completely enclosing it within the new tower. The new tank was located immediately above the old one. This would, presumably, have necessitated dividing the original supply zone, with the higher areas of the town supplied from the newer, high level tank. Hunstanton's 'Russian dolls' water tower was demolished some years ago. A similar situation occurred at Goldthorpe, South Yorkshire, in 1926 when a restricted site compelled the Dearne Valley Water Board to construct a 250,000 gallon concrete tower round an existing water tower consisting of a 50,000 gallon cast iron tank on a short, octagonal brick tower. The existing tower was encased within the central shaft of the new tower, leaving no external indication other than an oversize shaft ringed by its eight circumferential columns. The old, low level tank was retained for some time as a reserve supply for use when the new concrete tank was taken out of service for cleaning.

At first thought, the simplest and most obvious way to increase the capacity of a water tower would be to enlarge the tank. Unless the tower had been designed from the outset with this in mind it will, on reflection, be realised that (except perhaps with a Braithwaite tower) significant problems could arise in ensuring that not only the supporting structure but the tank itself is capable of carrying the greatly increased and possibly differently distributed load. It should not be overlooked that altering the top and bottom water levels in the enlarged tank could have implications for the hydraulic performance of the existing pumping plant and the water distribution network. At Barming, it should be noted, the water levels were deliberately left unchanged.

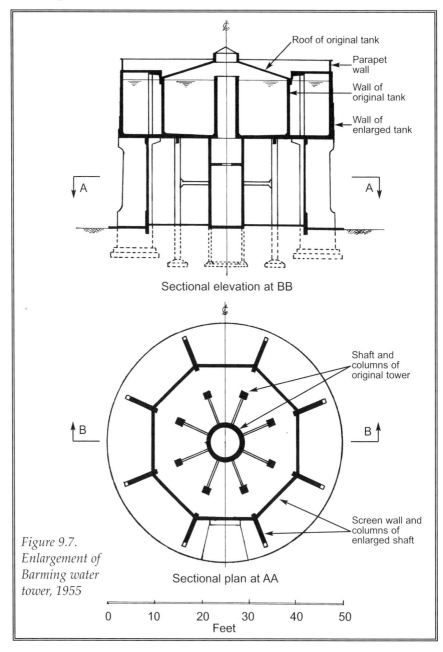

Sectional elevation at BB

Sectional plan at AA

Figure 9.7. Enlargement of Barming water tower, 1955

A somewhat different modification was carried out to Chester's Boughton water tower. The tower, a 268,000 gallon circular cast iron tank on a 64 foot high brick shaft, had originally been built circa 1854 but as the city expanded the head of water was insufficient to supply the remoter parts of the mains network so in 1889 the tank was jacked up and the shaft raised by an additional 20 feet. The added courses of brickwork at the top of the shaft are clearly visible but do not detract from the tower's appearance.

It is very probable, and quite understandable, that many of the less serious failures or difficulties experienced with water towers achieve only limited local attention and never feature in the technical journals, let alone the newspapers. In many cases anecdotal accounts, often vague and second hand, are the only source of information and can no longer be verified by recorded evidence. Even so,they should not be disregarded as they are often amusing and sometimes bizarre.

One such account relates to the refurbishment of Caister water tower, near Great Yarmouth, in the late 1970s. While the work was in progress the float switch which controlled the pumps was disconnnected and the overflow must also have been valved off or temporarily sealed. A minor failure of communications resulted in the refurbished tank being refilled prematurely. The tank overflowed and water cascaded down inside the shaft, filling the base of the shaft to a depth of over six feet before the entrance doors burst open and water sluiced through an adjoining housing estate, fortunately without causing serious damage or injury.

One water tower which never realised its full potential (and about which tantalisingly little is known) was Grennell water tower at Sutton in Greater London. This concrete tower was built in 1934 but failed its acceptance tests and was, apparently, never brought into use. It was eventually demolished shortly after the end of World War II. Grennell tower was intended to maintain mains pressure in a distribution system extended to supply a very large new housing estate remote from an existing service reservoir. Top water level in the tower was designed to be some 20 feet less than that in the reservoir but it appears that at peak periods the system became hydraulically unstable and the reservoir emptied prematurely. Attempts were made to balance the system but to no avail and the whole episode is shrouded in mystery. There are undoubtedly numbers of other water towers throughout Britain about which similar tales could be told. It is reported that Erwarton tower in Suffolk had an even longer history of underutilisation before its demolition in 1998.

There are two other more general hazards to which it might be expected that water towers could be particularly subject though, fortunately, neither hazard seems to have proved a major problem in Britain to date. Both are the result of natural phenomena.

The first of these hazards is earthquake. Earthquakes occur infrequently in Britain and when they do they are rarely of such a severity as to cause significant structural damage. As long ago as 1894 a water engineering textbook recognised the potential vulnerability of water towers with their top heavy configuration, especially when fully loaded. The author noted that the 1891 earthquake in Japan had demolished almost all the railway water towers over a wide area but gave no hint of what replaced them. It can easily be appreciated how a full tank on an iron or steel framework or a concrete tank supported only on columns, or even a concrete 'wineglass', would be vulnerable to rapid horizontal ground movements. Some water towers, particularly more modern ones, have the dynamic characteristics of an inverted pendulum and must therefore be considered susceptible to toppling. It is now rather belatedly common practice to design water towers to withstand the stresses imposed on the structure by an earthquake but there are clearly many hundreds of older water towers throughout Britain which were not.

The most severe earthquake to hit Britain in modern times was that of 1884 which had its epicentre at Wivenhoe, near Colchester. Structural damage was caused over a fairly wide area of Essex and Suffolk. The earthquake predated most of the existing water towers in the area although Colchester's Balkerne tower (*Jumbo*) had only just been completed. It seems to have survived almost unscathed and its massive bulk must have been to its considerable advantage, although a contemporary witness reported that, "I staggered against the side of a shop but I couldn't keep my eyes off *Jumbo*. It seemed to sway several times on its legs ... if the earthquake had gone on a moment longer I'm sure it would have fallen." It is of course possible that it was the observer who was swaying, not *Jumbo*. Even so, it is reported that there is cracking of the brickwork on one of the arches across the heads of the columns, supposedly caused by the earthquake, and the cast iron tank is said to have been strengthened by the addition of tie-bars anchored to external pattress plates. The original internal tie-bars would of course have been attached to lugs cast onto the insides of the plates during manufacture.

There are no reports of the towers at Braintree, Halstead and Clacton being affected though, unlike *Jumbo*, they were all some distance from the epicentre. The earthquake was certainly powerful enough to crack the concrete rendering inside the service reservoir at Sudbury, 15 miles northwest of Colchester, and to reduce significantly the yield of the town's public supply borehole. In 1897 it was discovered that more than half of the water leaving the service reservoir was not reaching the consumers (an intermittent supply was being provided, with the system shut down for seven hours each day) and several major leaks in the water mains were discovered, almost certainly a legacy of the 1884 earthquake. Sudbury did not get its first water tower until 1931 when urban development spread uphill from the river valley and engulfed the service reservoir — a very common situation.

There are at present in Britain no regulations or codes of practice concerning the effects of earthquakes on civil engineering structures. The implementation of *Eurocode 8* (*Design Provisions for Earthquake Resistance of Structures*) has been considered by the United Kingdom Government but rejected on economic grounds. Only the nuclear and petrochemical industries routinely take earthquakes into account in the design of their structures, though they are certainly considered for the largest bridges, dams and tunnels. Compliance with recent health & safety legislation would, however, suggest that the likelihood and consequences of earthquake damage should now be taken into account as part of a wider project risk assessment and, if necessary, action taken to reduce any significant risk identified, even if that action only entails a minor relocation of the proposed tower.

A well known British manufacturer of sectional steel panel tanks now also markets grp tanks. These are supplied by a Japanese corporation whose publicity material states that their elevated tanks, including of course the supporting structure, are designed with a 'seismic coefficient K = 0.3 G but (this) can be increased to between 0.6 and 1.0G for more severe conditions.' For Britain as a whole, a peak ground acceleration in an earthquake of about 0.05G can be expected, on average, once in 500 years.

The other natural hazard to which water towers can be vulnerable is severe frost. Britain's maritime climate means that prolonged periods of sub-zero temperatures are, fortunately, comparatively rare. Nevertheless severe winters do occur from time to time and it seems to have been standard practice from the beginning for the exposed pipework beneath elevated tanks to be lagged where the pipes are not enclosed within a shaft. On the other hand, experience seems to suggest that tank lagging is unnecessary, even with exposed steel panel tanks where, unlike concrete, the material of the tank itself offers virtually no thermal insulation. One exception already encountered is the steel 'wineglass' at Greenhow Hill, high in the Pennines, where the tank lagging was incorporated in the original design, presumably as a precaution. Lagged tanks are, however, not infrequently encountered in continental Europe.

In the severe winter of 1962/3 the then Sudbury (Suffolk) water tower, a cast iron tank on a steel framework, continued to function even though parts of the distribution network suffered from frozen pipes and households had to be supplied by bowser, the town crier being employed to announce its arrival. That water in the buried pipes should freeze before the water tower may seem surprising but there are a number of reasons why water towers should be less vulnerable to severe frost than might initially be supposed. In the first instance, if the water pumped into the tank is obtained from an underground aquifer the water leaving the ground will be at a virtually constant temperature, around 10°C, all year round. Secondly, the large mass of water in the tank will possess a substantial latent heat and will therefore take time to cool to freezing point. Since water is constantly entering and leaving the tower there will be a slow but steady circulation in the tank such that the colder water against the walls and floor of the tank is mixed with the slightly warmer water entering the tank before it has a chance to freeze. Lastly, and perhaps the least obvious, periods of prolonged freezing air temperatures tend in Britain to occur at times of settled periods of high barometric pressure, characterised by clear freezing nights alternating with calm, bright albeit bitterly cold days. It is during such days that the elevated tank is also directly exposed to the heating effect of solar radiation.

Even though frost seems never to have posed a major problem for British water towers it is instructive to consider how this problem is tackled in the continental United States where exposed steel tanks and harsh winters are the norm. The consequences of severe icing can be catastrophic and have resulted in the collapse of several American water towers over the years. This usually happens in one of two ways. In the first, overflow may occur for a number of reasons (eg, frozen ball valve or water level recorder) and the overflow pipe then becomes blocked with ice. The tank overfills and water then overflows through the access manhole or air vent and cascades down the side of the tower, freezing as it does so, and the increasing weight of ice eventually becomes too great for the supporting structure to bear. The second potential danger occurs if a thick layer of ice forms in the tank, or the overflow or ventilator is iced up. Under these conditions a partial vacuum can be created inside the tank when the water in the tank is drawn down. The tank then gently implodes.

One method used in the United States to combat freezing is to inhibit icing by overriding the automatic pump control system and operating the pumps manually, thereby maintaining a constant circulation of water within the tank and maximising the volume of relatively less cold water entering the tank during the night when outside temperatures are at their lowest. Fire hydrants are sometimes opened and water run to waste to assist this process. Alternatively a small recirculating pump may be temporarily installed in the tower to maintain a constant movement of water in the tank but this expedient will only delay, not prevent, the formation of ice. If icing does occur, the most popular method of dealing with the problem before it becomes acute is to use steam, and specialist tank maintenance contractors using mobile boilers attached to long, flexible steam hoses routinely offer this service to American municipal water undertakers.

In Britain, back in the steam era it was common winter practice on the railways to place smouldering braziers beneath the water columns used for replenishing locomotives, the braziers being fuelled by coal from the locomotive tenders. It should however be pointed out that the volume of water stored in these columns was minimal and that it could be static for long periods at a time and water columns were therefore at much greater risk of freezing than water towers. Even so, it was not only Adam Anderson who saw frost as a potential danger to his pioneering cast iron tank. The very early railway water tower at Curthwaite has the flue from a stove in the room beneath the tank carried up through the tank itself. The same device was employed over 30 years later at Appleton water tower on the Royal Estate at Sandringham but it never became a common feature, probably because the complications involved in the design and fabrication of a tank modified in this manner and the potential weaknesses which it introduced in the tank itself were considered, in Britain's temperate climate, to outweigh the benefits.

Technological progress is rarely without its drawbacks and the use of new materials can sometimes give rise to new and unexpected problems. When glass reinforced plastic (grp) sectional tanks were first introduced some, such is the nature of the material, were found to be slightly translucent. Unlike tanks of more traditional materials, the interior of these grp tanks was no longer completely dark and this resulted in rapid rates of algal growth inside the tank with inevitable and unacceptable consequences for the quality of water put into supply. The problem was quickly solved by blending the grp with a dye dense enough to make the tank panels completely opaque.

CHAPTER TEN

Re-use of Water Towers

Although the operational lifespan of water towers varies widely, from less than 30 to well over 100 years — many Victorian towers are now into their third century — there eventually comes a time when a water tower reaches the point where it is no longer adequate to meet increasing demands, or ceases to have an operational role in an enlarged supply network, or is beyond economic refurbishment or repair. The water tower's owner is then faced with the problem of what to do with it.

In a considerable number of cases the redundant tower is simply left where it is, particularly if it shares a still operational site with a service reservoir, depot or office. The tank is emptied, the pipework disconnected, the shaft is used for storage of surplus materials or equipment and the tower remains standing. Unless the structure becomes dangerous (and then probably because of spalling concrete or crumbling brickwork) the cost to the owner of allowing it to remain in situ is far less than the cost of demolition. Only if the tower's appearance is so shabby that it has become an embarrassment to the water undertaker will it be necessary for some form of action to be taken. Until this happens local residents and the general public will be almost entirely unaware that the tower is disused.

Where the redundant water tower occupies a site on its own the situation is rather different. It is remarkable how quickly vandals seem able to sense that a building is abandoned, and even if a disused water tower is sufficiently well armoured to prevent forced entry it can still become a target for criminal damage and graffiti. The site becomes an eyesore and possibly a danger to younger children — certainly not a good advertisement for the water undertaker. Disposal or demolition become the only two viable options, and the quicker the better. Disposal, unless there are overriding operational reasons why the site cannot be sold to an outside party, is clearly the cheaper option.

Most water towers thus disposed of seem to become private houses and, as the frequency of 'lifestyle' articles in newspapers and magazines suggests, the conversion of water towers for residential purposes is no longer unusual. There seem to be as many ways of doing this as there are types of water tower. A large municipal brick or masonry tower can even be converted into flats and, like Shoeburyness (Essex), altered almost beyond recognition. An infinitely more sensitive conversion has been that of the old Grade II listed Southall gasworks water tower which was converted to 37 luxury flats in the early 1980s. In other cases the tower can be retained almost intact as an adjunct to a new, ultra-modern house as has been done with the water tower at Coleshill (Bucks), though usually the tower itself is converted into a home. There is of course no reason why a water tower should only be converted to a dwelling house and at the time of writing there are plans to transform the small Victorian masonry tower at Lymm (Cheshire) into a video recording studio.

The most straightforward house conversion is that of a 'Victorian' municipal tower with an enclosed tank, where the tank can be removed without in any way affecting the external appearance of the tower yet greatly increasing the amount of living space available. This will clearly facilitate the planning application though, as with any water tower conversion, the relative absence of windows and the need to increase the number or enlarge existing ones could pose problems. Where the tower supported an exposed tank, removal of the tank may well give the tower a stunted appearance. It will also make it necessary to construct a completely new roof. At one site (Potterhanworth, Lincs) the cast iron tank has been retained as part of the conversion, with windows inserted into the sides of the tank. Whether this type of conversion is entirely satisfactory remains to be seen; potential problems with condensation, heat insulation and acoustics can all be foreseen.

The conversion of a water tower to a private house can be a protracted process. Munstead, a 130 foot high late Victorian octagonal brick tower in Surrey, took the owner seven years. Part of this can be due to the time taken to obtain planning approval and, in some instances, listed building consent. Building regulations can also place obstacles in the path of the unwary owner in the need to satisfy such requirements as means of escape in case of fire. At Munstead the riveted steel tank base was retained to form a dramatic ceiling to the fourth floor kitchen and the float-operated tank inlet valve relocated as part of the fifth floor living room decoration! The owner's efforts proved worthwhile, for on completion the conversion won the Surrey Historic Buildings Trust award, the Downlands Design award and a Royal Institute of British Architects regional award.

Few concrete water towers have, as yet, found their way into private hands for conversion to homes. A tower with a full-width central shaft is clearly the most suitable shape for conversion, though no doubt other more enterprising (or foolhardy) souls might see a 'wineglass' or a tank supported only on columns as a challenge — a final-year project for a student of architecture, perhaps. One concrete tower which has recently been converted to a dwelling is the rather small structure at Dunnington (North Yorkshire) with its octagonal

Figure 10.1. Dunnington water tower, North Yorkshire, 1961

tank and shaft (Figure 10.1). With an all-concrete tower there is no point, and probably no question, of removing the tank which is both architecturally and structurally integral with its supporting structure. The tank has to be included in the conversion even if, as at Dunnington, apertures have to be cut in the side of the tank for windows. This will inevitably involve cutting through the steel reinforcement within the concrete. Although the stresses in the reinforcement of the empty tank will be far less than they would have been under the working loads for which the structure was designed, this operation should, nevertheless, not be undertaken without professional engineering advice.

Though the work and expense involved in converting a water tower will be considerable, and the internal layout of the new home may not be ideal (though less inconvenient than a windmill) especially for those for whom stairs may be a problem, the result will be well worth the effort. The most obvious attraction is the superb views from the upper stories. A less immediately apparent advantage will be having a house that should, quite literally, be as solid as a rock. The structure was after all designed to take the load imposed on it by a tank full of water, hundreds if not thousands of tons of it. What is more, the tower has probably withstood this load for decades and it is hardly likely to keel over now. And for those that way inclined, the ability to look down on ones neighbours, literally as well as figuratively, may be an irresistible attraction. This might not appeal to the neighbours though. Planning permission for the conversion of the larger of the two disused brick water towers at Colne Road, Halstead (Essex) was refused as a result of complaints by the neighbours who objected vigorously to being overlooked.

There is at least one instance of a water tower being converted to a house when it had previously been converted to a water tower from a windmill. Tainter's Hill water tower in Kenilworth began life as a tower mill in 1778 and became the town's water tower in 1884. In due course the town expanded uphill and engulfed the old windmill which, although its tank was enlarged in 1925, was superseded by a new concrete water tower on the edge of the Borough at Burton Green in the early 1930s. This too, a small cylindrical drum on four columns, has been redundant for many years but, unlike its predecessor, has found no alternative use.

The conversion of water towers for residential use is not an entirely recent phenomenon. As long ago as 1928 the Windmill Road water tower at St Leonards (East Sussex) was converted to a house for the waterworks superintendent, though even by then this tower had already undergone one transformation. Built in 1885 by the then Hastings Union Rural Sanitary Authority, it was transferred to the Borough Waterworks in 1897 but from 1908 was used to store untreated water for flushing Hastings' sewers. Square in plan, it was originally built to a rather unusual open design using eight brick columns, connected at the top with semi-circular arches, to support an exposed cast iron tank on a pronounced cornice. The open space between the columns was infilled with brick curtain walling to form the three-storey house.

Residential use is not the only purpose to which redundant water towers have been put. Perhaps the most unusual conversion was that involving the old municipal water tower at Hornsea (Humberside). Built in about 1876 within 1200 yards of the sea, water from the public supply borehole on the site became brackish as demands and abstraction increased. Hornsea then had no option but to take its supply from Hull and a new water tower was built some distance inland, at Mappleton, in 1928. Hornsea Council then found themselves with an unwanted water tower which, with commendable ingenuity, they converted into an incinerator for the disposal of the town's domestic waste. Eventually this become uneconomic to operate and was abandoned, though the tank-less tower and its adjoining chimney still stand (Figure 10.2).

It is gratifying to be able to report that Adam Anderson's Round House at Perth (Chapter 3) has been saved by an imaginative reuse. Following its abandonment as a pumping station in 1965 deterioration set in, but the Perth Civic Trust campaigned successfully for its conservation. A careful and lengthy restoration of the building was

Figure 10.2. Hornsea water tower, Humberside,
c 1876, subsequently converted to an incinerator

completed in 1974 and the Round House was reopened as the local Tourist Information Centre. A further change of use has since occurred and the Round House now serves as a municipal art gallery dedicated to the work of the Scottish artist, J D Fergusson, an appropriate use for such a distinguished building.

Not all re-use has been a success. In the mid 1960s the redundant Chaulden Lane water tower in Hemel Hempstead was given over to a local boy scout troop after their scout hut was destroyed by fire, only for their new headquarters in the old Victorian water tower to suffer the same fate. Perhaps the most bizarre use to which a disused water tower might have been put arose when a local climbing club sought planning permission to convert Freston water tower near Ipswich, an octagonal concrete tank and shaft, into a clubhouse and training ground, the relative absence of crags and cliffs in East Anglia being something of a handicap for budding mountaineers. Whatever the reason, the project does not seem to have materialised. Not, strictly speaking, a re-use but one episode of the popular BBC TV comedy series *Dad's Army*, first broadcast in the 1970s, featured a Victorian water tower in a rural setting which Captain Mainwaring and his home guard platoon had to 'capture.' Many of the outdoor scenes in the series were filmed in Thetford Chase and the water tower used was the nearby Elveden Estate tower.

Britain's first reinforced concrete water tower, Meyrick Park, had a chequered career. Its location in a public park encouraged Bournemouth Borough Council to install a spiral iron staircase the year after the tower was built and charge members of the public 6d ($2^{1}/_{2}$p) to climb the tower for the views from the top. In 1901 this was not cheap and the attraction did not prove popular. No more than a dozen or so tickets were sold each year and as late as 1934 the original stock of tickets had still not been used up. Public access ceased at the outbreak of World War II when the tower became a military observation post. From 1954 it took on yet another role as a local weather station, though whether the top of a water tower is a suitable location for reliable meteorological readings is open to question.

A recent development that has undoubtedly staved off the threat of disposal and demolition is the appeal of water towers to the growing number of operators of mobile telephone networks. The reason is all too readily apparent from the manner in which so many towers, both operational and disused, are now garlanded (or festooned, depending on your point of view) with radio aerials. In some cases this has been done reasonably unobtrusively but in others the appearance of the tower, except perhaps from a distance, has been radically altered. Its previously clean outline has been broken by an ugly clutter of metal ducting, cables and vertical metal panels, leaving the tower looking like an electronic Christmas tree or the nest of a giant mechanical stork. The tower in Figure 10.3 has not only the usual embellishments but an unsightly access stairway has been grafted on to the side of the tower for good measure

It has to be admitted that since the 1960s the water undertakers have themselves used their conveniently sited water towers as base stations for their own mobile radio communications systems, nor were some of them averse, even then, to renting out space on their towers to third parties for the same purpose. The difference was that until the end of the 1980s the water undertakers and their tenants used VHF radio systems which needed only small, unobtrusive end-fed dipole or 'Yagi' aerials. Modern mobile telephone systems, despite miniaturisation of the electronic components, utilise progressively higher frequencies and seem, paradoxically, to require ever more complex and obtrusive aerial arrays. The first British water tower known to have been used as a radio transmitter site was Manchester's M-V tower described in Chapter 7. An experimental radio station was

Figure 10.3. Halesworth water tower, Suffolk, 1932, showing accretion of aerials and access ladder

established at the Metropolitan-Vickers research department at Trafford Park from where the first BBC programme in the north of England was broadcast in early 1922. The aerial was attached to the conveniently adjacent water tower.

Although this chapter has been about the re-use of water towers, it should not be overlooked that water towers have at times been built with dual use in mind from the outset. Dual use, in this context, does not include the incorporation of a pumphouse, valve house or operational store within the shaft or at the base of the tower, all of which can be considered part of the wider function of the water tower. It is the use of the tower for purposes unconnected with water supply, of which Shrewsbury's 18th century Market Cross water tower was a prime and very early example.

Where a water tower is privately or estate owned it is not uncommon for the owner to seek to maximise his or her personal benefit from what has been a major capital investment. The Appleton tower on the Royal Estate at Sandringham housed a shooting lodge complete with fireplace and chimney on the second floor, and Wappingthorn water tower at Steyning (West Sussex) was fitted out for joint use as a summer house.

178

The desire of the water undertaker to utilise the empty space within a water tower is understandable. In practice, the desire cannot often be realised as the water tower is located inconveniently for anything other than the supply of water, and there is the ever-present problem of security. If the secondary use is to be exercised by the owner himself, then security is less of a problem. The classic example of this type of dual use is Spalding UDC's Chatterton Tower, situated almost in the town centre. Here the exceptionally large (94 foot square) tower was designed to house the Council's water department offices, drawing office, stores, workshop/garage and boardroom beneath the tank on the ground and first floors, and still have room to provide local office space for the National Health Service and Potato Marketing Board. Even though the tower is now owned by Anglian Water the office space is still used as such.

Security risks are significantly greater when the general public has open access to a water tower, even if it is located at a manned, operational site. If the tower is at an unmanned site, as the overwhelming majority of them are today, public access is clearly out of the question. The view from the top of any water tower almost always justifies the climb. Water undertakers are aware of this and, particularly in post-war Europe, have sometimes designed water towers incorporating public facilities. Sweden's first 'wineglass' water tower was built in 1957 with a public restaurant and viewing gallery at the top, accessed by lifts. This was emulated in Britain in 1960 when Sheffield's Oaks water tower was built with a cafe and rooftop observatory, also served by a passenger lift. The Oaks tower is no longer open to the public and appears not to have been so for some considerable time. The Oaks was not the first water tower in Britain in which a lift was installed. This is believed to be Glasgow's Ruchazie tower, completed in 1942, although here the lift was solely for operational use, as at Spalding's Chatterton Tower which was equipped with a 15cwt capacity goods lift.

British water undertakers have generally been wary of the Great British public and the only other example of public access to a public supply water tower known to the author was at Park Hill tower in Croydon where, before World War I, the public could climb to the top of the tower on payment of a penny. This implies some degree of supervision by waterworks staff. The reluctance to countenance public access is understandable when the potential risks to public health are considered. The numbers of water towers now exhibiting bricked-up windows and steel-clad entrance doors is an all too depressing reminder of the ever growing problems of vandalism and forced entry.

CHAPTER ELEVEN

The Future of the Water Tower

The water tower is a slowly disappearing feature of the English landscape (I use 'English' deliberately as water towers have never been a notable feature of the Scottish or Welsh landscapes) although it may well be many generations before those that remain have become a mere curiosity. It is nevertheless the case that many more are being demolished or dismantled than are being built, and this is a trend it is hard to see being reversed. It is by no means a recent trend. As long ago as 1963 a prominent British water engineer in a discussion following the presentation of a paper on concrete water towers to a meeting of the Institution of Water Engineers publicly referred to water towers as 'a relic of the past', though he was immediately and openly rounded on by some of his professional colleagues for saying so.

The successive upheavals that have reshaped the structure of the British water industry in the past 30 years do not, perhaps rather surprisingly, seem to have influenced attitudes to water towers within the industry one way or the other. In 1967 the water industry in England and Wales was, despite a period of steady consolidation, still relatively fragmented as the following table illustrates:

Category of undertaker	Numbers of undertakers	Percentage of population served
Water boards	105	44%
City & borough councils	80	30%
Water companies	49	23%
Urban district councils	61	1%
Rural district councils	67	2%
	362	100%

By 1967 no statutory or private water companies existed in Scotland where virtually all water was supplied by the regional water boards. The scope for further rationalisation is obvious from the table above, and this duly occurred in 1974 when the number of water undertakers in England and Wales was reduced to ten regional water authorities and 29 statutory water companies.

The new multi-functional water authorities now had responsibility for sewerage and sewage treatment, water resource planning, pollution prevention, flood defences (both inland and coastal), land drainage and river navigation as well as what some still regarded as their principal function of water supply and distribution. The smaller statutory water companies, with their traditional single function, now found themselves embedded within their larger and at times overweening neighbours. This situation lasted until 1989 when the water industry was privatised. The newly created but short lived National Rivers Authority took over the regulatory responsibilities and river-based functions of the 'old' regional water authorities, leaving the newly privatised regional bodies with the dual core functions of water supply and sewage disposal. Since privatisation there has been a further spate of amalgamations and mergers, all now commercially driven, not only between the old statutory water companies but also involving the larger dual-function regional companies.

The post-war surge of water tower building had already subsided to a trickle by 1967. A few scattered towers were still being built in the 1970s and 1980s but even before privatisation new construction had virtually ceased. The slow but inexorable demolition or disposal of redundant and troublesome towers continued, though there is no indication that this trend has been hastened either by regionalisation or privatisation.

The primary reason for this slow demise has already been touched on in Chapter 1; the introduction, or at least the availability of variable speed electric pumps and the ability to operate and control them automatically. Where a water tower exists, provided that it is structurally sound and still appropriate in capacity and location to its role in the distribution network, it will usually be refurbished and retained. This will almost invariably be a decision made on economic grounds. The cost of demolishing a large reinforced concrete tower can easily exceed that of the superficial repairs necessary to extend its asset life by a further 20 years or more.

The situation is very different in those situations where, in times past, a new water tower would have been the obvious solution. Laying aside any lingering concerns that the water supply engineer may have about the reliability and robustness of pump-pressurised systems, the cost of installing variable speed booster pumps will only be a small fraction of the capital cost of a substantial concrete tower. The decision only becomes marginal in those cases where a small, prefabricated, sectional tank can be erected, usually as a replacement for an older tower, thus avoiding the need to reconfigure an existing distribution system.

It is interesting to discover that the debate about the role of water towers had been going on throughout the 20th century. The 1914 water supply textbook quoted in Chapter 1 observed, somewhat contentiously, that water towers were 'sometimes employed as an alternative to a standpipe though the purpose is the same' but then rather grudgingly conceded that the water tower did have 'certain advantages,' citing discontinuous pumping as one. The 1927 textbook contented itself with the passing remark that 'the American practice of pumping either direct into the mains or into a standpipe is not favoured by British engineers.' Another textbook published the following year airily asserted that 'pumping machinery has been improved to such an extent that the tendency is to do away with water towers' but then effectively contradicted this by adding 'unless it is feasible to make them of such a size that will compensate for the variation in consumption during the 24 hours.' Precisely the same statement had been made by one of the authors in the first version of the book which appeared in 1894! The 1928 authors then went on to say that water towers were 'desirable' in small towns where the supply was pumped but merely 'matters of convenience' for large towns. Standpipes, it was noted, had by then been superseded by air pressure vessels. Any such reservations do not appear to have been shared by water engineers at large, for the next 30 years was to see the heyday of the rural water tower.

Although the argument still goes on, the water tower's protagonists in Britain now appear to be a diminishing minority but this is not by any means the case elsewhere. Construction of new water towers may have virtually petered out in Britain but this trend is by no means universal. Water towers are still being built in the Republic of Ireland where as recently as 1998 an exceptionally large concrete 'wineglass', not an isolated example, was erected at Kiltrough for Meath County Council. With a 1.1 million gallon (5000 cu m) capacity this 177ft (54m) tall structure was the biggest water tower ever built in Ireland.

We have seen how the introduction of prefabricated structural steelwork, reinforced concrete and (in a limited field) pre-formed welded steel plate have all in their turn had a rapid and significant impact upon the design, aesthetics and economics of the water tower. Is another such radical departure, which would give water towers a new lease of life, in the offing? If it is, there is as yet no sign of it. A tantalising glimpse appeared in the mid 1960s when it was reported that 'a new type of elevated water tank is being developed by a well known manufacturer, the design being based upon a steel mast, steel wire ropes and a special nylon and neoprene fabric' though the report concluded, with a touch of bathos, 'but full details are not yet available.' Clearly the idea never left the drawing board, even if it ever reached it.

Since only a handful of large water towers have been built in Britain in the past 20 years it is difficult to tell whether another possible reason for the passing of the age of the water tower is real or merely perceived, namely the potential difficulty that any new tower would have in obtaining the approval of the local town & country planning authority. This problem had already started to appear in the 1960s, as can be seen from the discussion on the paper referred to above. A recurring complaint was the apparent failure of the planners to appreciate that to fulfil their function water towers have to be built on a ridge or hilltop and will inevitably be in a prominent position. One contributor to the discussion had been asked, in all seriousness, why he could not site his water tower in a valley where it would be less conspicuous. The problems inherent in obtaining planning consent for a water tower today can easily be imagined, even though it can be argued that an imaginatively designed water tower is no more of an intrusion on the skyline than an electricity pylon or a cluster of wind-powered generators.

Some local planning officers may have been seen by water engineers as obstructive or unsympathetic although a senior planning officer from the Ministry of Housing and Local Government present at the 1963 meeting stated that the Ministry was 'increasingly concerned, as everyone must be, by the number of tower structures which were appearing in the landscape of this country' but he then went on to reassure the engineers that 'in many cases the answer was the plain, non-committal tower' and 'there seemed to be a place for the tower as a welcome and visually exciting element in the landscape.' Whether he would still hold that opinion today is open to question, but it is certain that water towers would now be the least of his concerns. It must nevertheless be conceded, however reluctantly, that not all water towers have been imaginatively let alone sensitively designed, although by 1963 the situation had undoubtedly improved in the 20 years since the distinguished engineer, Howard Humphries, had lamented that 'concrete boxes on stilts have been erected far and wide.'

On the other side of the same environmental impact coin is the increasing number of water towers that are being given listed building status, although to date these are almost exclusively those incorporating an ornate masonry or brick tower. The listing process seems to be weighted heavily in favour of aesthetic or architectural merit. On that basis it could be assumed that a tower with an exposed iron tank would not be regarded with favour but it is encouraging to note that the two early railway towers at Curthwaite (Cumbria) and Haltwhistle (Northumberland) are both now Grade II listed structures. As far as is known, no concrete water towers are currently listed, which is regrettable, given the rate at which they are disappearing. Not that listed building status is any guarantee of protection — Britain's first reinforced concrete water tower, Meyrick Park in Bournemouth, was a listed building but its owner, even in 1994 when more enlightened attitudes to our engineering heritage were at last showing signs of having taken root, had no difficulty in obtaining consent to demolish it.

The rate of attrition of early concrete towers, many now reaching the state where major repairs or renovation are becoming necessary, should be of growing concern to anyone interested in preserving Britain's engineering heritage. Pre World War I reinforced concrete water towers are becoming rarer by the year and by the time that those responsible for conferring listed building status become aware of this it will almost certainly be too late to retrieve the situation.

The predicament of those public utilities who own redundant water towers should not be disregarded. The structure may gradually become a liability, especially where public safety becomes an issue. Intruders have to be kept out (not usually too difficult — most towers were designed with that in mind and some are built like fortresses) or, more likely, prevented from approaching the structure if spalling concrete or crumbling brickwork pose a danger to anyone unfortunate enough to be standing beneath when a lump falls off. When the author visited the tower at Aldeburgh the area round it was roped off with bunting and warning notices for this very reason. On the other hand, there are large numbers of redundant towers which have been disused and effectively abandoned for a decade or more without causing undue concern to their owners. In this category can be included the growing number of towers that, whilst having outlived their water supply function, generate a modest but useful income for their owners from the rental paid for aerial space by mobile radio and telephone companies. So long as this income exceeds maintenance costs the water tower continues to be an economic asset.

This has brought us back to the reuse of water towers. Provided the site is no longer required for other operational purposes, the sale of a redundant water tower resolves a number of problems for the water undertaker who is no longer faced with the problems associated with preserving what may have become a liability or demolishing a fondly regarded local landmark. It is possible that the preservation of the water tower, at least as an architectural feature, lies ultimately in their acquisition and imaginative conversion by private individuals. It would be a pity if water towers, in all their wide and fascinating variety, were simply to disappear into history, their slow but inexorable passing unnoticed and unmourned.

Gazetteer of Water Towers in Britain

As part of its research, the Water Towers Sub-Group set out to compile a schedule of all public supply water towers, past and present, in the British Isles. This task proved considerably more difficult than was envisaged at the outset. At the time of writing nearly 1000 towers have been identified and listed, but hitherto unrecorded towers are still coming to light and being added to the list and it may not ever be possible to claim that the list is complete.

There are a number of reasons for this. Problems have arisen, as discussed in Chapter 4, in deciding whether a particular tower was, or had at some time been a public supply water tower. Another reason is the ephemeral nature of many water towers, particularly some of the earlier rural ones. They have come and gone and left little trace behind, either physically or in the form of written records. Towers demolished to make way for larger or more permanent towers on the same site, have also proved very elusive. Successive reorganisations in the water industry over the past century and a half have resulted in the widespread destruction or disappearance of records and the dispersal of the staff with the local knowledge that went with them. From small private company to district council to larger municipality to water board to regional water authority and back to private water company — the process seems endless, and may indeed be so.

Often where a tower has been positively identified, even if it is still extant and operational, finding out detailed information about it can be frustrating and time consuming. Operationally significant data on tank capacity and top water level is the most commonly available, followed by date of construction, though even here widely varying dates may be obtained from different sources. Names of engineer and contractor are even harder to pin down. Where engineering record drawings are available (and as often as not this depends on a lengthy process of tracking down the right person in the right office) only the name of the engineer will be recorded.

The Sub-Group's task was not made easier by the reluctance, until comparatively recently, of the Ordnance Survey to show water towers as such on their most widely available 1/50,000 scale maps. Their earlier 'one inch' scale predecessors hardly marked any water towers at all. The omission of the label 'Wr Twr' amidst dense urban clutter is understandable, but the inconsistency of the Ordnance Survey in identifying water towers, even on many of their larger scale maps, has made 'map trawls' an uncertain process.

Although the Sub-Group's national schedule of water towers was intended to be limited to public supply towers, details of other water

towers, some of mere curiosity value but many of considerable technical merit and historical interest, kept emerging. To compile a complete
schedule of all British water towers would clearly have been a far more
daunting and infinitely more open-ended task than compiling a schedule of public supply towers yet we felt that such information should
not simply be discarded or ignored. The result has been a compromise
and, like most compromises, a not entirely satisfactory one; data on
significant non-public supply water towers has been amassed and
appended to the national schedule, albeit in a somewhat subjective
manner. The Sub-Group's national schedule of water towers was sub-
divided into county lists for ease of reference. For this purpose the
counties established in the local government reorganisation of 1974
were used. Recent piecemeal reorganisations from which emerged the
new unitary authorities have rendered obsolete the use of the 1974
counties, but we have nevertheless retained the earlier pattern even
though some of the more artificial of the 1974 counties no longer exist.
This decision can be justified on practical grounds; firstly to avoid a
plethora of geographical sub-divisions — some of the new unitary
authorities cover a relatively small area — and secondly because most
of the unitary authorities fall conveniently within the boundaries of
their larger predecessor counties.

The national schedule of water towers is presented in this Appendix
in map and list format, each map covering a single county or group of
counties and accompanied by a reference table. Over large tracts of
Scotland and Wales water towers are few and far between and, for this
reason, they have each been represented by a single, national map
except for two regions, South Wales and the Glasgow area, where the
density of water towers is sufficient to justify a separate, larger scale
inset map. Selections of what are considered to be the most noteworthy of the non-public water supply towers are also included in the
maps and lists.

Ordnance Survey grid references have not been given for individual towers. This is a regrettable but deliberate omission, made in order
to address and allay the concerns expressed by a few of the water
undertakers who supplied the Sub-Group with information and feared
that publication of the information in full could constitute a security
risk. That any determined terrorist or saboteur can now locate most
water towers from OS maps or by simple observation — many water
towers are conspicuous features of the landscape — or that other
installations, such as pumping stations, would make more effective
targets, is immaterial. Whether or not such concerns are justified they
must be respected.

The reference table given with each map identifies each water tower
by name. All water towers have names. These are given to them by the
water undertaker, not out of any misplaced sense of romanticism but
for purely practical reasons — if you are responsible for operating a
dozen or more towers you have to be able to identify and locate them

individually, and distinguish between them. It is self evident that water towers should be named after the place where they are located; generally they are, though there are the odd exceptions. Defining a tower's location is not always as easy as might be supposed.

Water towers are built on hilltops and, in rural areas, are therefore often remote from centres of population. Most rural towers take the name of the parish in which they are built (a legal convenience at the planning stage) or of the nearest village — not always the same. In some instances the tower takes the name of the hill on which it is built, or the adjacent farm. Such names often have purely local significance, occasionally not even appearing on the Ordnance Survey map. There are a few instances of towers being named after the area they supply rather than the place where they were built. In some cases the name by which the local people refer to a tower may differ from the 'official' name, and the popular name may, eventually be adopted by the water undertaker.

In towns where there is only one water tower it will usually take the name of the town, but in larger towns or cities there may be a number of water towers. In these cases the tower will take the name of the district or suburb, or sometimes even the name of the street in which it stands. This can cause problems, for whereas the location of 'Church Street Tower' may be obvious to local people, from a wider perspective that name is virtually meaningless. In such cases we have therefore used the local name in conjunction with the name of the town.

Where a tower still exists its location can be fixed from current Ordnance Survey maps or a site visit. Problems arise when attempting to identify and locate towers that have long since been demolished. Older maps are, as has already been pointed out, fairly unhelpful. The first problem is that references to a tower at the design or construction stage in, for example, technical journals or trade magazines may use a name that was never adopted by the undertaker, or one which turns out to be misleading, or simply wrong. Secondly, it is not unheard of for a tower to change its name during the course of its lifetime, as for example, from the name of the locality to the name of the parish, or vice versa. The name of any water tower listed in the gazetteer that follows may not therefore be the name by which that tower is known locally, or even the name used by the present owner, but it is the name thought most likely to identify that tower without confusion or ambiguity for the majority of readers.

Since this is an historical study the lists of water towers in the gazetteer should ideally indicate their dates of construction. Mention has already been made of the difficulty in determining the date of many towers. A few towers have their dates cast into the structure or carry commemorative plaques. Unfortunately these plaques are sometimes stolen, or removed at a subsequent change of ownership. They also usually refer to the opening date, whereas a foundation stone may give an earlier date, and a date above the doorway (a favourite position) something in between. The date given for a water tower in an undertaker's records may not always be the date of construction. In some instances, particularly where a redundant military tower has been taken over for public supply, there is a strong suspicion that the date given may be the date the tower was adopted by the water undertaker.

Yet another potential pitfall in the dating of water towers is where there has been a succession of towers on the same site, some of which may have coexisted for a number of years. In these situations it is not always possible to determine with certainty whether a tower shown on an old map or referred to in a published article or in an undertaker's records is the existing tower, or the tower for which an old drawing or illustration has been found. Attempting to date a water tower by its style or type of construction can also be misleading. A few characteristically 'Victorian' brick towers were still being built as late as the 1930s. Many designs in concrete were used and reused by undertakers and consulting engineers alike over a lengthy period. Many of the designs from the 1930s reappear in almost identical form in the 1950s. The convenience and economy of taking a proven design off the shelf, dusting it down and using it once more are all too obvious, even when the completed work is palpably dated in appearance. For the various reasons given above it was decided not to include the dates of water towers in the gazetteer.

Water towers are shown on the maps by either solid or hollow circles, cross-referenced with the relevant list by a number or letter. Solid circles represent towers which are known or believed to be still extant, though they may be disused, derelict, converted to another use or even ruinous. Hollow circles show the location of water towers which no longer exist. These will be largely brick, masonry or concrete towers, or relatively recent Braithwaite tanks which appeared in the inventories of present day water undertakers. Considerable numbers of smaller and older Braithwaites and possibly even other types of tower erected by local, long forgotten water undertakers for small rural communities in the first half of the 20th century and long since superseded and demolished have almost certainly been overlooked. Where there has been a succession of towers on the same site, or where two sites are so close together as to preclude the use of separate circles on the map, a single circle will represent more than one tower. In such cases the existence or otherwise of any one of those towers in that vicinity will determine whether a solid or a hollow circle appears.

The great majority of water towers shown on the maps are public supply towers and these are identified numerically. Occasionally a name will appear in the reference list followed by numbers, as for example 'North Walsham 1, 2 & 3' in the Norfolk listing. This indicates that there have been three successive towers at that location. In this case the original tower has been demolished but the second and third are still extant. On each map a few water towers are identified alphabetically. These are towers constructed for purposes other than public supply, as described in Chapter 8. Only the more interesting or note-worthy examples in any area have been selected. They are, in the main, existing structures although a few non-public supply towers which are no longer extant have been identified (as hollow circles) where their historical importance is such as to necessitate their inclusion in the gazetteer.

It will be apparent from the above that it cannot be guaranteed that the national gazetteer of water towers that follows is either complete or entirely accurate. Even if it were, it would be out of date almost as soon as this book is published since water towers are slowly but inexorably disappearing. Nevertheless, it is offered as the best and most compre-hensive record that the Panel for Historical Engineering Works' Water Towers Sub-Group has been able to compile.

List of Maps

Map No	Area Covered
1	Devon and Cornwall
2	Somerset and Dorset
3	Avon and Wiltshire
4	Hampshire (including Isle of Wight)
5	Greater London, Surrey and West Sussex
6	Kent and East Sussex
7	Oxfordshire and Berkshire
8	Buckinghamshire and Bedfordshire
9	Hertfordshire
10	Essex
11	Cambridgeshire
12	Suffolk
12	Norfolk
14	Hereford & Worcester and Gloucestershire
15	Warwickshire and Northamptonshire
16	Shropshire, Staffordshire and West Midlands
17	Nottinghamshire, Derbyshire and Leicestershire
18	Lincolnshire
19	Merseyside, Greater Manchester and Cheshire
20	South Yorkshire and Humberside
21	North Yorkshire and West Yorkshire
22	Cumbria and Lancashire
23	Northumberland, Tyne & Wear, Co Durham and Cleveland
24	Wales (with South Wales as inset)
25	Scotland (with Glasgow Area as inset)

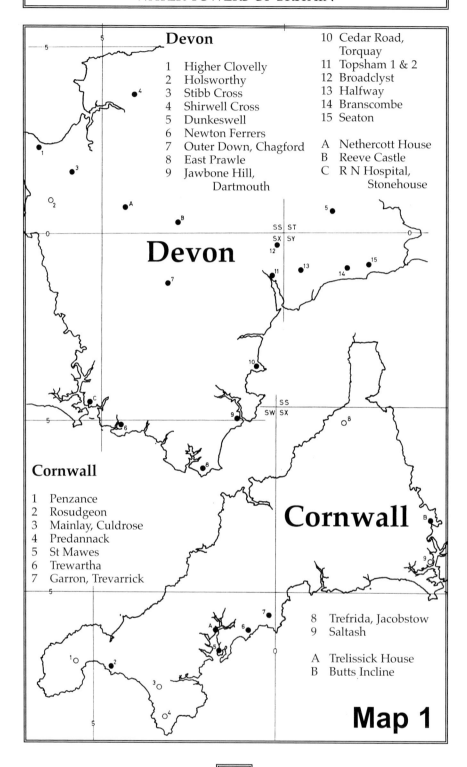

Devon

1 Higher Clovelly
2 Holsworthy
3 Stibb Cross
4 Shirwell Cross
5 Dunkeswell
6 Newton Ferrers
7 Outer Down, Chagford
8 East Prawle
9 Jawbone Hill,
   Dartmouth
10 Cedar Road,
   Torquay
11 Topsham 1 & 2
12 Broadclyst
13 Halfway
14 Branscombe
15 Seaton

A Nethercott House
B Reeve Castle
C R N Hospital,
   Stonehouse

Devon

Cornwall

1 Penzance
2 Rosudgeon
3 Mainlay, Culdrose
4 Predannack
5 St Mawes
6 Trewartha
7 Garron, Trevarrick

Cornwall

8 Trefrida, Jacobstow
9 Saltash

A Trelissick House
B Butts Incline

Map 1

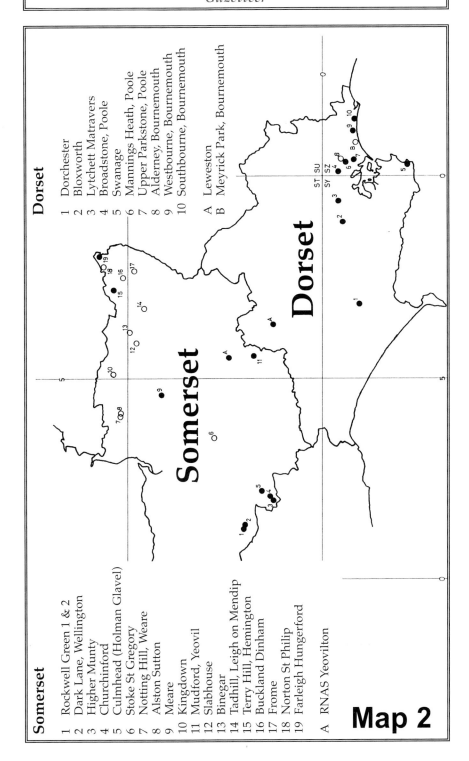

Somerset

1 Rockwell Green 1 & 2
2 Dark Lane, Wellington
3 Higher Munty
4 Churchinford
5 Culmhead (Holman Glavel)
6 Stoke St Gregory
7 Notting Hill, Weare
8 Alston Sutton
9 Meare
10 Kingdown
11 Mudford, Yeovil
12 Slabhouse
13 Binegar
14 Tadhill, Leigh on Mendip
15 Terry Hill, Hemington
16 Buckland Dinham
17 Frome
18 Norton St Philip
19 Farleigh Hungerford

A RNAS Yeovilton

Dorset

1 Dorchester
2 Bloxworth
3 Lytchett Matravers
4 Broadstone, Poole
5 Swanage
6 Mannings Heath, Poole
7 Upper Parkstone, Poole
8 Alderney, Bournemouth
9 Westbourne, Bournemouth
10 Southbourne, Bournemouth

A Leweston
B Meyrick Park, Bournemouth

Map 2

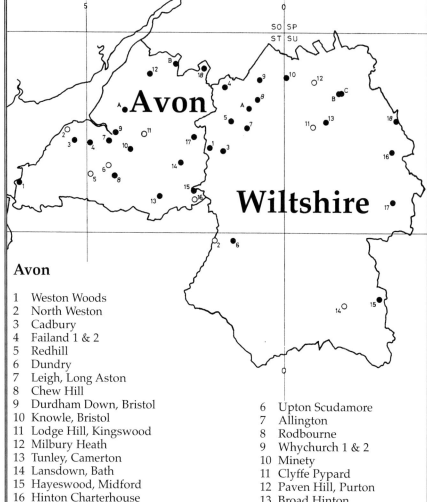

Avon

1   Weston Woods
2   North Weston
3   Cadbury
4   Failand 1 & 2
5   Redhill
6   Dundry
7   Leigh, Long Aston
8   Chew Hill
9   Durdham Down, Bristol
10 Knowle, Bristol
11 Lodge Hill, Kingswood
12 Milbury Heath
13 Tunley, Camerton
14 Lansdown, Bath
15 Hayeswood, Midford
16 Hinton Charterhouse
17 Marshfield
18 Tresham

A   Filton
B   Charfield Railway Station

Wiltshire

1   Colerne
2   Chapmanslade
3   Rudloe
4   Sherston
5   Yatton Keynell 1 & 2
6   Upton Scudamore
7   Allington
8   Rodbourne
9   Whychurch 1 & 2
10 Minety
11 Clyffe Pypard
12 Paven Hill, Purton
13 Broad Hinton
14 Bishopsdown, Salisbury
15 Winterslow
16 Ramsbury Tank
17 Wexcombe Down
18 Baydon 1 & 2

A   Hullavington
B   Swindon Railway Works 1
C   Swindon Railway Works 2

Map 3

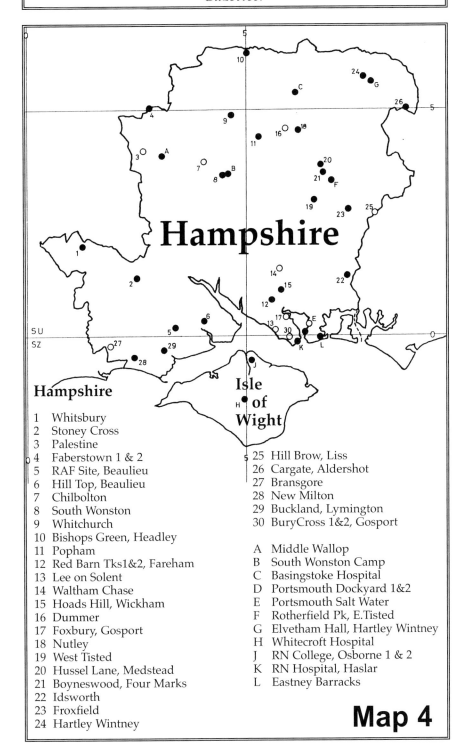

Hampshire

1   Whitsbury
2   Stoney Cross
3   Palestine
4   Faberstown 1 & 2
5   RAF Site, Beaulieu
6   Hill Top, Beaulieu
7   Chilbolton
8   South Wonston
9   Whitchurch
10 Bishops Green, Headley
11 Popham
12 Red Barn Tks1&2, Fareham
13 Lee on Solent
14 Waltham Chase
15 Hoads Hill, Wickham
16 Dummer
17 Foxbury, Gosport
18 Nutley
19 West Tisted
20 Hussel Lane, Medstead
21 Boyneswood, Four Marks
22 Idsworth
23 Froxfield
24 Hartley Wintney

25 Hill Brow, Liss
26 Cargate, Aldershot
27 Bransgore
28 New Milton
29 Buckland, Lymington
30 BuryCross 1&2, Gosport

A   Middle Wallop
B   South Wonston Camp
C   Basingstoke Hospital
D   Portsmouth Dockyard 1&2
E   Portsmouth Salt Water
F   Rotherfield Pk, E.Tisted
G   Elvetham Hall, Hartley Wintney
H   Whitecroft Hospital
J   RN College, Osborne 1 & 2
K   RN Hospital, Haslar
L   Eastney Barracks

Map 4

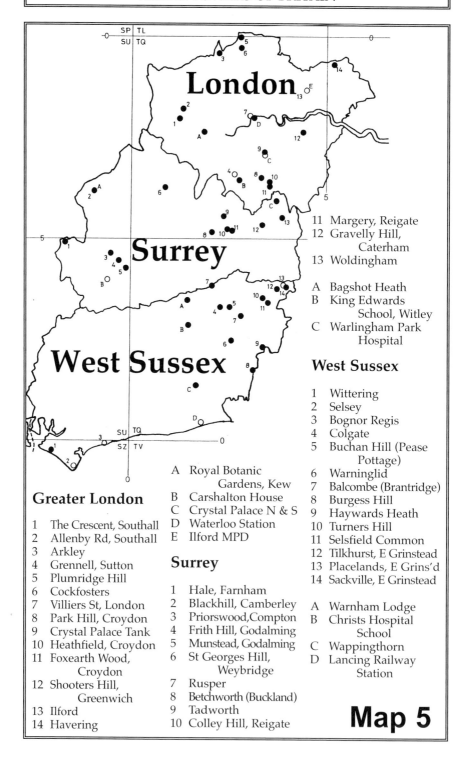

West Sussex

1 Wittering
2 Selsey
3 Bognor Regis
4 Colgate
5 Buchan Hill (Pease Pottage)
6 Warninglid
7 Balcombe (Brantridge)
8 Burgess Hill
9 Haywards Heath
10 Turners Hill
11 Selsfield Common
12 Tilkhurst, E Grinstead
13 Placelands, E Grins'd
14 Sackville, E Grinstead

A Warnham Lodge
B Christs Hospital School
C Wappingthorn
D Lancing Railway Station

11 Margery, Reigate
12 Gravelly Hill, Caterham
13 Woldingham

A Bagshot Heath
B King Edwards School, Witley
C Warlingham Park Hospital

Greater London

1 The Crescent, Southall
2 Allenby Rd, Southall
3 Arkley
4 Grennell, Sutton
5 Plumridge Hill
6 Cockfosters
7 Villiers St, London
8 Park Hill, Croydon
9 Crystal Palace Tank
10 Heathfield, Croydon
11 Foxearth Wood, Croydon
12 Shooters Hill, Greenwich
13 Ilford
14 Havering

A Royal Botanic Gardens, Kew
B Carshalton House
C Crystal Palace N & S
D Waterloo Station
E Ilford MPD

Surrey

1 Hale, Farnham
2 Blackhill, Camberley
3 Priorswood, Compton
4 Frith Hill, Godalming
5 Munstead, Godalming
6 St Georges Hill, Weybridge
7 Rusper
8 Betchworth (Buckland)
9 Tadworth
10 Colley Hill, Reigate

Map 5

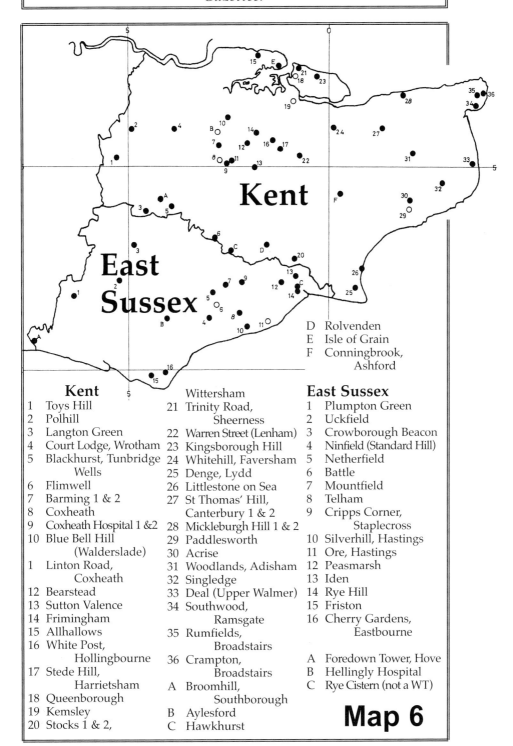

D Rolvenden
E Isle of Grain
F Conningbrook,
    Ashford

Kent

1 Toys Hill
2 Polhill
3 Langton Green
4 Court Lodge, Wrotham
5 Blackhurst, Tunbridge
    Wells
6 Flimwell
7 Barming 1 & 2
8 Coxheath
9 Coxheath Hospital 1 &2
10 Blue Bell Hill
    (Walderslade)
1 Linton Road,
    Coxheath
12 Bearstead
13 Sutton Valence
14 Frimingham
15 Allhallows
16 White Post,
    Hollingbourne
17 Stede Hill,
    Harrietsham
18 Queenborough
19 Kemsley
20 Stocks 1 & 2,

Wittersham
21 Trinity Road,
    Sheerness
22 Warren Street (Lenham)
23 Kingsborough Hill
24 Whitehill, Faversham
25 Denge, Lydd
26 Littlestone on Sea
27 St Thomas' Hill,
    Canterbury 1 & 2
28 Mickleburgh Hill 1 & 2
29 Paddlesworth
30 Acrise
31 Woodlands, Adisham
32 Singledge
33 Deal (Upper Walmer)
34 Southwood,
    Ramsgate
35 Rumfields,
    Broadstairs
36 Crampton,
    Broadstairs
A Broomhill,
    Southborough
B Aylesford
C Hawkhurst

East Sussex

1 Plumpton Green
2 Uckfield
3 Crowborough Beacon
4 Ninfield (Standard Hill)
5 Netherfield
6 Battle
7 Mountfield
8 Telham
9 Cripps Corner,
    Staplecross
10 Silverhill, Hastings
11 Ore, Hastings
12 Peasmarsh
13 Iden
14 Rye Hill
15 Friston
16 Cherry Gardens,
    Eastbourne

A Foredown Tower, Hove
B Hellingly Hospital
C Rye Cistern (not a WT)

Map 6

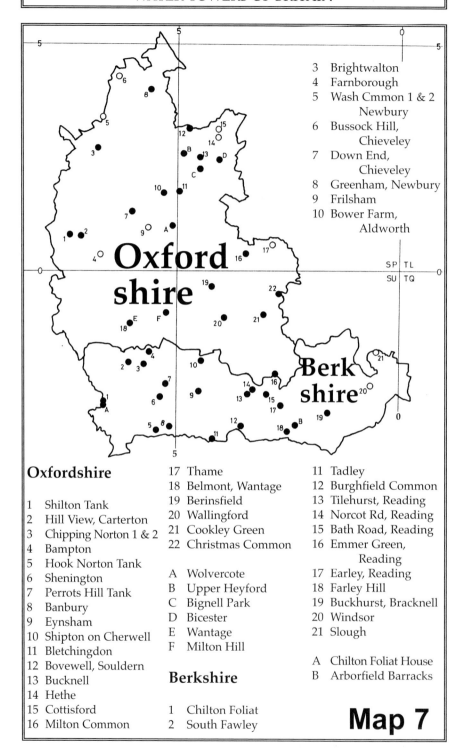

3 Brightwalton
4 Farnborough
5 Wash Cmmon 1 & 2
   Newbury
6 Bussock Hill,
   Chieveley
7 Down End,
   Chieveley
8 Greenham, Newbury
9 Frilsham
10 Bower Farm,
   Aldworth

Oxfordshire

1 Shilton Tank
2 Hill View, Carterton
3 Chipping Norton 1 & 2
4 Bampton
5 Hook Norton Tank
6 Shenington
7 Perrots Hill Tank
8 Banbury
9 Eynsham
10 Shipton on Cherwell
11 Bletchingdon
12 Bovewell, Souldern
13 Bucknell
14 Hethe
15 Cottisford
16 Milton Common

17 Thame
18 Belmont, Wantage
19 Berinsfield
20 Wallingford
21 Cookley Green
22 Christmas Common

A Wolvercote
B Upper Heyford
C Bignell Park
D Bicester
E Wantage
F Milton Hill

Berkshire

1 Chilton Foliat
2 South Fawley

11 Tadley
12 Burghfield Common
13 Tilehurst, Reading
14 Norcot Rd, Reading
15 Bath Road, Reading
16 Emmer Green,
   Reading
17 Earley, Reading
18 Farley Hill
19 Buckhurst, Bracknell
20 Windsor
21 Slough

A Chilton Foliat House
B Arborfield Barracks

Map 7

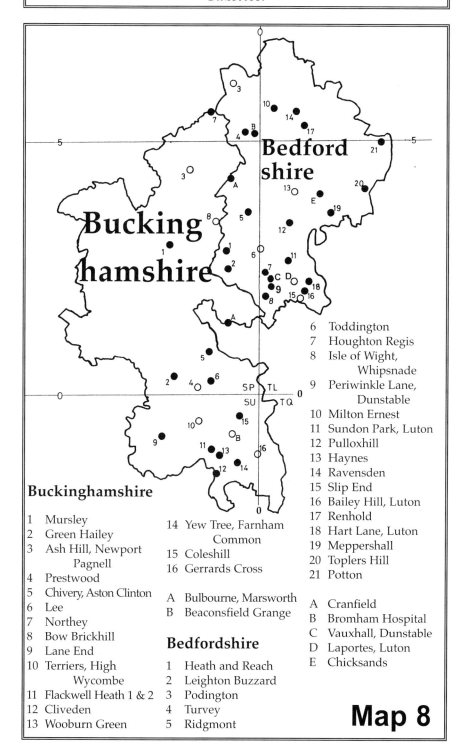

Bedford shire

Bucking hamshire

6 Toddington
7 Houghton Regis
8 Isle of Wight,
    Whipsnade
9 Periwinkle Lane,
    Dunstable
10 Milton Ernest
11 Sundon Park, Luton
12 Pulloxhill
13 Haynes
14 Ravensden
15 Slip End
16 Bailey Hill, Luton
17 Renhold
18 Hart Lane, Luton
19 Meppershall
20 Toplers Hill
21 Potton

Buckinghamshire

1 Mursley
2 Green Hailey
3 Ash Hill, Newport
     Pagnell
4 Prestwood
5 Chivery, Aston Clinton
6 Lee
7 Northey
8 Bow Brickhill
9 Lane End
10 Terriers, High
     Wycombe
11 Flackwell Heath 1 & 2
12 Cliveden
13 Wooburn Green

14 Yew Tree, Farnham
     Common
15 Coleshill
16 Gerrards Cross

A Bulbourne, Marsworth
B Beaconsfield Grange

Bedfordshire

1 Heath and Reach
2 Leighton Buzzard
3 Podington
4 Turvey
5 Ridgmont

A Cranfield
B Bromham Hospital
C Vauxhall, Dunstable
D Laportes, Luton
E Chicksands

Map 8

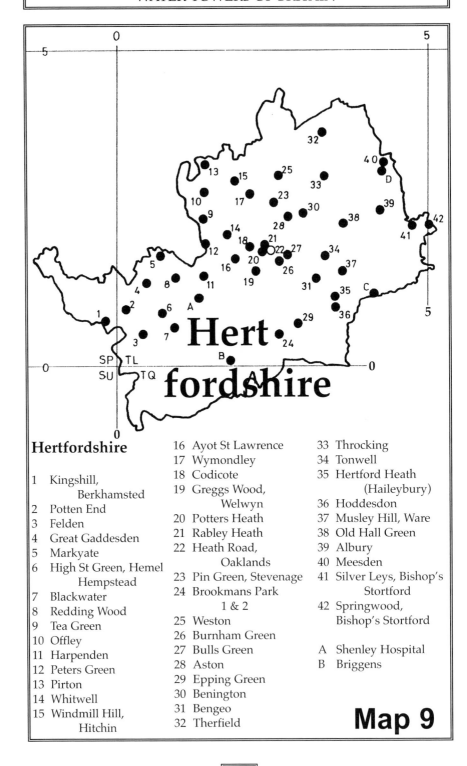

Hertfordshire

1 Kingshill, Berkhamsted
2 Potten End
3 Felden
4 Great Gaddesden
5 Markyate
6 High St Green, Hemel Hempstead
7 Blackwater
8 Redding Wood
9 Tea Green
10 Offley
11 Harpenden
12 Peters Green
13 Pirton
14 Whitwell
15 Windmill Hill, Hitchin

16 Ayot St Lawrence
17 Wymondley
18 Codicote
19 Greggs Wood, Welwyn
20 Potters Heath
21 Rabley Heath
22 Heath Road, Oaklands
23 Pin Green, Stevenage
24 Brookmans Park 1 & 2
25 Weston
26 Burnham Green
27 Bulls Green
28 Aston
29 Epping Green
30 Benington
31 Bengeo
32 Therfield

33 Throcking
34 Tonwell
35 Hertford Heath (Haileybury)
36 Hoddesdon
37 Musley Hill, Ware
38 Old Hall Green
39 Albury
40 Meesden
41 Silver Leys, Bishop's Stortford
42 Springwood, Bishop's Stortford

A Shenley Hospital
B Briggens

Map 9

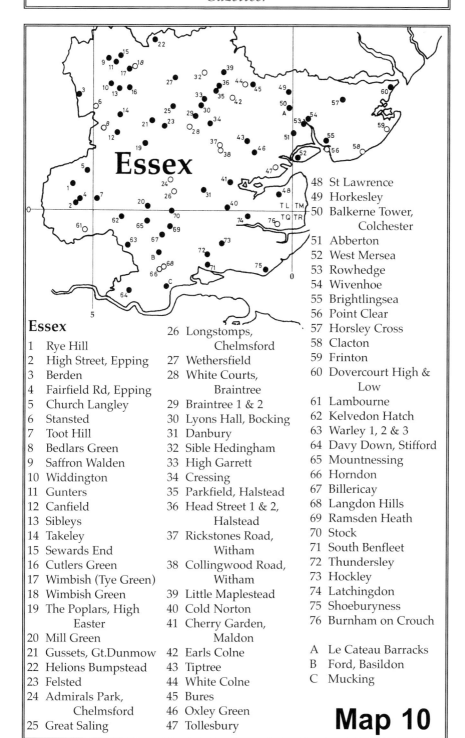

Essex

1 Rye Hill
2 High Street, Epping
3 Berden
4 Fairfield Rd, Epping
5 Church Langley
6 Stansted
7 Toot Hill
8 Bedlars Green
9 Saffron Walden
10 Widdington
11 Gunters
12 Canfield
13 Sibleys
14 Takeley
15 Sewards End
16 Cutlers Green
17 Wimbish (Tye Green)
18 Wimbish Green
19 The Poplars, High
   Easter
20 Mill Green
21 Gussets, Gt.Dunmow
22 Helions Bumpstead
23 Felsted
24 Admirals Park,
   Chelmsford
25 Great Saling

26 Longstomps,
   Chelmsford
27 Wethersfield
28 White Courts,
   Braintree
29 Braintree 1 & 2
30 Lyons Hall, Bocking
31 Danbury
32 Sible Hedingham
33 High Garrett
34 Cressing
35 Parkfield, Halstead
36 Head Street 1 & 2,
   Halstead
37 Rickstones Road,
   Witham
38 Collingwood Road,
   Witham
39 Little Maplestead
40 Cold Norton
41 Cherry Garden,
   Maldon
42 Earls Colne
43 Tiptree
44 White Colne
45 Bures
46 Oxley Green
47 Tollesbury

48 St Lawrence
49 Horkesley
50 Balkerne Tower,
   Colchester
51 Abberton
52 West Mersea
53 Rowhedge
54 Wivenhoe
55 Brightlingsea
56 Point Clear
57 Horsley Cross
58 Clacton
59 Frinton
60 Dovercourt High &
   Low
61 Lambourne
62 Kelvedon Hatch
63 Warley 1, 2 & 3
64 Davy Down, Stifford
65 Mountnessing
66 Horndon
67 Billericay
68 Langdon Hills
69 Ramsden Heath
70 Stock
71 South Benfleet
72 Thundersley
73 Hockley
74 Latchingdon
75 Shoeburyness
76 Burnham on Crouch

A Le Cateau Barracks
B Ford, Basildon
C Mucking

Map 10

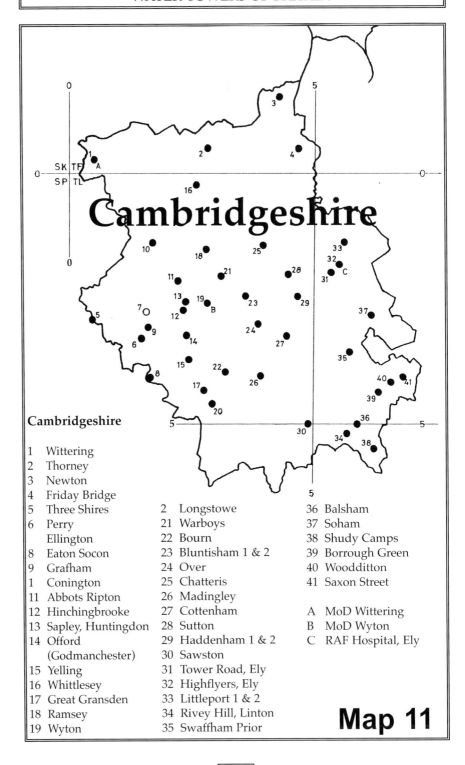

Cambridgeshire

1 Wittering
2 Thorney
3 Newton
4 Friday Bridge
5 Three Shires
6 Perry
  Ellington
8 Eaton Socon
9 Grafham
1 Conington
11 Abbots Ripton
12 Hinchingbrooke
13 Sapley, Huntingdon
14 Offord
   (Godmanchester)
15 Yelling
16 Whittlesey
17 Great Gransden
18 Ramsey
19 Wyton

2 Longstowe
21 Warboys
22 Bourn
23 Bluntisham 1 & 2
24 Over
25 Chatteris
26 Madingley
27 Cottenham
28 Sutton
29 Haddenham 1 & 2
30 Sawston
31 Tower Road, Ely
32 Highflyers, Ely
33 Littleport 1 & 2
34 Rivey Hill, Linton
35 Swaffham Prior

36 Balsham
37 Soham
38 Shudy Camps
39 Borrough Green
40 Woodditton
41 Saxon Street

A MoD Wittering
B MoD Wyton
C RAF Hospital, Ely

Map 11

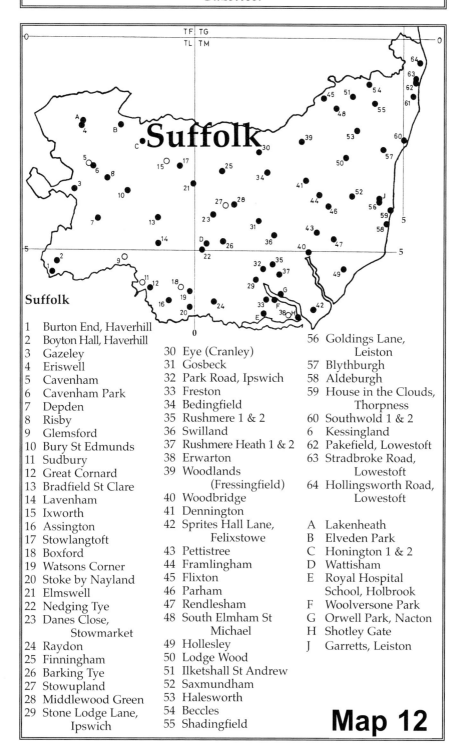

Suffolk

Suffolk

1 Burton End, Haverhill
2 Boyton Hall, Haverhill
3 Gazeley
4 Eriswell
5 Cavenham
6 Cavenham Park
7 Depden
8 Risby
9 Glemsford
10 Bury St Edmunds
11 Sudbury
12 Great Cornard
13 Bradfield St Clare
14 Lavenham
15 Ixworth
16 Assington
17 Stowlangtoft
18 Boxford
19 Watsons Corner
20 Stoke by Nayland
21 Elmswell
22 Nedging Tye
23 Danes Close,
   Stowmarket
24 Raydon
25 Finningham
26 Barking Tye
27 Stowupland
28 Middlewood Green
29 Stone Lodge Lane,
   Ipswich

30 Eye (Cranley)
31 Gosbeck
32 Park Road, Ipswich
33 Freston
34 Bedingfield
35 Rushmere 1 & 2
36 Swilland
37 Rushmere Heath 1 & 2
38 Erwarton
39 Woodlands
   (Fressingfield)
40 Woodbridge
41 Dennington
42 Sprites Hall Lane,
   Felixstowe
43 Pettistree
44 Framlingham
45 Flixton
46 Parham
47 Rendlesham
48 South Elmham St
   Michael
49 Hollesley
50 Lodge Wood
51 Ilketshall St Andrew
52 Saxmundham
53 Halesworth
54 Beccles
55 Shadingfield

56 Goldings Lane,
   Leiston
57 Blythburgh
58 Aldeburgh
59 House in the Clouds,
   Thorpness
60 Southwold 1 & 2
6 Kessingland
62 Pakefield, Lowestoft
63 Stradbroke Road,
   Lowestoft
64 Hollingsworth Road,
   Lowestoft

A Lakenheath
B Elveden Park
C Honington 1 & 2
D Wattisham
E Royal Hospital
   School, Holbrook
F Woolversone Park
G Orwell Park, Nacton
H Shotley Gate
J Garretts, Leiston

Map 12

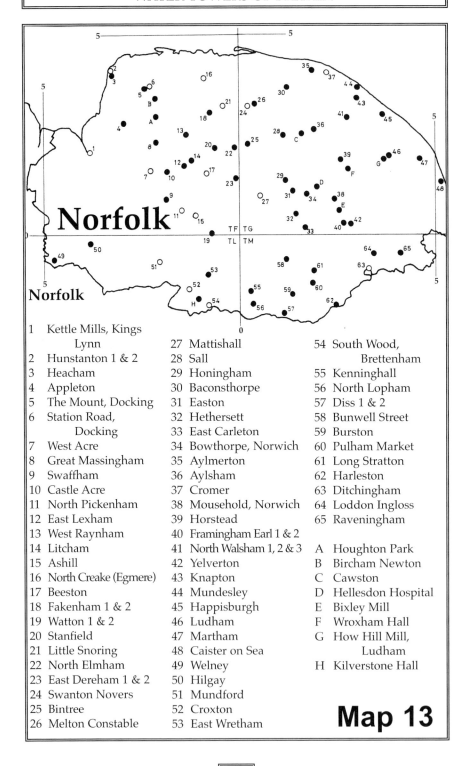

Norfolk

1	Kettle Mills, Kings Lynn	27	Mattishall	54	South Wood, Brettenham
2	Hunstanton 1 & 2	28	Sall	55	Kenninghall
3	Heacham	29	Honingham	56	North Lopham
4	Appleton	30	Baconsthorpe	57	Diss 1 & 2
5	The Mount, Docking	31	Easton	58	Bunwell Street
6	Station Road, Docking	32	Hethersett	59	Burston
7	West Acre	33	East Carleton	60	Pulham Market
8	Great Massingham	34	Bowthorpe, Norwich	61	Long Stratton
9	Swaffham	35	Aylmerton	62	Harleston
10	Castle Acre	36	Aylsham	63	Ditchingham
11	North Pickenham	37	Cromer	64	Loddon Ingloss
12	East Lexham	38	Mousehold, Norwich	65	Raveningham
13	West Raynham	39	Horstead		
14	Litcham	40	Framingham Earl 1 & 2	A	Houghton Park
15	Ashill	41	North Walsham 1, 2 & 3	B	Bircham Newton
16	North Creake (Egmere)	42	Yelverton	C	Cawston
17	Beeston	43	Knapton	D	Hellesdon Hospital
18	Fakenham 1 & 2	44	Mundesley	E	Bixley Mill
19	Watton 1 & 2	45	Happisburgh	F	Wroxham Hall
20	Stanfield	46	Ludham	G	How Hill Mill, Ludham
21	Little Snoring	47	Martham	H	Kilverstone Hall
22	North Elmham	48	Caister on Sea		
23	East Dereham 1 & 2	49	Welney		
24	Swanton Novers	50	Hilgay		
25	Bintree	51	Mundford		
26	Melton Constable	52	Croxton		
		53	East Wretham		

Map 13

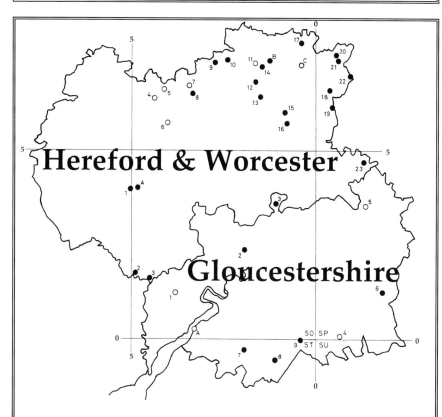

Hereford & Worcester

1 Broomy Hill, Hereford
2 Welsh Newton
3 Doward
4 Leysters
5 Oldwood, Tenbury Wells
6 Bredenbury (Grendon Green)
7 High Wood
8 Broad Heath
9 Rock
10 Long Bank, Bewdley
11 Summerfield, Kidderminster
12 Bishops Wood, Crossway Green
13 Uphampton
14 Hartlebury
15 Yew Tree Hill, Droitwich
16 Crowle
17 Romsley Hill
18 Headless Cross, Redditch 1&2
19 Astwood Bank
20 Weatheroak Hill 2
21 Weatheroak Hill 1
22 Gorcott Hill (Bransons Cross)
23 Pebworth

A County Hospital, Hereford
B Winterfold
C Barnsley Hall, Bromsgrove

Gloucestershire

1 Speech House
2 Maisemore (Woolridge)
3 The Mythe, Tewkesbury
4 Harnhill
5 Springhall Tank
6 Windrush Tank
7 Kingscote
8 Tetbury
9 Tarlton

A Sharpness Docks

Map 14

Warwickshire

1 Lapworth
2 Bearley
3 Lye Green
4 Atherstone on Stour
5 Little Shrewley
6 Hampton on the Hill
7 Budbrooke
8 Wellesbourne
9 Burton Green
10 Tile Hill
11 Market St, Warwick
12 Tainters Hill,
    Kenilworth
13 Arley
14 Corley
15 Tuttle Hill,
    Nuneaton
16 Gaydon
17 Bedworth
18 Offchurch
19 Harbury
20 Bulkington
21 Edge Hill
22 Deppers Bridge
23 Stretton on
    Dunsmore
24 Ashlawn Rd, Rugby

A Hatton Asylum 1 & 2
B Avon Carrow

Northamptonshire

1 Barby
2 Preston Capes
3 Halse
4 Everdon Stubbs
5 West Haddon
6 Flore
7 East Haddon
8 Whittlebury
9 Harpole
10 Paulerspury
11 Brixworth
12 Yardley Gobion
14 Roade (E)
15 Boughton
16 Hardingstone
17 Harrington
18 Stimpson Avenue,
    Northampton
19 Dingley
20 Desborough
21 Brafield on the Green
22 Rothwell
23 Ecton
24 Broughton
25 Mears Ashby
26 Beanfield, Corby 1 & 2
27 Earls Barton

28 Great Doddington
29 Isham
30 Rockingham
31 Willowbrook, Corby
32 Tanfields, Corby
33 Gretton
34 Stannion Lane,
    Corby 1 & 2
35 Wollaston
36 Finedon
37 Irchester
38 Grafton Underwood
39 Manton, Rushden
40 Brigstock
41 Woodford
42 Bedford Rd, Rushden
43 Collyweston
44 Denford Ash
45 Raunds
46 Southwick
47 Hemington
48 Ashton Wold

A Blisworth Rly Stn
B Roade(S)
C Abington Park,
    Northampton
D Castle Ashby
E Corby Steelworks W
F Corby Steelworks E

Map 15

Staffordshire

1   Ashley Heath
2   Hanchurch
3   Swynnerton
4   Meir Heath
5   Longsdon
6   Essington 1 & 2
7   Bednall
8   Morrilow Heath
9   Pye Green,
        Hednesford
10 Hanbury
11 Rolleston on Dove
12 Winshill, Burton on
        Trent

A   Michelin, Stoke on
        Trent
B   St Edward's Hospital,
        Leek
C   Burton Workhouse 1 & 2

Shropshire

1   Wilcott (Nesscliffe)
2   Shelton, Shrewsbury
3   Market Cross 1 to 4 &
        St Mary's, Shrewsbury
4   Market Drayton
5   Cheswardine Hall,
        Chipnal
6   Clee View, Ludlow
7   Netchwood
8   Tasley, Bridgnorth

A   RAF Shawbury
B   Old Woodhouse
C   Lady Forester Hosp-
        ital, Much Wenlock

West Midlands

1   High Acres, Wordsley
2   Goldthorn Hill,
        Wolverhampton
3   Turners Hill, Rowley
        Regis
4   Warley

A   Hollymoor Hospital

Map 16

Nottinghamshire

1 Swingate, Kimberley
2 Hucknall
3 Newstead
4 Nornay, Blyth
5 Stanton on the Wolds
6 Ordsall Rd, Retford
7 Gringley on the Hill
8 Danethorpe

A Nottingham Univers-
    ity Hospital
B Newton on Trent
C Balderton Hospital

Derbyshire

1 Trusley
2 Radbourne Lane,
    Derby
3 Boundary Tower,
    Woodville
4 Allestree (Quarndon)
5 Morley Smithy
6 Hady, Chesterfield
7 Tagg Hill, Heanor
8 Mapperley

9 Newton
10 Ilkeston
11 Hillstown, Bolsover

A Bradley Hall
B Staveley

Leicestershire

1 Ashby de la Zouch
2 Ellistown
3 Bagworth
4 Hoton
5 Wymeswold
    Aerodrome
6 Melton Mowbray
7 Somerby
8 Waltham on the Wolds
9 Wymondham
10 Buckminster

11 Sewstern
12 Buckminster Ashes
13 Burley on the Hill
14 Pilton
15 Hinckley
16 Barwell
17 Ullesthorpe
18 Bitteswell
    Aerodrome
19 Enderby
20 Lutterworth
21 Husbands Bosworth

A Gopsall Park
B Central Fire Station,
    Leicester
C Leicester University
    Engineering Building
D Thorpe Satchville
E Cottesmore

Map 17

Lincolnshire

1 Ash Grove, Gainsborough
2 Coxs Hill, Gainsborough
3 Gorse Lane, Grantham
4 Blyborough
5 Woodnook
6 Lobthorpe
7 Barkston Heath
8 Fillingham
9 Hareswood
10 Westgate, Lincoln
11 Bracebridge Heath
12 Nettleham Fields
13 Brocklesby
14 Swinstead
15 Toft Newton
16 Newton Bar
17 Ashby de la Launde
18 Clay Hill, Sleaford
19 Potterhanworth
20 Lenton
21 Dorrington
22 Folkingham 1 & 2
23 Scopwick
24 Ruskington
25 Evedon
26 Martin
27 Anwick
28 Billingborough
29 Bardney
30 Burton Pedwardine
31 Heckington
32 Great Hale
33 Billinghay
34 Ludford
35 Baumber
36 Quadring
37 Crowland
38 Holland Fen (Brothertoft)
39 Pinchbeck
40 Chatterton Tower, Spalding
41 Pinchbeck Road, Spalding
42 Kelstern
43 Stenigot 1 & 2

44 Weston
45 Sutterton
46 Canister Bridge
47 Fulletby
48 Whaplode Drove 1
49 Garfits Lane, Boston
50 Whaplode Drove 2
51 Revesby
52 Horncastle Road, Boston
53 Grain Silo, Boston
54 Fishtoft
55 Grimoldby
56 Old Leake
57 Gedney 1 & 2
58 Little Sutton
59 Wingland
60 Mablethorpe

61 Mumby
62 Skegness 1 & 2

A Hemswell
B Le Talls Mill, Lincoln
C St Johns, Bracebridge Heath
D Waddington 1&2
E Cranwell
F Stamford Railway Station
G Rauceby Hospital
H Digby 1&2
J Bass Maltings, Sleaford
K Binbrook
L Manby

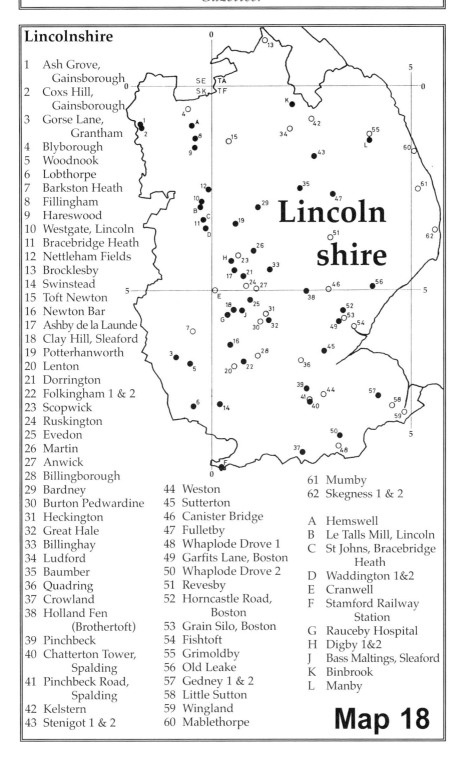

Lincoln shire

Map 18

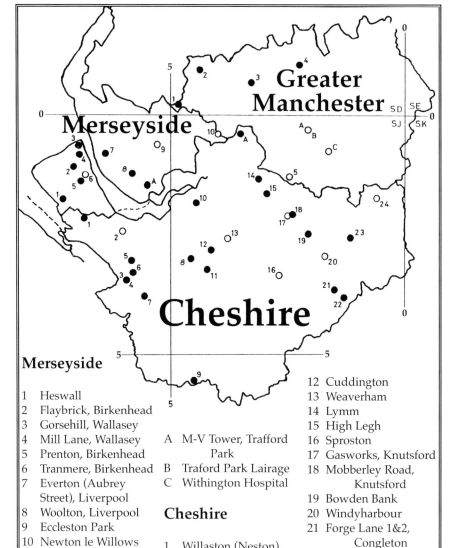

Merseyside

1 Heswall
2 Flaybrick, Birkenhead
3 Gorsehill, Wallasey
4 Mill Lane, Wallasey
5 Prenton, Birkenhead
6 Tranmere, Birkenhead
7 Everton (Aubrey Street), Liverpool
8 Woolton, Liverpool
9 Eccleston Park
10 Newton le Willows

A Ford, Halewood

Greater Manchester

1 Billinge
2 Standish
3 Syndale, Bolton
4 Ainsworth (Starling Redcliffe)
5 Bowdon

A M-V Tower, Trafford Park
B Traford Park Lairage
C Withington Hospital

Cheshire

1 Willaston (Neston)
2 Whitby, Ellesmere Port
3 Overleigh, Chester
4 Bridgegate, Chester
5 Upton, Chester
6 Boughton, Chester
7 Saighton
8 Eddisbury Hill
9 Wirswall
10 Norton, Runcorn
11 Oak Mere

12 Cuddington
13 Weaverham
14 Lymm
15 High Legh
16 Sproston
17 Gasworks, Knutsford
18 Mobberley Road, Knutsford
19 Bowden Bank
20 Windyharbour
21 Forge Lane 1&2, Congleton
22 Moss, Congleton
23 Whirley Barn, Macclesfield
24 Hilltop, Higher Poynton

A Newchurch Hospital, Culcheth

Map 19

South Yorkshire

1 Hoyland
2 Upper Cudworth
3 Darfield
4 Goldthorpe 1&2
5 High Woods,
       Mexborough
6 Hooton Pagnell
7 Hickleton
8 Skellow
9 Adwick Ridge
10 Scawthrope
11 Askern
12 Armthorpe,
       Doncaster

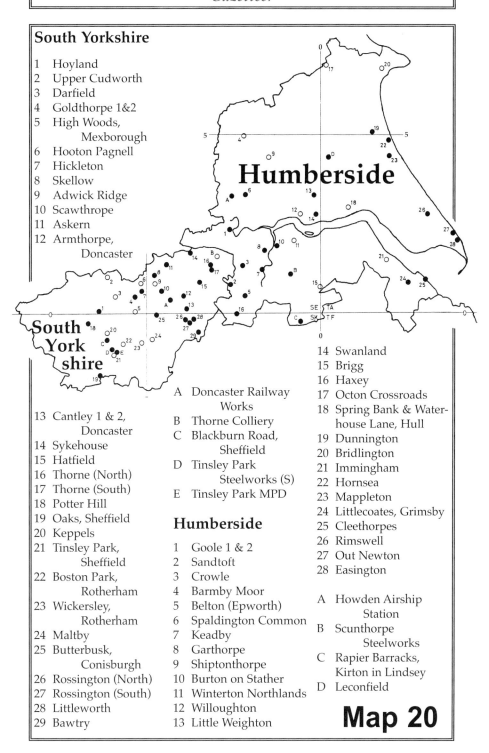

Humberside

South York shire

13 Cantley 1 & 2,
       Doncaster
14 Sykehouse
15 Hatfield
16 Thorne (North)
17 Thorne (South)
18 Potter Hill
19 Oaks, Sheffield
20 Keppels
21 Tinsley Park,
       Sheffield
22 Boston Park,
       Rotherham
23 Wickersley,
       Rotherham
24 Maltby
25 Butterbusk,
       Conisburgh
26 Rossington (North)
27 Rossington (South)
28 Littleworth
29 Bawtry

A Doncaster Railway
       Works
B Thorne Colliery
C Blackburn Road,
       Sheffield
D Tinsley Park
       Steelworks (S)
E Tinsley Park MPD

Humberside

1 Goole 1 & 2
2 Sandtoft
3 Crowle
4 Barmby Moor
5 Belton (Epworth)
6 Spaldington Common
7 Keadby
8 Garthorpe
9 Shiptonthorpe
10 Burton on Stather
11 Winterton Northlands
12 Willoughton
13 Little Weighton

14 Swanland
15 Brigg
16 Haxey
17 Octon Crossroads
18 Spring Bank & Water-
       house Lane, Hull
19 Dunnington
20 Bridlington
21 Immingham
22 Hornsea
23 Mappleton
24 Littlecoates, Grimsby
25 Cleethorpes
26 Rimswell
27 Out Newton
28 Easington

A Howden Airship
       Station
B Scunthorpe
       Steelworks
C Rapier Barracks,
       Kirton in Lindsey
D Leconfield

Map 20

North Yorkshire

West Yorkshire

West Yorkshire

H N Eastern Railway
   Works, York (2no)
J Queen Street
   Railway Works, York
K York University
L Drax Grammar
   School

West Yorkshire

1   Roils Head
2   Tinshill, Leeds
3   Broad Oak
4   Gawthorpe
5   West Bretton 1 & 2
6   Middleton, Leeds
7   Kirkhamgate
8   Moortown, Leeds 1 & 2
9   Wooley Edge
10 Blackmoor
11 Nostell
12 Garforth
13 Featherstone
14 Park Hill, Pontefract
15 Airedale (Redhill),
        Castleford
16 Ackworth (Castle
        Syke)
17 Upton Beacon
A   Keighley Rly Stn
B   Leeds University
C   Heath Common
D   Headley Hall
E   Knottingley

North Yorkshire

1   Gallowgate, Richmond
2   Ingleby Arncliffe
3   Hutton Rudby
4   Botton Hall
5   Sandsend
6   Greenhow Hill
7   Thruscross
8   Birstwith
9   Harlow Hill, Harrogate
10 Walton Head, Pannal
11 Lovesome Hill
12 Skelton on Ure
13 Marton cum Grafton
14 Bilbrough
15 Askham Richard
16 Askham Bryan
17 Severus Hill, York
18 Rievaulx
19 Sutton on the Forest
20 Lendal Tower, York

21 Selby
22 Riccall
23 Siwards How, York
24 Dunnington
25 Terrington
26 Hemingbrough
27 Flaxton
28 Wheldrake
29 Harton
30 Settrington Beacon
31 Ling Hall
32 Silpho 1 & 2
33 Ganton Wold
34 Mill Hill, Filey

A   Aske Park
B   Newby Hall, Ripon
C   Myton on Swale
D   Grimston Park
E   Milford Junction
F   Gascoigne Wood
G   Clifton Hospital, York

Map 21

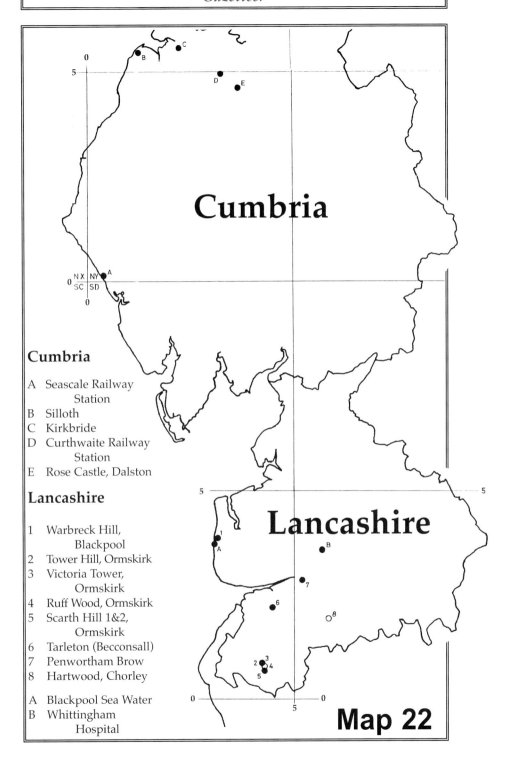

Cumbria

A   Seascale Railway
        Station
B   Silloth
C   Kirkbride
D   Curthwaite Railway
        Station
E   Rose Castle, Dalston

Lancashire

1   Warbreck Hill,
        Blackpool
2   Tower Hill, Ormskirk
3   Victoria Tower,
        Ormskirk
4   Ruff Wood, Ormskirk
5   Scarth Hill 1&2,
        Ormskirk
6   Tarleton (Becconsall)
7   Penwortham Brow
8   Hartwood, Chorley

A   Blackpool Sea Water
B   Whittingham
        Hospital

Map 22

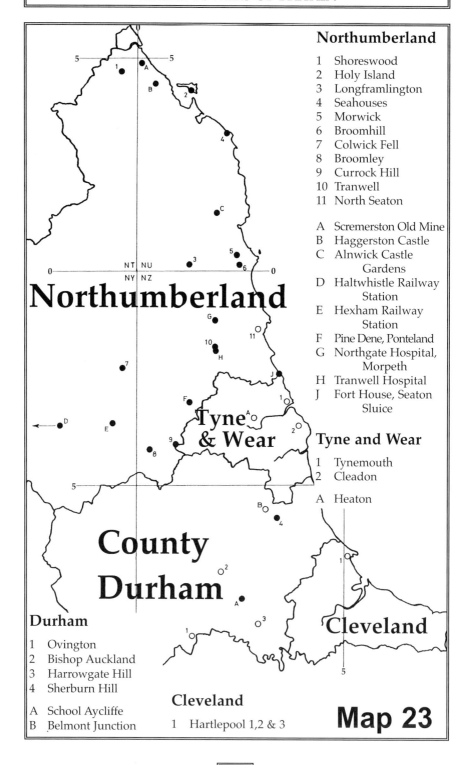

Northumberland

1 Shoreswood
2 Holy Island
3 Longframlington
4 Seahouses
5 Morwick
6 Broomhill
7 Colwick Fell
8 Broomley
9 Currock Hill
10 Tranwell
11 North Seaton

A Scremerston Old Mine
B Haggerston Castle
C Alnwick Castle Gardens
D Haltwhistle Railway Station
E Hexham Railway Station
F Pine Dene, Ponteland
G Northgate Hospital, Morpeth
H Tranwell Hospital
J Fort House, Seaton Sluice

Northumberland

Tyne & Wear

County Durham

Cleveland

Tyne and Wear

1 Tynemouth
2 Cleadon

A Heaton

Durham

1 Ovington
2 Bishop Auckland
3 Harrowgate Hill
4 Sherburn Hill

A School Aycliffe
B Belmont Junction

Cleveland

1 Hartlepool 1,2 & 3

Map 23

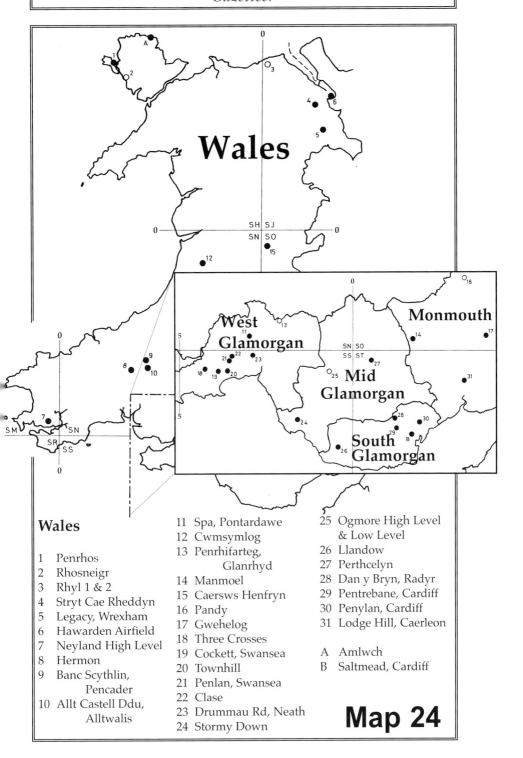

Wales

1 Penrhos
2 Rhosneigr
3 Rhyl 1 & 2
4 Stryt Cae Rheddyn
5 Legacy, Wrexham
6 Hawarden Airfield
7 Neyland High Level
8 Hermon
9 Banc Scythlin,
     Pencader
10 Allt Castell Ddu,
     Alltwalis

11 Spa, Pontardawe
12 Cwmsymlog
13 Penrhifarteg,
     Glanrhyd
14 Manmoel
15 Caersws Henfryn
16 Pandy
17 Gwehelog
18 Three Crosses
19 Cockett, Swansea
20 Townhill
21 Penlan, Swansea
22 Clase
23 Drummau Rd, Neath
24 Stormy Down

25 Ogmore High Level
     & Low Level
26 Llandow
27 Perthcelyn
28 Dan y Bryn, Radyr
29 Pentrebane, Cardiff
30 Penylan, Cardiff
31 Lodge Hill, Caerleon

A Amlwch
B Saltmead, Cardiff

Map 24

Scotland

43 Carrickstone, Cumbernauld
44 Muirhouse, Motherwell
45 Smyllum, Lanark
46 Forth
47 Easter Dalmeny
48 Spion Kop, Lochgelly

Scotland

1 Graven, Zetland
2 Orams Fancy, Stronsay
3 Crossbost, Leurbost
4 Grimshader, Leurbost
5 Ranish, Leurbost
6 Tong, Tolsta
7 Swainbost, Ness
8 Adabrock, Ness
9 Knockaird, Ness
10 Nybster
11 Fairburn
12 Raitloan, Nairn
13 Schoolbrae, Garmouth
14 Clerkhill, Peterhead
15 Round House, Perth
16 Ladybank
17 Leslie
18 Gallowshill, Dundee
19 Menzieshill, Dundee
20 Law Road, Dundee
21 Keptie Hill, Arbroath
22 Lochside Cistern, (North
   Esk Road), Montrose
23 Auchendores
24 Drumchapel, Glasgow
25 Pollock C, Glasgow
26 Priesthill, Glasgow
27 Pollock D, Glasgow
28 Patterton

29 Barloch, Milngavie
30 Ruchill, Glasgow
31 Bearyards, Bishopbriggs
32 West Netherton,
   East Kilbride
33 Woodhill, Auchinairn
34 South Cathkin,
   Carmunnock
35 Whitecross, East Kilbride
36 Ruchazie 1&2, Glasgow
37 Cranhill, Glasgow
38 Craigend, Glasgow
39 Garthamlock, Glasgow
40 Queenslee, Glasgow
41 Fauldhead, Kirkintilloch
42 Tannochside, Uddingst'n

49 Carberry, Kirkcaldy
50 Eskbank Road, Dalkeith
51 Greencroft, Whithorn
52 Annan

A Benbecula
B Leverburgh
C Invergordon
D Caterpillar, Tannochside
E Larkhall
F Ravenscraig Steelworks
G Muirhall, Addiewell
H Broxburn
J Portobello Baths,
   Edinburgh
K St Boswells Station

Map 25

Bibliography

INTRODUCTION

Becher, B & Becher, H, *Wasserturme,* Schirmer/Mosel, Munich, 1988, also as *Water Towers,* MIT Press, Cambridge, Mass, USA, 1988.

Cox, R C, & Gould, M H, 'The Water Tower in Ireland,' *Journ Inst Engrs Ireland,* Vol 122, pp 19-36, 1998/9

Cross-Rudkin, P S M, *et al,* 'The Assessment of Civil Engineering Heritage,' *Proc Inst Civ Engrs (Mun Engr),* pp 211-216, Vol 139, Dec 2000.

Griffiths, A, 'Towers of Water,' *Water* magazine, pp 21-24, January 1981.

Headley, G & Meulenkamp, W, *Follies, Grottos and Garden Buildings,* Aurum Press, London, 1999.

Merkl, G, *et al, Historische Wasserturme,* R Oldenbourg Verlag, Munich, 1985.

Van Craenenbroeck, W (Ed), *Unité dans la Diversité, La Belgique des Chateau d'Eau,* Anseau, Brussels Symposium, May 1991.

Van der Veen, H, *Watertorens in Nederland,* Uitgeverij 010, Rotterdam, 1989

CHAPTER ONE
The Function of the Water Tower

Adams, H C, *Waterworks for Urban and Rural Districts,* Sir Isaac Pitman, London, 1938.

Bjorklund, H, 'Design and Construction of Service Reservoirs and Water Towers,' *Proc Int Water Supply Congress* (Subject No 3), London, 1955.

Burton, W K, *The Water Supply of Towns and the Construction of Waterworks,* Crosby, Lockwood & Son, London, 1894.

Burton, W K, & Dumbleton, J, *The Water Supply of Towns and the Construction of Waterworks,* (2 vols), Crosby,

Lockwood & Son, London, 4th Edn, 1928.

Garnett, W, *A Little Book on Water Supply,* Cambridge University Press, 1922.

Hughes, S, *A Treatise on Waterworks for the Supply of Cities and Towns,* J Weale, London (3rd edn, 1875), 1856.

Humber, W, *A Comprehensive Treatise on the Water Supplies of Cities and Towns,* Crosby, Lockwood, London, 1876.

Johnstone-Taylor, F, *Modern Waterworks Practice,* Ernest Benn, London, 1927.

Maxwell, W H, *Current Waterworks Practice,* Batsford, London, 1946.

McConnel, S, *Small Water Supplies,* Constable & Co, London, 1964.

McPherson, J A, *Waterworks Distribution — a Practical Guide,* Batsford, London, 1900.

Thresh, J C, *Water and Water Supplies,* Redman Pub Co, London, 1896.

Tudsberry-Turner, J H & Brightmore, A W, *The Principles of Waterworks Engineering,* Spon, London, 1893.

Twort, A C, *A Textbook of Water Supply,* Edward Arnold, London, 1963.

Uren, F C, *Waterworks Engineering,* Castle Litho, Bristol, 1914.

Veal, T H P, *The Supply of Water,* Chapman & Hall, London, 2nd edn, 1950.

Walters, R C S, *The Nation's Water Supply,* Ivor Nicholson & Watson, London, 1936.

CHAPTER TWO
The Origins of the Water Tower

Anon, *An Inventory of the Historic Monuments in the City of York* (Vol 2, The Defences), R C H M E, London, 1972.

Anon, *The Story of the Water Supply to Kingston upon Hull, 1292 to 1983,* Yorkshire Water Authority, Leeds, 1983.

Barty-King, H, *Water. The Book,* Quiller Press, London, 1992.

Brace, J, *The Warwick Waterhouses,* Warks Ind Arch Soc, Warwick, Aug 1996.

Hayes, J, 'Prior Wilbert's Waterworks,' *Canterbury Cathedral Chronicle,* Vol 71 pp 17-26, 1977.

Isaac, P, 'Roman Public Health Engineering' (and discussion), *Proc ICE (Design & Construction),* Vol 70, May 1981

Lewis, M J T, 'Our Debt to Roman Engineering — The Water Supply of Lincoln to the Present Day,' Rolt Memorial Lecture, *AIA Conference,* Lincoln, 1983.

Otter, R A (Ed), *Civil Engineering Heritage — Southern England,* Thomas Telford, London, 1994.

Radley, J, 'York Waterworks and Other Waterworks in the North before 1800,' *Trans Newcomen Soc,* Vol 39, pp143-156, 1967.

Robins, F W, *The Story of Water Supply,* Oxford University Press, 1946.

Skeat, W O (Ed), *Manual of Water Engineering Practice* (Ch1, Historical Development), Institution of Water Engineers, London (4th edn), 1969.

Stark, A, *History of Gainsborough,* (second edn), Gainsborough, 1843.

Switzer, S, *An Introduction to a General System of Hydrostaticks and Hydraulicks,* (2 Vols), T Astley *et al,* London, 1729.

White, A, *Grantham Conduit* (Lincolnshire Museums Archaeology Series No 9), Lincolnshire C C, Lincoln, 1979.

White, A, *St Mary's Conduit, Lincoln* (Lincolnshire Museums Archaeology Series No19), Lincolnshire C C, Lincoln, 1980.

Williamson, F, 'George Sorocold of Derby — a Pioneer of Water Supply,' *Journal of the Derbyshire Archaeological Society,* Vol 57, pp 43-96, 1936.

Williamson, F, & Crump, W B, 'Sorocold's Waterworks at Leeds, 1694,' *Thoresby Society Miscellanea* (Vol 37, pt 2) pp 166-182, 1941.

Wood, R, *The Remarkable Cistern at Rye,* Sussex Industrial History,Vol 7 pp 24-28, 1976.

CHAPTER THREE

The Victorian Municipal Water Tower

Anon, 'Croydon Water Tower,' *Engineering,* pp 543-5, 5 June, 1868.

Anon, *Leeds Corporation Water Undertaking Centenary, 1852 to 1952,* Leeds Corporation Waterworks Department, 1952.

Binnie, G M, *Early Victorian Water Engineers,* Thomas Telford, London, 1981.

Briggs, A, *Victorian Cities,* Penguin Books, 1968.

Cameron, K J, *The Schoolmaster Engineer, Adam Anderson of Perth and St Andrews, c1780 - 1846,* Abertay Historical Society, Dundee,1988.

Cormie, J E D, *The Round House, Marshall Place, Perth, A Brief History of Perth's First Waterworks,* Perth Tourist Association, Perth, 1975.

Crosby, A, *The Public Water Supply Industry in Essex, 1850 - 1939; a Study of its History, Technology and Architecture,* (Comparative Surveys of Modern Archaeological/ Architectural Remains in Essex, No 12), Essex C C, Chelmsford, 1999.

Deacon, G, 'The Vyrnwy Works for the Water Supply of Liverpool,' *Min Proc Inst Civil Engineers,* Vol 126, pp 24-67, 1895/6.

Hall, H, *The History of Montrose Water Supply, 1720 to 1914,* Montrose Town Council, 1914.

Hassan, J, 'The Water Industry in the Nineteenth Century' (Three parts) *Water Services,* 14 Jan (pp 12-13), 21 Jan (pp 6-7) and 28 Jan (pp 14-15), 1983.

Hillen, J, *History of the Borough of Kings Lynn,* Kings Lynn (Reprinted by E P Publishing, 1978) 1907.

Humphreys, W H, *York Water Works,*

1677 to 1903; a Short Historical and Descriptive Account, York, 1903.

Orbach, J, *Victorian Architecture in Britain,* Blue Guide Series, A&C Black, London, 1987

Rennison ,R W, *Water to Tyneside; a History of the Newcastle & Gateshead Water Company,* Newcastle & Gateshead Water Co, Newcastle, 1979.

Walmesley, C A, 'History of Perth's Water Supply, 1751 to 1870,' Presidential Address, *Perthshire Soc of Natural Sciences,* 27 March, 1953.

CHAPTER FOUR
Early Rural
Water Towers

Anon, 'Huntingdon Rural Water Supply,' *Civil Engineering,* pp 174-6, May 1937.

Hainsworth, I H, *County of the West Riding of Yorkshire, Water Survey — Summary of report by I H Hainsworth,* Ministry of Health, London, 1949.

Harland, R S, *A short history of rural water supplies in Craven,* Pub No 27 (Journal No 8), North Yorkshire County Record Office, Northallerton, 1981.

Lennox Boyd, C, *Appleton Water Tower — Notes on its History and Architecture,* The Landmark Trust, Maidenhead (draft edn) 1998.

Peacock, O, *Cottenham's Troubled Waters,* Cottenham Village Soc (Info & Edn Gp), 1978.

Warren, D, *Rural Water Supply in Somerset,* SIAS Survey No10, Somerset Industrial Archaeology Society, Taunton, 1998.

CHAPTER FIVE
Early Concrete
Water Towers

Anon, 'Characteristics of the Chief Systems of Reinforced Concrete Applied to Buildings in Great Britain,' *Concrete & Const Eng,* Vol 2, pp 427-444, 1907.

Anon, 'Recent British Examples of Reinforced Concrete: The Cleethorpes Reinforced Concrete Water Tower, Lincolnshire,' *Concrete & Const Eng,* Vol 3, pp 77-81, 1908.

Anon, 'New Uses for Concrete: Water Tower at Great Marlow,' *Concrete & Const Eng,* Vol 5, pp 295-7, 1910.

Anon, 'Ferro-Concrete Water Towers and Elevated Reservoirs,' *Ferro-Concrete,* Vol 9, pp 159-171, 1917.

Anon, 'Reinforced Concrete Water Tower at Topsham, Devon,' *Concrete & Const Eng,* Vol 12, pp 43-6, 1917.

Anon, 'Water Tower at Aylesford,' *Concrete & Const Eng,* Vol 18, pp 84-7, 1923.

Anon, 'Progress During a Quarter of a Century,' *Concrete & Const Eng,* Vol 21, pp 111-149, 1926

Anon, 'Designs for Water Towers,' *Concrete & Const Eng,* Vol 22, pp 561-3,1927.

Adams, H, & Matthews, E R, *Reinforced Concrete Construction in Theory and Practice,* Longmans, Green & Co, London, 1920.

Andrews, E J, *The Reinforced Concrete Regulations of the London County Council,* Batsford, London, 1916.

Castle, J H, 'Municipal Works at Goole,' *Proc Inst Mun & Cty Engrs,* Vol 55, pp 605-6, 1928.

Chrimes, M M *et al,* 'Historic Concrete,' *Proc I C E (Structures & Buildings),* Vol 116, Nos 3&4, Special Issue (a collection of 14 papers) Nov 1996.

Gould, M H, & Barton, B M J, 'Early Reinforced Concrete Water Towers, 1900 to 1930,' *Trans Newcomen Soc,* Vol 71, No 2, pp 269-281, 2000.

Haegerman, G, Huberti, G & Moll, H, *Vom Caementum zum Spannbeton - Band 1,* Bauverlag, Wiesbaden & Berlin, 1964.

Heaven, F H, 'Design for a Water Tower, *Concrete & Const Eng,* Vol 15, pp 182-6, 1920.

Jones, B E (Ed), *Cassell's Reinforced*

Concrete, Waverley Book Co, (2nd edn), 1920.

Marsh, C F, *Reinforced Concrete*, Constable, London, 1904, (3rd edition 1906 with W Dunn).

Marsh, C F, & Dunn, W, *Manual of Reinforced Concrete and Concrete Block Construction*, Constable, London, 1908.

Reynolds, C E, *Reinforced Concrete Designers Handbook*, Concrete Publications, London, 1932.

Ritchie, H C, 'Reinforced Concrete for Water Retaining Structures' *Trans Inst Water Engrs*, Vol 27, p 86, 1922.

Scott, W L, & Glanville, W H, *Explanatory Handbook on the Code of Practice for Reinforced Concrete*, Concrete Publications, London (later editions to 1965), 1934.

Senior, S M, 'New Water Tower at Hertford,' *Water & Water Eng*, Vol 32, pp 317-9, 1930.

Silcock, E J, 'Goole Water Tower,' *Proc Inst Mun & Cty Engrs*, Vol 63, pp 1712-6, 1937.

Stanley, C C, *Highlights in the History of Concrete*, Cement & Concrete Assn, Slough, 1979.

Twelvetrees, W N, *Concrete — Steel*, Whittaker & Co, London, 1906.

Twelvetrees, W N, *Concrete — Steel Buildings*, Whittaker & Co, London, 1907.

CHAPTER SIX

Modern Concrete
Water Towers

Anon, 'Harpenden Water Tower - an Improved Method of Construction,' *Water & Water Engineering*, Vol 32, pp 419-21, 1930.

Anon, 'Water Tower and Reservoir, Southall,' *Water & Water Engineering*, Vol 33, pp 160-4, 1931.

Anon, 'Water Tower at Norwich,' *Concrete & Constructional Engineering*, Vol 29, pp 55-8, 1934.

Anon, 'National Water Supplies,' *Water & Water Engineering*, Vol 37, pp 484-5, 1935.

Anon, *Code of Practice for Reinforced Concrete Structures,*' Institution of Civil Engineers, London, 1938.

Anon, 'Structural and General Notes on a Two Million Gallon Reinforced Concrete Reservoir and Water Tower; The Ruchazie Reservoir of Glasgow Corporation Water Department,' *Water & Water Eng*, Vol 50, pp 306-9, 1947.

Anon, *Concrete in Water Supply,* Cement & Concrete Assn, London, 1948.

Anon, 'A Village Water Tower of Unusual Construction,' *Concrete Quarterly*, Vol 21, pp 32-3, 1954.

Anon, 'The Chatterton Water Tower of the Spalding UDC,' *Water & Water Engineering*, Vol 58, pp 235-241, 1955.

Anon, 'The Siwards How Water Tower of the York Waterworks Company,' *Water & Water Engineering*, Vol 60 pp 377-382, 1957.

Anon, 'Novel Water Tower Construction in Sweden,' *Water & Water Engineering*, Vol 60, pp 263, 1957.

Anon, *Tower Power*, Water Services, No1230, Vol 102, July 1998.

Aylwin, E, & Ward, R C, 'Development and Utilisation of Water Supplies in the East Riding of Yorkshire,' *Occasional Papers in Geography* No 10, University of Hull, 1969.

Batty, I, & Westbrook, R, *The Design of Water Retaining Structures*, Longman Scientific & Technical, 1991.

Bray, T J, *A Course in Reinforced Concrete Design*, Chapman & Hall, London, 1946.

BS CP2007, *Design and Construction of Reinforced and Prestressed Concrete Structures for the Storage of Water and other Aqueous Liquids*, British Standards Institution, 1960.

BS 5337, *Code of Practice for the Structural use of Concrete for Retaining Aqueous Liquids* (now withdrawn), British Standards Institution, 1976.

BS 8007, *Code of Practice for the Design of Concrete Structures for Retaining*

Aqueous Liquids, British Standards Institution, 1987.

Carpenter, H, 'The Calculation of Cylindrical Tanks with Rectangular, Triangular or Trapezoidal Wall Section,' *Concrete & Const Eng*, Vol 37, pp 345-53, 1942.

Creasy, L R, *Prestressed Concrete Cylindrical Tanks*, Contractors Record Ltd, (J Wiley & Sons), London, 1961.

Faber, J, & Mead, F, *Oscar Faber's Reinforced Concrete*, Spon, London, (New Edn), 1961.

Gamblin, G, & Waters, W D A, 'Modern Waterworks Construction — with Special Reference to Service Reservoirs, Tanks and Large Diameter Mains,' *Journ Inst Mun Engrs*, Vol 92, pp 335-9, Sept 1965.

Gould, M H, & Cleland, D J, 'Development and Design Form of Reinforced Concrete Water Towers, *Proc I C E (Structures & Buildings)* Vol 146, Issue 1, pp 3-16, 2001

Gray, W S, & Manning, G P, *Concrete Water Towers, Bunkers, Silos and other Elevated Structures*, Cement & Concrete Assn, London, (5th edn, 1st edn by W S Gray, 1933), 1973.

Hall, C, *Running Water*, Robertson McCarta, London, 1989.

Haughton, H, 'Great Yarmouth Water Supply — a new 750,000 Gallon Water Tower,' *Water & Water Engineering*, Vol 35, pp 12-16, 1933.

Hawes, F, 'Lee Valley Revisit,' *Concrete Quarterly*, pp 20-23, Winter 1991.

Hibbert, F, 'Steel and Concrete Water Tower,' *Civil Engineering*, pp 47-9, May 1932.

Howard-Humphreys, G, 'Reinforced Concrete Water Towers,' *Concrete & Constructional Engineering*, Vol 38, March 1943.

Hurd, M K, 'Formwork for Cone, Funnel and Cylindrical Structures,' *Concrete Construction*, pp 369-372, April 1989.

Intze, O, 'Theoretical Investigation of the Principle of Construction of Tanks,' *Zeitschrift des Vereines Deutscher Ingenieure*, Vol 30, p 25, 1886.

Manning, G P, *Reinforced Concrete Reservoirs and Tanks*,' Cement & Concrete Assn, London, (reprinted 1972), 1967.

Percey, E C, 'The Emancipated Water Tower,' *Concrete*, pp 22-27, Sept 1975.

Rowe, K, 'Water Towers are Works of Art,' *Surveyor*, pp 8-11, 10 Jan 1980.

Rowe ,K, 'Recent Water Towers in Norfolk,' *Water Services*, pp 236-242, May 1981.

Waters, A H S, *Shropshire County — Report on Water Supply*, A H S Waters, Consulting Civil Engineer, Birmingham, Jan 1946.

Williams, G M J, Houghton, D S, & Moss, G M, 'Design of Two Unusual Structures at York University,' *Structural Engineer*, Vol 45, No 5, pp 175-185, 1967.

CHAPTER SEVEN
All-metal Water Towers

Anon, 'Engineering Details at the Crystal Palace, No1,' *The Engineer*, pp 108-9, 1 Feb 1901.

Anon, 'Steel Water Tower at East Providence, *Water*, Vol 7, No 81, pp 335-6, 1905.

Anon, 'Water Tower; Westinghouse Works, Manchester,' *The Engineer*, pp 363-5, 10 April 1913.

Anon, 'A Welded Water Tower,' *Civ Eng and Public Works Review*, p 463, Sept 1948.

Anon, 'The Plan Takes Shape,' *Bedford Transport Magazine*, Vol 20 No 4, pp 122-6, 1955.

Anon, 'Motherwell Company's Horton Ellipsoidal Water Tower' (Vauxhall WT, Dunstable), *Water & Water Engineering*, Vol 59, pp 362, 1956.

Anon, 'New Elevated Water Tank at the Caterpillar Tractor Company's Tannochside Plant, Glasgow,' *Water & Water Engineering*, Vol 61 p 499, 1958.

BS 1563, *Specification for Cast Iron*

Sectional Tanks (Rectangular), British Standards Institution, London, 1949.

BS 1564, *Specification for Pressed Steel Sectional Rectangular Tanks*, British Standards Institution, London (rev 1975 & 1983), 1949.

BS 7491, *Glass Fibre Reinforced Plastic Cisterns for Cold Water Storage, Part 3 - Specification for Sectional Tanks*, British Standards Institution, London, 1994.

Bestow R C, 'The Design of a Small Water Tower as a Steel Frame Building,' *Proc Inst Mun & Cty Engrs*, Vol 63, pp 1001-16, 1937.

Buchanan, A, Jones, S K & Kiss, K, 'Brunel and the Crystal Palace,' *Ind Archaeol Review*, Vol 17 No 1, pp 7-21, 1994.

Gould, M H, 'The Development of the All-Metal Water Tower,' *Ind Archaeol Review*, Vol 23 No 2, pp 113-123, 2001.

Hopkins J C, 'End of the M-V Tower,' *AEI News*, Vol 24 No 1, p 5, 1955.

Johnstone-Taylor, F, 'Dished-Bottom Tanks and Steel Post Water Towers,' *Water & Water Engineering*, pp 133-6, 20 April 1925.

Ramm, D W, 'Design of Elevated Steel Tanks,' *Proc Australian Inst of Steel Construction*, Vol 12, No 1, 1978.

CHAPTER EIGHT

Water Towers
for other Purposes

Anon, 'Reinforced Concrete Water Towers at York,' *The Engineer*, pp 244-510, March 1911.

Anon, 'A 1,500,000 Gallons Elevated Water Tank at Staveley,' *Concrete & Const Eng*, Vol43, pp 343-6, 1948.

Anon, *The North Midland Railway Guide, 1842*, Turntable Enterprises, Leeds, (republished) 1973.

Armstrong ,Sir W G, 'The History of the Modern Development of Water Pressure Machinery,' *Proc I C E*, Vol 50, 1877.

Ball, J D W, *Reinforced Concrete Railway Structures*, Constable & Co, London, 1913.

Bowden-Smith, R, *The Water House, Houghton Hall, Norfolk*, Avenue Books, Woodbridge, Suffolk (Sponsored by Christie's), 1987.

Brees, S C, *Glossary of Civil Engineering*, Tilt & Bogue, London, 1841.

Coad, J G, *The Royal Dockyards, 1690 - 1850*, Scolar Press, Aldershot (for RCHME), 1989.

Cockrill, J W, 'The Use of Sea Water for Street Watering, Sewer Flushing and Other Purposes,' *Proc I C E*, Vol 110, 1892.

Douet, J, *British Barracks, 1600 - 1914*, Stationery Office, London, 1998.

Fawcett, W, 'Belmont Junction Water Tower,' *Bull North East Ind Arch Soc*, 1971.

Francis, P, *British Military Airfield Architecture*, Patrick Stephens, 1996.

Franklin, J, *The Gentleman's Country House and its Plan, 1835 to 1914*, Routledge & Kegan Paul, London, 1981.

Innes, G B, *British Airfield Buildings of World War II*, Midland Publishing, 1995.

Riley, R C, 'The Evolution of the Docks and Industrial Buildings in Portsmouth Naval Dockyard, 1698 - 1914,' *The Portsmouth Papers*, No 44, Portsmouth City Council, 1985.

Temple, J C, & Francis, P, *New Guidelines for Listing Military Airfield Buildings in England*, published privately by the authors, 1994.

Waddington, H S, 'Early Hydraulic Supply by Elevated Tank,' *PHEW Newsletter*, Aug 1980.

CHAPTER NINE

Problems with
Water Towers

Allin, R V, 'The Righting and Stabilising of a 200,000 Gallon Water Tower,' *Concrete & Constructional Engineering*, Vol 29, pp 3-13, 1934.

Anon, 'Water Tower at Goldthorpe,' *Concrete & Const Eng*, Vol 24, pp 411-4, 1929.

Anon, *Jubilee of Ownership, 1880 - 1930; A Short History of the Waterworks*, City of Nottingham Water Department, 1930

Anon, 'The Repair of Water-Containing Structures,' *Concrete & Constructional Engineering*, Vol 29, pp 452-5, 1934.

Anon, 'Water Tower at Sutton,' *Concrete & Constructional Engineering*, Vol 29, pp 483-7, 1934.

Anon, 'Shrewsbury's Water Supply - the new Shelton Scheme,' *Water & Water Engineering*, Vol 37, pp 477-495, 1935.

Anon, 'Moving a 1900 Ton Water Tower,' *Civil Engineering & Public Works Review*, Vol 48, No 560, pp 152-3, 1953.

Cusdin, S E T & Milne, J W, 'Concrete Water Towers' (& discussion), *Journ Inst Water Engrs*, Vol 17, pp 407-442, 1963.

Haining, P, *The Great English Earthquake*, Robert Hale, London, 1976.

Hayward, T W A, 'Six Years Municipal Work at Sudbury' (Eastern District Meeting, 13/6/1903), *Proc Inc Assn Mun & County Engrs*, 1903.

Larson L A, 'Cold Weather Operation of Elevated Tanks' (in *Distribution Systems - Actions & Innovations*), American Water Works Assn, 1980.

Owen, H, *Some Account of the Ancient and Present State of Shrewsbury*, Shrewsbury (reprinted E J Morten, Manchester, 1972), 1808.

Phillips, T, *History and Antiquities of Shrewsbury*, Shrewsbury, 1779.

Ritchie, J O C, 'Water Towers,' *The Structural Engineer*, Vol 35, No 1, January 1957.

Ruck, F W M, 'The Leaning Tower of Skegness,' *Trans Soc of Engineers*, Vol 43, pp 117-122, 1952.

Smith, D G, *Effects of Earthquakes on Water Towers*, Informal Report, SECED, ICE, London, August 2001.

CHAPTER TEN
Re-use of Water Towers

Anon, 'Saving a Surrey Water Tower,' *Country Life*, p1245, Vol168, No4338, 1980.

Anon, 'Diamond Cut for a Perfect Match,' (Leweston WT), *Concrete Cutter*, Vol 2, Issue 2, p 11, Jan 2001.

Gillilan, L, 'Towering over their Neighbours,' *Independent on Sunday* newspaper, pp 80-82, 18 June, 1995.

Osborne, B E, *Tadworth Tower — Ultimum Refugium*, Spas Research Fellowship, Tadworth, Surrey, 1999.

Index

All subjects, names and items are indexed by page number. Where a particular subject extends over a number of consecutive pages, only the number of the initial page in the sequence is given. Illustrations are indexed independently in bold type. Individual water towers are shown in small capitals.

N n

Q o

P p

Q q

R r